Books by RUTH MOORE

THE EARTH WE LIVE ON

(1956, 1971)

NIELS BOHR: THE MAN, HIS SCIENCE,
AND THE WORLD THEY CHANGED

(1966)

THE COIL OF LIFE

(1961)

CHARLES DARWIN

(1955)

MAN, TIME, AND FOSSILS

(1953)

THESE ARE BORZOI BOOKS
PUBLISHED IN NEW YORK BY ALFRED A. KNOPF

THE EARTH WE LIVE ON

THE EARTH
WE LIVE ON

The Story of Geological Discovery

by RUTH MOORE

Drawings by SUE ALLEN

Second Edition, Substantially Revised

NEW YORK   ALFRED A. KNOPF   1971

THIS IS A BORZOI BOOK
PUBLISHED BY ALFRED A. KNOPF, INC.

ISBN: 0–394–46968–2
Library of Congress Catalog Card Number: 56–8924
Manufactured in the United States of America

PUBLISHED NOVEMBER 2, 1956
REPRINTED THREE TIMES
SECOND EDITION, SUBSTANTIALLY REVISED
PUBLISHED APRIL 1971

PREFACE

THE STORY OF THE EARTH, of the evolution of its continents and mountains, of its upheavals, its hidden interior, its origin and its amazing past, could be told in an almost limitless number of ways. This book will try to ask the questions that curious, interested man has always asked about these problems and asks today, and will attempt to tell the dramatic story of how many scientists have imaginatively and carefully developed some of the answers, or some of the likely answers.

In recent years the new mathematics and new scientific instruments have carried the search very largely into the realms of geophysics and geochemistry. Material has become more formidable and less accessible for the non-scientist, but more stirring and startling than ever. To follow the story into these complexities was frightening. It was, however, irresistible.

My approach had to be that of a reporter. Therefore, even to have attempted this book would have been impossible without the generous co-operation and assistance of many people, and particularly of the scientists who are working on these far frontiers. I want to express my most sincere appreciation to all of them. When I sought the scientists out in their laboratories, they answered my questions and generously gave me additional materials. I was thus able to interview all of the living American scientists whose work is reported in this book. I am deeply grateful to them, too, for reading many of the chapters in the book, and for making suggestions and corrections.

I should particularly like to thank Dr. Harold Clayton Urey of the University of Chicago, Dr. J. Tuzo Wilson of the University of Toronto, Dr. A. C. Waters and Dr. Ernst Cloos of Johns Hopkins University, Dr. Brian Mason of the American Museum of Natural History, and Dr. J. Laurence Kulp of Columbia University. I should like to add my thanks to Dr. C. A. Robinson, Jr., of Brown University for reviewing the chapters dealing with classical materials, and to Dr. F. O. Pettijohn of Johns Hopkins University for reading the historical matter.

But the new findings are understandable only in the light of what has gone before. Writing of the outstanding students of the earth from Hesiod on required access to fine libraries. I drew constantly on the rich resources of Crerar and Newberry libraries in Chicago.

Many others went to great trouble in helping me to find photographs and other materials. I should like to thank the United States Geological Survey, the Geological Survey of Canada, the American Museum of Natural History, the British Information Services, the French Embassy Press and Information Division, the Royal Canadian Air Force, the United States Department of Defense, the United States Forest Service, Harvard College Observatory, the Wisconsin Conservation Department, the Smithsonian Institution, the Carnegie Institution, the University of Chicago, and *Life* magazine.

To two others I owe a special measure of gratitude: to the *Chicago Sun-Times* for generously granting me a lengthy leave of absence to work on this book, and to Harold Strauss, editor in chief of Alfred A. Knopf, Inc., for his constant and clear-sighted guidance and his brilliant editing.

RUTH MOORE

July 1956
Chicago, Illinois

CONTENTS

I. MYTH AND REASON

IV. INTO INVISIBLE FORCES

L I S T   O F   P L A T E S

FOLLOWING PAGE 240

LIST OF DRAWINGS

IN THE TEXT

Part One

MYTH AND REASON

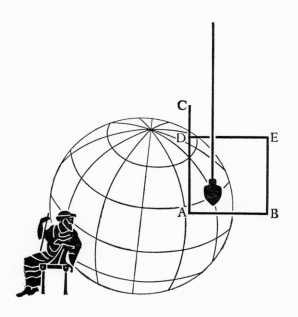

GODS, REASON, AND THE EARTH

AT FIRST we could only wonder and speculate and reason about this earth we live on.

Many centuries passed before men learned, in the eighteenth century, to examine the earth itself for the answers to their questions about the "outward form and inner workings of nature." And then there came a swift enlargement in the understanding of the earth, and a sudden upset in old beliefs. Quiet mountains were revealed as once fiery volcanoes and dry lands as former beds of the sea, and, most shockingly, men found that the earth was not the unaltered remainder of Noah's Flood, but an earth that had changed and still was changing.

Not long afterward came another surge forward. At the end of the nineteenth century a study of the process of change showed how great canyons had been cut and how the substance of the mountains had accumulated on the subsiding shores of the seas.

And now there has come another time when a new approach and a new insight are increasing men's understanding of the earth. By experiment and by the application of the principles of physics and chemistry men are able with new assurance to explore "the hidden heart of things," the origin of the earth, its deep interior, and its—to us—all important surface. The new studies, nearly all of them the work of the first decade after the close of World War II, are again overthrowing and changing many long-held beliefs. A different, a fuller, and a surprising picture of the earth is taking form. Already it can be said:

The earth in all probability was not torn from the sun, as

men assumed during the last one hundred and fifty years. A very different origin is being postulated.

At one period in its past the earth may have "rolled about," turning the North Pole into a tropical land and the tropics into a frozen waste.

The continents drift around the globe, and the crust, upwelling from below, is renewed before returning again to the mantle.

The earth and all its products on which men depend—the metals, the coals, the stones—are the end products of a breaking down and reassortment of the elements with which the planet began.

The earth is nearly twice as old as even the boldest theorists believed only a decade ago.

If even the attentive reader has heard little of these new findings, it is not surprising. The work that is so expanding the understanding of the earth is very recent, and it is normally couched in some of the most technical and abstruse of mathematical notation. Reports on the geological discovery of the earth are no longer as easy to read as a lively book of travels, and they make their first appearances in many scientific journals of limited circulation. Only lately have several distinguished anthologies brought the often startling new materials together for the use of the scientists themselves.

The growth in our knowledge of the earth was not a planned evolution. It was not a systematic or a steady search for the answers to our eternal and essential questions about how the earth, its mountains, its plains, and its resources came to be. Each age has worked at the problem with the tools available to it, and as individual scientists have seen and imaginatively developed the possibilities open to them.

The scientist of today is the first to venture successfully into the invisible. The amazing new geochemical and geophysical studies had to await the development of the mathematics, the experimental instruments, and the understandings that would permit the exploration of structures and forces that man can never see and will never directly know. The measurement of unseen waves coursing through invisible depths, the recording of radiation from imperceptibly minute traces of billion-year-old materials, the mapping of the forever hidden structure of matter have at last enabled the scientist to draw verifiable deductions about the nature of the earth and about why it is the rugged, rich-surfaced globe we know.

The scientists of the previous two centuries, as they pursued the same quest for knowledge of the earth, were forced to rely on the measurement and observation of the visible earth and on the study of the easily perceivable remains of former states— the fossils and the rocky strata.

Their predecessors of the Middle Ages, and the ancients could employ only reason, tradition, and the deep instincts of man to explain the often fearsome earth. Theirs was often a voyage into the unknown too, but without compass or test.

This is the developing story this book will try to tell; it is a story of men and their long search for the truth, of high adventure and painstaking research, of triumph and sometimes of defeat before the inscrutibility and concealment of the earth.

It begins with the gods.

One day, perhaps in the eighth century before Christ, Hesiod was tending his lambs on the green slopes of holy Mount Helicon. Suddenly—or so Hesiod tells us in his poem the *Theogony* —the three Muses, the sweet-singing daughters of Great Zeus, appeared before him and taught him "glorious song," and bade him tell "how at first gods and earth came to be, and the boundless sea with its raging swell, and the gleaming stars, and the wide heaven above. . . ."

The happy poet eagerly obeyed. With a shoot of olive, a "marvelous thing" that the Muses had plucked and given to him, Hesiod wrote one of the first full accounts we have of the beginnings of heaven and earth, and of the earthly and heavenly phenomena that sustain men or in times of upheaval awe and destroy them.

But long before Hesiod and long before Homer, that other early chronicler who dealt to some degree with these vital matters, men had wondered about the earth they live on. They wondered and sought for explanations just as men do today and as they have done in all the long ages in between. They needed to know about their beautiful and yet tumultuous earth. Only by understanding could they hope to dispel the fears they felt when mountains burst into flame and the earth shook so violently that no mortal man could be sure that the end was not near.

There was an explanation. As the Muses related the story to Hesiod, the earth had been brought into being by natural forces. It had come into existence with the gods, mighty creatures who not only had given it being, but performed its vast tasks much as humans did their lesser ones. Thus, through storm and calm Atlas bore on his back "the cruel strength of the crushing world and the vault of the sky."

These Greek explanations, or myths, as the modern world calls them, were based on what a man could see of the earth and all that he sensed about it.

"A real myth has nothing to do with religion," said that great student of Greece and mythology Edith Hamilton. "It is an explanation of something in nature; how for instance any and everything in the universe came into existence; men, animals, this or that tree, the sun, the moon, the stars, storms, eruptions or earthquakes, all that is and all that happens. . . . Myths are early science, the results of men's first trying to explain what they saw around them."

And if these sights and accounts seem now to be a matter of fancy, they were not without their reality in those early days. When men lived near to the earth and closely attuned to her moods, it was not difficult to catch a glimpse of the Muses dancing upon highest Helicon or moving abroad at night "veiled in thick mist" to utter their lovely song. Or, standing on the shore of an early morning, one might easily "have sight of Proteus rising from the sea."

Through men's dreams, too, moved the divine figures, majestic in mien and impressive in their stature. "To these figures they attributed sentience because they were seen to move their limbs and give voice to their stately features and stalwart frames," explained Lucretius many years later.

Hesiod was a man of such sensibilities. A shepherd and a farmer, he lived in Bœotia, a simple land of fields and mountains which lay to the north and west of Athens. But as he watched his sheep he listened always for the music of the Muses' song. The genealogy and genesis of the earth which the song inspired Hesiod to write deeply influenced those who came after him and still colors our language and thought.[1]

At first, the Muses revealed to Hesiod, there was chaos, "dark, wasteful, wild." Then, into this gloom and void, this immeasurable abyss, "wide-bosomed Earth" was born. Without cause, without creator, Earth, "the ever sure foundation of all," came into being; it suddenly was—a vast disk floating on a turbulent waste of waters.

Many other peoples and many other traditions and legends have likewise described the beginnings of this earth. "And the earth was without form, and void; and darkness was upon the face of the deep," says the Bible. And modern science, with all of its resources and with its new concept of an earth assembled from the dust of space, has not materially altered this nearly universal and deeply felt belief that in the beginning there was formlessness and emptiness.

"Earth," says Hesiod, then bore "starry Heaven equal to herself to cover her on every side," and brought forth the long hills, and Pontus, the watery deep.

Out of chaos also had come Erebus, the underworld where death dwells, and Black Night. By some miracle these two figures of darkness in their turn gave birth to Ether, the bright,

[1] Hugh G. Evelyn White, who made the Oxford translation of Hesiod, questions that Hesiod wrote the *Theogony*. It may have been the work of a later poet who attributed it to him.

pure upper atmosphere, and to Day. Out of darkness came light.

Here, then, was a beginning, an understandable beginning in which the major parts of the world—the earth, the heavens, and the nether world—had been brought into being by a process of birth and into a relationship that men knew they bore. But this illimitable expanse of earth and sky and waters was

DAWN, ROSY-FINGERED, ARISES "TO BRING LIGHT TO GODS AND MORTALS."

empty. No man had yet moved across its vastness; long before living creatures the earth had come into existence.

The filling in and shaping of this fresh young universe was, as Hesiod relates the story, a long process of struggle and trial. Great natural forces that Hesiod always personifies as gods and demigods were at work.

The first to come upon the vacant earth were children born of the union of Earth and Heaven. Among them were Oceanus, the deep-swirling ocean river that encircled the earth, and "lovely Tethys," who, with Oceanus, would bear the eddying river Nilus (Nile), the Meander, the fair stream Ister, and many another great river.

"There are three thousand neat-ankled daughters of Ocean who are dispersed far and wide and in every place alike serve the earth and the deep waters, children who are glorious among goddesses," said Hesiod. "And as many other rivers are there, babbling as they flow, sons of Ocean whom queenly Tethys bare, but their names it is hard for a mortal to tell, though people know those by which they severally dwell."

Other offspring of Heaven and Earth gave birth to great Helius, the sun, to Selene, the moon, and Eos, "the dawn that shines both upon the earth and the gods who live in the heavens above." And from a union of Eos and the Dawn-wind came the winds, brightening Zephyrus, headlong Boreas, and boisterous Notus, whose fierce gales often accompanied the heavy autumn rains of Zeus.

Hesiod had no love for Boreas, the north wind, and the cruel frosts that he blew over the earth until many a lofty oak was brought low and even the wild beasts shuddered and set their tails between their legs. Then a man had need to lace on his felt-lined boots, his outer coat of kidskin, and his cap of felt. That was the only way, as he returned from his fields, that he could stop Boreas from wrapping round him, making his body clammy and soaking his clothes.

But the earth was not to take its final form without great changes and near disasters. Men sensed that fact, for the earth bore many marks of past violence. The earth itself, it was told, was shaken as Zeus and the younger gods struggled to unseat Cronus, the first ruler of the gods, the father who had relentlessly tried to destroy his son Zeus at birth.

"The boundless sea rang terribly and the earth crashed loudly," said Hesiod. "Wide heaven was shaken and groaned and high Olympus reeled from its foundation under the charge of the undying gods, and heavy quaking reached dim Tartarus. . . ."

At this terrible moment Zeus came forth hurling the supreme weapon, the lightning and thunder. "The life-giving earth crashed around in burning and the vast wood crackled loud with fire," Hesiod continued, "all the land seethed and Ocean's streams and the unfruitful sea. The hot vapor lapped round the earth-born Titans and flames unspeakable rose to the bright upper air."

ZEUS HURLS "HIS BLAZING THUNDERBOLT."

Even gods could not withstand such a charge. The old gods were conquered. Many of them were bound in chains and hurled as far beneath the earth as heaven is above, which was "nine times the space that measures night and day to mortal man."

Around their prison ran a bronze fence, and night spread about it in a triple line like a "neck circlet." Just above grew the roots of the earth and the sea. If a man were once within the outer bronze gates that led to this vast gulf it would take him a year to reach its floor, wrote Hesiod. And it would be a bitter year for any venturer, for cruel blast upon cruel blast of wind would carry him first this way and then that.

Out of mercy Zeus decided to spare the life of gigantic Atlas. But in punishment for his resistance Zeus assigned him to uphold the wide heavens for all eternity. Some said that Atlas was Mount Atlas in northwest Africa, the great peak that seemed to reach up until it supported the whole sky. Hesiod did not attempt to settle the point; he had given men an explanation of how the heavens held firm above them, and had relieved them of the fear that the great arch might someday come crashing down.

It was after the titanic battle of the gods that Earth bore her youngest child, Typhœus. From his shoulders grew a hundred-headed dragon, from his eyes flashed fire, and he "uttered every kind of sound unspeakable." His voice was at once the bellow of a furious bull, the roar of a lion, and the kind of hiss that makes a mountain echo. When Typhœus, or Typhoon, so much as arose, the earth seethed and the sea turned into a tempest.

Zeus moved quickly and with all of his strength to stay this consuming monster who threatened the very continuance of the earth. With a scorching thunderbolt Zeus struck him down and cast him deep into the nether world. Even there, however, Typhoon was not wholly overwhelmed. He retained a disastrous remnant of his power. From Tartarus, said Hesiod, he sometimes sends forth whirling winds that rush upon the sea, scattering ships and destroying sailors. Men are defenseless before their power. Other winds from Typhoon sweep over the earth, spoiling the fields of men and filling the earth with dust and uproar.

But this was the last major challenge. Although the earth had been shaken and Typhoon would occasionally cause trouble, the world had taken form and had come safely through. The gods pressed far-seeing Zeus to reign thenceforth over heaven and earth. And this he did.

So Hesiod sang. So did the Muses reveal to him the story of how the earth, the heavens, the oceans, the rivers, and the storms and earthquakes came to be. It was an account that was never to be forgotten.

· · ·

Some four centuries later, another observer of the earth, a professor, strolled slowly through the shady loggia of the Lyceum and out into the gardens with his group of advanced students. All the while the professor—Aristotle—was talking, sometimes thoughtfully, sometimes incisively, and often with a glance and gesture toward the blue morning sky and the bright-shining sun.

Heraclitus, he was saying, had maintained that the sun was about the size that it looked to the man in the street, "about a foot across." That, declared Aristotle with cheerful disdain, was a "childish opinion." Perhaps the jibe brought the peripatetics to a halt. No one, Aristotle went on, driving home his point, could hold such a childish opinion if he had studied what mathematics could demonstrate about the earth and heavens.

"It is too simple to believe that each of the moving bodies [celestial] is really small in size because it so appears to us when we look at it from the earth," he added.

On the contrary, the great Greek philosopher argued, the sun was huge, and the earth—the sphere from which he and his students were watching the heavens—"a mere nothing when compared in size with the surrounding universe."

This did a Greek discuss the earth in fourth-century Athens; so far had science come from the gods of Hesiod. The old idea of the earth's predominant place in the universe had gradually been yielding to the new mathematics, though it still was a startling concept to declare the earth to be relatively "nothing." Even now, some twenty-three centuries later, we do not find it easy to realize that the earth which looms so large to us is a lone, almost infinitesimal point in an infinite universe.

It was such thinking, opening new worlds and placing what was known in new dimensions, that brought some of the most alert young men in knowledge-loving Greece to Aristotle's school, the Lyceum. In almost every way—in its faculty and students, in its classrooms and library, its loggias and gardens—

the Lyceum was intellectually and physically similar to a university of today. It lay just northeast of the city in a grove sacred to Apollo and the Muses.

Study in the Lyceum's quiet may have had a value all the deeper because of the disturbed and disturbing conditions in the world outside. In 334 b.c., the year Aristotle opened his school, a twenty-one-year-old new king of Macedonia was overturning the predominant place of Greece in the ancient world almost as completely as Aristotle was reversing the old relationship of earth to universe. The twenty-one-year-old was Alexander, thereafter to be known as "the Great."

By one of those odd turns of fate, Aristotle, who had been born in northern Stagira not far from Macedonia, had served as the tutor of the young world conqueror. Though Alexander acted contrary to the teaching of Aristotle, his conquests provided the stability that permitted the philosopher to open and develop his school. When Alexander died in 323, Aristotle, who was always under suspicion because of his northern connections, was compelled to leave the Lyceum and withdraw from Athens. Within another two years he too was dead.

As Aristotle and his pupils paced the gardens of the Lyceum, the earth was only a part of their study. Their total inquiry was into the universe and the thought and acts of man. However, Aristotle's work had suggested the need for a reordering, a rearranging, and a rethinking of the theories of the earth developed by a great succession of Greek philosophers who had followed Hesiod. He incorporated his findings and conclusions— many of them changing what was previously thought or accepted—into his courses on physics, on the heavens, on generation and decay, and most particularly on meteorology. These skillful, polished lectures are the only form in which his works on the earth have come down to us.

For centuries they were to mold, if not to control, men's ideas about the earth.

The shape of the earth was as much a problem as its size. Was this earth on which men lived a sphere? Or was it, as some maintained, flat and drum-shaped?

Hesiod had pictured the earth as a flat disk borne up on the primordial waters. Thales, the first of the Greek philosophers to seek a natural rather than a mythical explanation of how the earth came to be, held almost to the same concept—a flat earth afloat on the deep.

Aristotle bluntly labeled the idea "simple-minded." As he always did in approaching any subject, he first reviewed the positions of his predecessors and then systematically brought out the objections to them. Aristotle was a man of wit as well as learning, and he was not above dazzling the students who trailed him with a brilliant display of irony and a blunt scoffing at some of the "absurd" claims that had been made.

"As if the same account had not to be given of the water which carries the earth as of the earth itself," he exclaimed with light sarcasm. "It is not the nature of water any more than of earth to stay in mid-air; it must have something to rest upon. But observation shows that this is not the case. Any piece of earth goes to the bottom, the quicker the larger it is. These thinkers seem to push their inquiries some way into the problem, but not as far as they might."

Anaximenes, Anaxagoras, and Democritus also had believed that the earth was flat. "They say that it covers the air beneath it like a lid," Aristotle explained to his students. "The air not having room enough to change its place stays there in a mass, like the water in the case of the water clock. And they adduce an amount of evidence to prove that air, when cut off and at rest, can bear a considerable weight."

There was one fatal trouble with both the water and the compressed-air arguments; the earth could not be buoyed up by a sea or supported on a column of air for the simple reason that it was not flat. The earth was a sphere, Aristotle declared with certainty. "Its shape must necessarily be spherical."

The movement of all things toward a center, and the whirling motion of the spheres—Aristotle thought they revolved around the earth—would make the earth round, he correctly reasoned. The evidence of the senses also supported his conclusion. In an eclipse of the moon, when a shadow of the earth was cast on the moon's shining surface, that shadow always was curved. This projected image of the earth showed it to be round.

The stars testified to the same roundness. In Egypt and in Cyprus, it was well known, stars were visible which could not be seen in more northerly lands, and vice versa.

"All of which goes to show," said Aristotle, "not only that the earth is circular, but also that it is a sphere of no great size, for otherwise the effect of so slight a change of place would not be so quickly apparent."

And Aristotle was completely right. His proofs are in large part the proofs that modern scientists still use to prove the sphericity of the earth.

Aristotle had a mind that leaped on ahead. If the earth were round, it seemed likely that the same ocean might link the Pillars of Hercules (at the Strait of Gibraltar) and "the parts around India." Some eighteen centuries later this remarkable insight of Aristotle's was to be a factor in sending Columbus out into the dread, still unknown ocean in a daring attempt to reach India and prove that the earth was round. When the Italian adventurer landed on some semi-tropical islands he accordingly named them the West Indies, and later the strange red inhabitants of the land to the north were to be called Indians.

The problem of how the seas and the rivers could sustain themselves on such an earth also had to be faced. The explanations that had been given in the past, Aristotle told his class, were no better than what might have been thought of by the man in the street.

Some philosophers had said that all the rain that fell was collected beneath the earth in a great hollow or hollows and that it was from these reservoirs that all rivers flowed. This nicely explained why some rivers ran higher in winter than in summer, and why some were perennial and some were not. If the store of water was great enough to last until the return of the winter rains, a river would flow continuously. But if the supply were scanty, it might soon be exhausted and the rivers would dry up. This was an advance over Hesiod's explanation that the rivers were the offspring of lovely Tethys and Ocean, but it was not much more satisfactory.

Aristotle cited one major reason why the reservoir theory was "close to ridiculous." Anyone who tried to compute the volume of water flowing in the rivers each day would soon see that a reservoir would have to be nearly as large as the earth itself. Tossing out such an impossibility, Aristotle contended that rivers originated in a very different way.

"Mountains and high places act like a thick sponge overhanging the earth and make the water drip through and run together in small quantities in many places," he declared. Seeping through and collecting, the water finally gushed forth in springs, some of them large enough immediately to create rivers. Thus, rivers were formed in the mountains, a fact that might be verified by looking at the map.

Aristotle probably gave this lecture in his classroom. On the walls were maps of the world which he needed for his exposition. One large map showed two broad habitable zones on either side of a central equator-like line that stretched from the "equinoctial sunset" in the outer ocean beyond the Pillars of Hercules to the "equinoctial dawn" somewhere in the vicinity of India. Beyond these two zones, scholars assumed, the world was too hot or too cold to be habitable by man.

You can see, said Aristotle, pointing to Asia, that the largest rivers flow from the mountain range of Parnassus, the highest mountains in the direction of the winter dawn. (These were probably the Hindu Kush Mountains in northwest India, an extension of the Himalayas.) From these mountains came many great rivers, including the Indus, "the greatest of all rivers." Aristotle's hand must have traced its course south through what is now India into the "outer ocean" (the Arabian Sea).

Moving on toward the west, he indicated the Caucasus, a range so high that its peaks were sunlit for a third part of the night, and at the opposite end of the ancient world (in Spain) the Pyrenees. From both of them flowed many rivers, large and long. Aristotle went on to Africa. The Silver Mountains (probably Mounts Kilimanjaro and Kenya in east central Africa) gave rise to the Chrementes (perhaps the Senegal) and formed the most important of the sources of the Nile.

Further investigation would show, he continued, that all other rivers similarly flowed from mountains. Some few, it was true, might seem to originate in marshes, but one would always find that the marshes lay beneath mountains or other rising ground.

"We can now see," said Aristotle summing up, "that the supposition that rivers spring from definite hollows in the earth is a false one."

As rivers grew mighty or failed, Aristotle observed that the land they served changed too. His study of rivers, and of the sea, led him into one of the prime questions about the earth—how it has changed and is changing. He saw clearly a fact that is always difficult for men to grasp: where there is now land, there has often been water, and where water, land.

"The same parts of the earth are not always moist or dry, but change their character according to the appearance or failure of rivers," he said. "So also mainland and sea exchange places and one area does not always remain earth, another sea, for all time, but where there is now sea there is at another time land."

Aristotle thought of it as a process of maturing and aging, much like that affecting the bodies of plants and animals. "These changes escape our observation because the whole natural process of the earth's growth takes place by slow degrees and over periods of time which are vast compared to the length of our life, and whole peoples are destroyed and perish before they can record the process from beginning to end."

This was exactly what had happened in Egypt. Clearly the whole country was a deposit of the Nile, though the beginning of the deposit had been lost in time and records were lacking. But there was indirect evidence. Homer, writing of Egypt, had significantly made no mention of Memphis. Probably this city standing at the head of the delta had not then existed, or had been quite unimportant, for the low, marshy country at the river's mouth would normally be the last settled.

Aristotle had seen with his own eyes how land could be built up by water. During his years in Ionia he had watched the current through the Bosporus create a sandbank off the shore of Asia and had seen a small lake form behind it. Later a "further sandbank formed in front of this one, and another lake, and so the process went on."

Slowly, with a gradualness that passed unnoticed during the brief lives of men and peoples, the earth changed. But the nature of the process that Aristotle understood so well was too difficult, too confounding, too unbelievable for men generally to bear in mind or accept. Aristotle's insight into the process of change was to be lost as far as most men were concerned until its independent rediscovery in the nineteenth century. Then it would startle the world and remake the science of the earth.

But no scientist of the nineteenth century and no scientist of today could state this key principle of the earth's slow changing more clearly or brilliantly than Aristotle did in the *Meteorologica:*

"If rivers come into being and perish and if the same parts of the earth are not always moist the sea must necessarily change correspondingly. And if in places the sea recedes while in others it encroaches, then evidently the same parts of the earth as a whole are not always sea, nor always mainland, but in the process of time all change."

The sea and its nature inevitably had to be considered by a man and his students bent on exploring "everything that happens naturally." How had it come to be and why was so great a volume of water salty?

The ancients concerned with theology—a reference to Hesiod —had tried to provide both land and sea with a source, Aristotle told his students as he began his discussion of this subject. Perhaps they had thought that this would "give a more dramatic and grander air to their theories," Aristotle suggested.

Others with a more secular approach—the philosophers—had assumed that in the beginning the whole region about the earth was water. As the sun struck the great expanse of moisture, evaporation began. The seas were what remained of this primary water, and since the process was an endless one, ultimately they would evaporate too.

Still others had maintained that the sea was the sweat of the earth, sweated out when the sun beat hot upon the earth. Like all sweat, it was salty.

Plato, for his part, had argued in the *Phædo* that the sea, as well as the rivers, had its origin in a body of water at the center of the earth, in Tartarus. As this tremendous underground lake surged back and forth, the waters that supplied the sea flowed in and out through channels pierced in the earth.

Aristotle invited his students to take a critical look with him at each of these theories. Could the sea have come from one source? No, for it was well known that water which has a source is either running water or water that has to be lifted artificially, as in a well. That definition did not fit the sea. Although the sea might seem to flow as it rushed through a narrow strait or moved from one depth to another, this was not a true flow. Aristotle had no real understanding of the tides, but he recognized that the sea's ebb and flow was different from the flow of rivers.

Was the sea formed by a process of drying up and would it in the end disappear, as Democritus had said? That, said Aristotle, sounded like something out of Æsop's fables. Æsop told about Charybdis, the hideous daughter of Earth and Poseidon, who with her fellow monster Scylla lurked atop Sicilian cliffs to lure unwary sailors to their destruction. When she took one gulp of the sea, the mountains appeared; when she took a second, the islands came into view. At her third, Æsop predicted, the sea would be drained.

Lightly Aristotle joked: "This was a suitable retort for Æsop to make when the ferryman annoyed him, but it is hardly suitable for those who are seeking the truth." More seriously, Aristotle added that, whatever had made the sea come to rest where it did, the same cause must clearly make it stay there for all time. He pointed out that the water which was lost by evaporation was replaced by the rains. Therefore, he concluded, the sea would never dry up.

Was the sea, then, the sweat of the earth? Still in fine argumentative fettle, Aristotle called this contention "absurd." "Such a statement is perhaps satisfactory in poetry, for metaphor is a poetic device, but it does not advance our knowledge of nature," he commented.

Aristotle dealt more seriously, though just as devastatingly, with Plato, the master with whom he had studied for so long. If the sea ran out of the depths of the earth, as Plato had said, the water would have to perform that "proverbial impossibility" of flowing uphill. And where would the water drawn up as rain vapor come from if the same amount of water always flowed back into Tartarus' pool? And manifestly all rivers that did not flow into one another made their way to the sea, not to Tartarus.

No, Aristotle concluded, the sea was the terminus, not the source, of the earth's waters. If the universe had had a beginning, so had the sea, for the "two are supposed to have come into being at the same time." One of the students must have looked or asked the "old question" that this raised: If the sea was the terminus and immense rivers poured their waters into it constantly, why did it not become larger?

Aristotle indulgently answered. In doing so he explained the phenomenon of evaporation, which he had long observed and understood well. The sun drew up the finest and sweetest water each day. Dissolved into vapor, it rose into the upper regions, where it was condensed by the cold and fell again as rain.

The question of the sea's saltiness still had to be directly taken up. The more thoughtful had attributed the salt to the admixture of the salty earth, though why the admixture should have so strong an effect in a body as large as the ocean and not in the rivers posed a problem.

Here Aristotle did experiment. To test his belief that the fresh water was drawn up and the salt left behind, he evaporated some salt water. Then he condensed the vapor. There was little or no salt in the water he obtained.

Aristotle also experimented with the admixture theory. Taking a jar made of wax, he tightly stoppered it and dropped it into the sea. The water that came through the walls was fresh, he said; the earthy matter that produced the saltiness of the sea had been kept out as by a filter. H. D. P. Lee, Cambridge University translator of the *Meteorologica*, points out that this test does not work as Aristotle said. He is inclined to think that Aristotle took it on hearsay, though the great Greek speaks of doing it himself.

But it did not matter. The saltiness of the sea was accounted for; an ancient puzzle and contradiction was solved. It was possible to understand why the sea was salt though the waters that fed it were fresh.

Aristotle was collecting a famous library for the Lyceum. He received books and reports from many places. In Hiera, one of the Æolian islands lying just north of Sicily and off the toe of Italy, the earth had risen with an awful noise into a crest-shaped mound. Then came a violent explosion, the report said. The tremendous blast of wind that "broke out" carried such a quantity of cinders and ash into the air that the neighboring city of Lipara was smothered. A similar disaster had occurred in Heracleia on the Black Sea. At the onset of an earthquake the wind burst forth from the earth with all the force and fury of a hurricane, and the trembling of the ground did not cease, it was indicated, until it had been vented.

It seemed undeniable to Aristotle that wind, "the farthest mover" and a force of the greatest velocity, power, and violence, was the cause of earthquakes. He was convinced that the winds arose from an "exhalation of the earth," and this fitted well with his theory. He reminded his pupils that when rain falls upon the heated earth "a considerable amount of wind is generated." If the wind flowed inward instead of outward and if it were then constricted into a narrow space underground, he reasoned, pressures great enough to make the earth tremble would certainly be generated.

Aristotle liked nothing better than to draw analogies from the human body. Earthquakes, he urged, were exactly like the tremors and throbbings produced when wind was pent up inside the human body. How great its violence could be was well demonstrated in tetanus and spasms, both of which were caused by wind, he said. A victim in their grip was so powerfully seized and shaken that not even a number of men could control his movements. "And if we compare great things with small, we must suppose that the same sort of thing happens to the earth," declared Aristotle.

Many centuries later these mistaken theories of Aristotle still were accepted as law, and Shakespeare was to write:

> *Diseased nature oftentimes breaks forth*
> *In strange eruptions; oft the teaming earth*
> *Is with a kind of colic pinch'd and vex'd*
> *By the imprisoning of unruly wind*
> *Within her womb; which, for enlargement striving,*
> *Shakes the old beldam earth and topples down*
> *Steeples and moss-grown towers.*

Close student of the earth that he was, Aristotle was of course aware that the shocks of an earthquake sometimes continued "for forty days or so," and that the "symptoms" might later recur. "The cause of the severity is the amount of the wind and the shape of the passages through which it has to flow," he explained. "When it meets with resistance and cannot easily get through, the shocks are severest and air is bound to be left in the narrow places, like water that cannot get out of a vessel. Therefore, just as throbbings in the body do not stop at once or quickly, but gradually as the affliction dies away, so the originating cause of the exhalation and the source of the wind clearly do not expend all at once the material that produces the wind which we call an earthquake."

The tidal waves that so frequently followed an earthquake were caused, Aristotle said, by an opposition of winds. He described to his students how a great mass of water might pile up if a wind causing an earthquake was unable "to drive out the sea" because another wind was pushing the waves toward the shore. If the first wind then gave way, the water would be driven in and would break with an awful flood over the land.

The windy exhalations were also capable, Aristotle maintained, of producing an equal tumult in the heavens. They gave rise to lightning, thunder, whirlwinds, firewinds, and thunderbolts. But in addition to these phenomena in the heavens, they had two other important effects within the earth.

Beneath the ground the dry, smoky "exhalation" produced such "infusible" materials as sulfur and ocher. The vaporous exhalation, on the other hand, gave rise to all the metals that were either fusible or ductile, including gold, copper, and iron. When the vaporous exhalation was caught between stones whose dryness compressed or solidified it, the metals were produced much as dew or frost condense out of the same exhalation above ground. Where reason did not serve to explain the phenomena of the earth, Aristotle was himself trapped.

Many other manifestations of the universe were examined by the thought-provoking professor and his students as they strolled through the gardens and loggias of the Lyceum, for it was the world in all its aspects and all its richness which Aristotle sought to understand. During the thirteen years at the Lyceum, Aristotle fixed the main outlines of the sciences and carried many of them to the highest point they had yet reached. And that included the study of the earth proper.

And yet when Alexander died and the hatred the Greeks bore for their northern conqueror could break forth unrestrained, its force also turned, like one of Aristotle's perverse trouble-making winds, against the northern-born philosopher. A charge of impiety was brought against him. It was a trumped-up thing based on a hymn and an epitaph that he had written on his old friend Hermeias.

Aristotle did not fight the charge, however. Determined not to let the Athenians "sin twice against philosophy"—bring about another death as they had Socrates'—Aristotle turned his school over to a friend and withdrew to Chalcis. It was there that, about a year later, he died.

Classical Greece was at an end, but the understanding of the earth had taken a long leap forward.

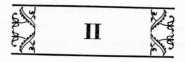

II

NOAH
OF THE FLOOD AND THE EARTH

BETWEEN THE BARREN, high-lying Syrian desert to the west and the Persian mountains to the east lies the valley of the Tigris and the Euphrates. Originally it was a shorter valley than it is now, for the salt waters of the Persian Gulf then extended farther inland. But silt brought down by the two big rivers and by a pair of rivers that emptied into them at right angles gradually turned what had been an arm of the sea into a great delta. Every spring when the flood waters came down from the mountains the rivers ran over their nearly flush banks and covered both the delta and the marshy valley behind it with a brown, turgid sheet of water. As the flood receded, the light stoneless soil left behind was "as rich as any in the world."

Many centuries later—in 1922—Sir Leonard Woolley led an archæological expedition into this ancient valley of lower Mesopotamia. When he began to study its geological history he was irresistibly reminded of the story in Genesis of the creation of this world as man's home. It was a story, he believed, taken over by the Hebrews from the people of the valley.

"And God said, Let the waters under the heaven be gathered together unto one place, and let the dry land appear." This was the way it had come about in the valley.

The Bible account continues: "And the earth brought forth grass, and herb yielding seed after his kind, and the tree yielding fruit, whose seed was in itself, after his kind: and God saw that it was good." If it was this valley to which reference was made, men also saw that it was good. They moved into this delta of the Tigris and the Euphrates, first occupying the islands and the mounds that rose above the marsh and, as more land became dry, taking that over too. Here they founded one of the world's earliest civilizations, and here they engaged in one of the greatest of all dramas.

One year, all accounts agree, there came a flood so broad, so deep, and so surpassingly devastating that it wiped out all

"AND GOD SAID, LET THERE BE LIGHTS IN THE FIRMAMENT OF THE HEAVEN TO DIVIDE THE DAY FROM NIGHT."

the civilization that had been. Only one patriarch survived, and with him the members of his family and the living things that he took into the ark he had been forewarned to build.

It was long afterward that men learned to scratch pictorial symbols on clay tablets, but when they did, the story of the Great Flood was one of the first they recorded. Later still, when the Bible was written down, the story was told again as one of the central facts in man's being. It was a story never to be forgotten.

During the Middle Ages and well into the nineteenth century the Flood was the subject of a deep-cutting religious controversy. To prove that the Bible was a true and inspired text, men of faith went to prodigious lengths to show that the Flood could have occurred and that Noah had survived to give the race of man its second beginning.

But it is with another effect of this magnificent legend that this book is concerned. As religious scholars studied and debated the Flood, the conviction grew that the rush and sweep of its waters had shaped the face of the earth into what it has since been. The waters of the Flood, it was argued, had formed the alignments of the continents, they had piled up the mountains, and they had filled the rocks with the dead bodies of animals that had perished in the catastrophe. The Flood explained the world's geology and geography.

In this way the theologians could demonstrate that the Flood must have inundated the world exactly as they believed the Bible said. Laymen and scientists could point to the configurations of the continents and to fossils as conclusive, though indirect, evidence of the Flood. But, for all of the faith and all of the rationalization, the story of the Flood still had the quality of a legend. No one, or certainly very few, ever dared to dream that actual evidence of the Great Flood could be found. Even after Troy had been found, and Nineveh, and the labyrinth of Minos, it seemed impossible, even unimaginable, that men could discover the historical record of the Flood.

Sir Leonard Woolley certainly was not thinking about the Flood when he took the British Museum-University of Pennsylvania expedition into Mesopotamia early in the 1920's. Their spades were set to dig for another part of the past.

Back in 1854, J. E. Taylor, British consul at Basra, had dug into a low mound that lay about halfway between the modern city of Baghdad and the Persian Gulf. The site is about ten miles west of the present course of the Euphrates. Not far below the surface Taylor had come upon some inscriptions that identified the desert-covered ruins as the famed city of Ur. Ur of the Chaldees! Ur, the home of Abraham! Although Taylor's work was not carried much further, its great importance was recognized and there was hope of going on with it as soon as possible.

Many difficulties stood in the way. Not the least was the country itself. On three sides of the mound that was Ur the desert stretched parched and burning all the way to the horizon. The sandy waste was inhabited only by a few wandering Bedouins, and any foreigner ventured in at his own risk. For these and other reasons only a few small-scale attempts were made to uncover more of the ancient city that Taylor had discovered. Not until 1922 could a large, systematic exploration be undertaken. Then the work was carried on for twelve years.

Woolley's first step was to dig trial trenches that might trace the great wall with which Nebuchadnezzar had enclosed the Sacred Area of Ur. He found parts of the walls, but as his workmen deepened the trenches, vases, bowls, small bronze objects, and beads, some of them of gold, began to turn up in clusters. Woolley realized that he had happened upon the cemetery of Ur. Excavating it was a job that would require the utmost care and study. Despite the protests of his Arab workmen, Woolley stopped work on the "gold trench" until all should have acquired more experience, and started to explore some promising mounds that lay four miles north of Ur at a place known as al 'Ubaid.

The surface of one unimposing low mound was strewn with flint implements and fragments of a pottery known to be "prehistoric." Woolley dug into it. Under only a few inches of dust and broken pottery he came upon a three-foot stratum of hard mud, in which were embedded quantities of painted pottery, flint and obsidian tools, and fragments of a clay plaster that bore the imprint of reeds. Beneath lay a clean water-laid soil.

The tools, he recognized with an archæologist's pleasure at an important find, belonged to the Stone Age; not a sign of a metal implement lay in the mud. Hoes had been chipped from flint or chert, and knives and awls made from rock crystal or obsidian.

Woolley could interpret the story this deposit told. A Stone Age people had lived in huts made of reeds and mud on an island slightly raised above the marsh. Several generations of huts had been built, one on the ruins of another, and then suddenly, while men still had only tools of stone, the village had ceased to exist. This was a puzzling matter. Woolley gave it considerable thought, but at the time he could see no explanation.

Later he investigated another low mound near Ur, one where the Arabs had often picked up flint hoes. There he discovered another deserted Stone Age village, very like the first. Again he asked what could have happened.

During the next four years the expedition, now skilled at its job, returned to the excavation of the cemetery at Ur. In sixteen royal graves and thousands of common ones they made one of the notable hauls of archæology—tombs stocked with implements and ornaments of gold and precious stones, fine pottery, and a clear record of a strange civilization in which richly appareled retainers calmly followed their kings into death.

It was a high civilization that lay revealed there in the desert, but by what steps had these valley people reached their imposing level of art and culture? Could the abandoned Stone Age villages have been their forerunners, and if so, how much time had elapsed between their simple culture and the elaboration of Ur, between the Stone Age and the First Dynasty? Woolley badly needed to know the order of events, the history of the region. The only way to arrive at an outline was to dig deeper at Ur to see if the record could be filled in.

As a test Woolley sank a five-foot-square shaft below the grave level. It went down through a lot of mixed rubbish, mud, bricks, ashes, and broken pottery. Then abruptly all of this debris of man ended. All at once there was only clean mud. The Arab diggers called Woolley to report that they had reached virgin soil and that there was no need to go any deeper.

Woolley took a first look and was about to agree. But with an archæologist's caution he took his levels and learned that the "virgin soil" was not nearly so deep down as he had expected. This was surprising. Woolley instructed his men to go on digging. With considerable disgust they spaded through eight feet of clean water-laid soil that yielded no sign of human activity.

And then came another great moment. At this point, flint implements and broken pottery closely similar to that at al 'Ubaid appeared before their startled eyes. Woolley climbed down into the pit and examined the newly found level with an intense excitement that he scarcely dared to admit. An idea had flashed immediately into his mind, but it seemed impossible, incredible. He quickly summoned two other members of the staff and showed them the astonishing strata. What did they think? They stared, like Woolley unable to put into words the unbelievable thing they knew they were seeing.

At this moment Mrs. Woolley arrived. She looked at the upper layers, at the eight feet of clean soil, and at the ancient remains beneath, and did not hesitate. "Of course," she cried, "it's the Flood!"

The shaft, however, was not much more than a yard square at the bottom. With such limited evidence a careful archæologist would not announce the discovery of a flood that for centuries had been regarded as one of the determinative events in the history of man. More proof had to be sought.

The next season, on the low ground where the royal cemetery had been, Woolley marked out a rectangle seventy-five feet by sixty. There he had dug a huge pit that finally was taken down sixty-four feet.

Below the grave level the new pit first disclosed the ruins of houses built of a peculiar brick with a convex top, and below them eight other levels of houses. Next came an amazing eighteen feet of broken pottery. It was soon apparent that a vase factory had once stood on the site and that the pit was cutting through the dump where broken and discarded pots had been tossed. A thin layer of sherds at the bottom of the pile came from the same kind of handmade ware that had been found at al 'Ubaid, though the painting had been much more carelessly done.

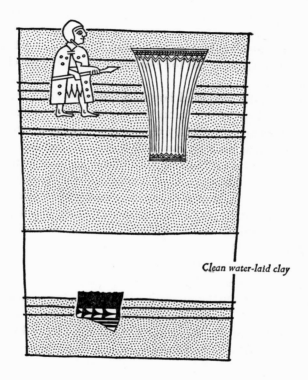

Clean water-laid clay

THE ACTUAL FLOOD. ELEVEN FEET OF CLEAN WATER-LAID CLAY TESTIFIED TO THE GREAT FLOOD THAT HAD SWEPT THE VALLEY OF THE TIGRIS AND THE EUPHRATES. BELOW THE CLAY LAY STONE-AGE POTTERY. ABOVE WERE PILED THE REMAINS OF LATER CIVILIZATIONS.

And again there was the clean silt, the clay that Woolley this time confidently noted was "piled up by the Flood." Here, however, the silt was eleven feet thick and, except for one streak of darker mud, was uniform throughout. Microscopic examination confirmed that it was water-laid and made up of materials brought down from the middle course of the Euphrates.

Below the flood silt came more decayed brick, ashes, and broken pottery, infallible evidence of human occupation. Woolley could faintly distinguish three successive pre-Flood levels. Scattered throughout was an abundance of Stone Age pottery of the hand-turned al-'Ubaid type, flints, clay figurines, and fragments of plaster still showing the form of the reed against which it once had pressed.

Here, too, the reed-mud huts had originally been set up on a little rise of ground surrounded by water. The pottery pieces scattered around at a slightly deeper level all lay horizontally as though they had been thrown into water and had settled gently down to the soft mud bottom. Below these remains of Stone Age man was only stiff green clay pierced by the brown stains of roots. All traces of human occupation had petered out. Woolley knew that at last he was at the bottom of Mesopotamia.

The spit of mud on which the huts had stood had been considerably lower than the near-by city mound of Ur. When the great flood came the huts must have been quickly and completely overwhelmed. Woolley knew at last what had happened to the huts at al 'Ubaid and to his other Stone Age island village. The deluge had written their abrupt end.

Eleven feet of silt, the maximum the expedition found, indicated a flood of not less than twenty-five feet. Genesis had fixed the Flood's depth at twenty-six feet. In the flat valley, Woolley calculated, such a flood would have covered an area three hundred miles long and one hundred miles wide. The entire valley would have been submerged, with the exception of the higher parts of the mound-built cities.

"It was not a universal deluge," declared Woolley. "It was a vast flood in the valley of the Tigris and Euphrates which drowned the whole habitable world between the mountains and the desert; for the people who lived there that was all the world.

"The great bulk of those people must have perished, and it

was but a scanty and dispirited remnant that from the city walls watched the flood recede at last. No wonder that they saw in this disaster the gods' punishment of a sinful generation, and if some household had managed to escape by boat from the drowned lowlands the head of it would naturally be chosen as the hero of the saga."

Life was never the same again in the valley; the continuity of civilization had been broken. The Flood was an end and a beginning.

In time new waves of people swept into the valley to take advantage of its fertile soil. Woolley could trace them by the pottery they left. Eventually great temples and ziggurat palaces rose on the city mounds. The flood silt lay far below. And yet the Flood remained a central and unforgotten fact in the lives of the people of the valley and in their concept of the world.

On both sides of a clay tablet the scribes of one post-Flood people scratched the story of Ziusudra, a great and good patriarch who was told by the gods to build a boat against the flood that was coming, and who did so and survived. A still later people who lived in the valley inscribed the account on twelve large tablets preserved, as befitted so important and sacred a history, in the library of the god Nabû at Nineveh.

The gods warned Utnapishtim the faithful that a flood was coming. As he lay asleep in his reed hut he was awakened by the these words:

> *Reed hut, reed hut! Wall, wall!*
> *Reed hut hearken! Wall, consider!*
> *Man of Shurippak, son of Ubara-Tutu!*
> *Tear down [thy] house, build a ship!* [1]

Humbly Utnapishtim replied: "Ea, my lord . . . what thou has commanded, [I] will honor and carry out."

[1] Alexander Heidel: *The Gilgamesh Epic and Old Testament Parallels.* Chicago: University of Chicago Press; 1949.

The flood came and overwhelmed the land, but Utnapishtim, his family, and the game and the beasts of the field which he had taken to safety with him came through unharmed, though the rest of mankind "had turned to clay." As the waters abated, Utnapishtim successively sent forth a dove, a swallow, and a raven. When the raven did not return, the group in the ark knew that they could emerge from their refuge. As they sorrowfully but thankfully stepped forth on the peak of Mount Nisir, where the ark had grounded, their first act was to pour a libation to the gods.

Other men remembered too and kept alive the story of that Great Flood. In still another account written on tablets of clay the name of the patriarch is Atrahasis. In Greece many years later they told the story of Deucalion's Flood and of Deucalion, the King of Pythia, who had been saved in the ark he built.

And then came the Bible and the majestic account known so well to men of the Western world: "In the six hundredth year of Noah's life, in the second month, the seventeenth day of the month, the same day were all the fountains of the great deep broken up, and the windows of heaven were opened. And the rain was upon the earth forty days and forty nights."

Thus the Biblical account of the deluge begins. Fed by ceaseless torrential rains and by the outpourings of the depths, the waters rose. They overflowed the banks of the rivers, they filled the valleys, and they continued to rise until they submerged the tops of the highest mountains and stood fifteen cubits above them. (A cubit is approximately a foot and a half.)

As in the earlier versions of the Flood story, one man alone was ready for this catastrophe, this end of the world as men had known it. He was the faithful, righteous Noah, a man who had stood aside from the violence and corruption to which the other descendants of Adam had given themselves. True to his precepts, he had unquestioningly obeyed when God had commanded him to build an ark, and in further obedience to those commands he had taken into it his wife, his sons, their wives,

NOAH'S ARK. THE LITTLE COCKLESHELL OF AN ARK, AND THE HOUSE ON A HULL OF THE 15TH CENTURY; THE 16TH AND 17TH CENTURIES' VERSIONS: ARKS ALMOST LARGE ENOUGH "TO CONTAINE THOSE SUNDRY CREATURES FROM WHOSE BEING CAME ALL LIVING THINGS MAN POSSIBLY COULD NAME"; AND KIRCHER'S FAMOUS ARCA NOE, THE "SCIENTIFIC ARK," WITH 300 STALLS ON THE FIRST DECK, A GRANARY ON THE SECOND, AND SPACE FOR 2,000 CAGES AND NOAH'S FAMILY ON THE THIRD.

and two of every sort of beast and bird and "every thing that
creepeth upon the earth." The great storm broke, the door of the
ark was shut, and as the flood rose the ark was lifted up and
floated free.

For five months Noah's ark rode out the awful turmoil, the
darkness, the buffeting of the winds, the forty days and forty
nights of torrential rain and the succeeding days of lesser tempest.

Not until the seventeenth day of the seventh month of the
year, according to the Hebrew Bible, did the ark ground on the
mountains of Ararat.[2] This was one hundred and fifty-one days
after the beginning of the flood, and only then had the waters
started to subside. Another seventy-four days passed before the
tops of the mountains became visible and forty days more before
Noah dared to open the window of the ark. Encouraged by the
sight of the re-emerging peaks, he sent forth a raven, which
winged its way across the waters and did not return. Seven days
later Noah tried again; this time he sent forth a dove. But the
waters still "were on the face of the whole earth" and the weary
dove returned to the one point of rest and safety.

Noah waited another seven days. Once more he opened the
window and released the dove. This time she returned to him at
evening bearing a freshly plucked olive leaf. Noah knew by this
token that the waters had fallen to the level of the lowlands
where olive trees grew.[3] Cautiously, though, he waited another
seven days and for the third time sent the dove forth. This time
she did not come back; the lowlands as well as the mountains
were nearly free of water.

It was the first of the following year, however, before the
flood waters had entirely receded from the saturated earth, and
almost two months more before men or animals could set foot on
the soggy ground. Only then, one year and eleven days after en-

[2] The Genesis account is not more specific about location. Some transla-
tors have rendered it as "the mountains of Armenia."

[3] Strabo, the Greek historian (*c.* 63 B.C.–*c.* A.D. 23), reported that olive
trees grew on the Armenian lowlands.

tering the ark, could Noah, his family, and the animals emerge and give thanks to God.

A changed world, muddy and desolate, lay before them; but the earth had received its new stock.

Every detail of the Flood was later to become of the utmost importance in shaping men's ideas of the earth. In the seventeenth century the Christian world discovered with a shock that some of the books of the Bible might be subject to a variety of readings. Scholars going back to Biblical sources had found inconsistencies in translations and in interpretations. The exactitude on which men had relied was shaken and the predicament was grave.[4]

But there was one promising way out. If it could be proved that the miracles of the Bible were true and that they could be rationally and scientifically explained, variations in translations and contradictions in words would cease to matter. A new citadel could be built, and built impregnably on science and logic. A new authority could supersede revelation.

And the Flood was one of the major miracles of the Bible, second only to the creation itself. During the latter half of the seventeenth century it became almost an obsession with scientists and scholars to prove that the deluge had occurred exactly as the Bible and legend related and that it had shaped the world exactly as the seventeenth century knew it.

Many difficult problems were inherent in this approach. Where had the water come from? How had there been enough of it to cover the entire world, even to the tops of the highest mountains? What had become of the waters at the end of the Flood? Such questions had to be faced if the Flood was to be rationalized.

It had early occurred to some thinkers that if the surface of the antediluvial world had been flatter than the mountainous

[4] The whole crisis that arose between reason and the text of the Bible is most interestingly discussed in Don Cameron Allen's *The Legend of Noah* (Urbana: University of Illinois Press; 1949). This book also presents an excellent review of all the literature on the Flood.

face of their earth, a much smaller rise in the waters could have submerged the entire globe. In fact, Antonio de Torquemada had suggested in 1614 in his *Jardin de Flores Curiosas* that "the whole world before the time of the flood was plaine and levell, without any hill or valley at all."

This intriguing idea later set a noted Cambridge cleric to pondering. Once started, Thomas Burnet (1635–1715) was not one to stop short of seeking the whole truth. In the early 1680's Burnet began by computing that it would have taken eight oceans of water to create the deluge, "that great Ocean rowling in the Air without bounds or banks." But his figures also showed that forty days and forty nights of the heaviest rainfall, plus the "Breaking open of the fountains of the deep," would have produced only one ocean of water.

"Whither shall we go," he asked, "to find the more than seven oceans of water that we still want?"

Burnet refused to "cut the knot" by simply saying that God created the waters and then annihilated them again. Did not Augustine, Moses, and St. Peter all say that the Flood had occurred by natural means? It was Burnet's object to prove that it had.

Neither would Burnet accept the explanation that the Flood was only a local inundation. If that had been the case, the "borderers" could surely have escaped by crossing to higher land, and there would have been no need for Noah to build his ark.

The Flood, as Burnet saw it, would also have had to be universal to carry out God's purpose of eradicating all sinners. He calculated that in the sixteen hundred years that had passed between the creation and the Flood, 10,737,418,240 men and women had been born. Surely they would have spread around the world and to all of its continents. To wipe them out, the Flood would certainly have had to be global. Burnet considered it significant that the people of Mexico, China, and other lands also had legends of a great flood that had devastated the world.

Thus, eight oceans of water there had to be; they "lay heavy" on Burnet's thoughts. To obtain them, the Cambridge scholar worked out a hypothesis that had to be at the same time a hypothesis of how the earth came to be and of how it had assumed its outer form.

In the beginning, Burnet held, the earth had been different. It must, he reasoned, have come nearer to "plainness and equality," and it could therefore have been more easily "overflowed" and the deluge could have been "performed with less water." The "paring off" of the mountains made the inundation possible, but it did not solve the problem of what had happened to the water at the end of the Flood. How had it been disposed of?

Burnet had looked contemplatively and well at the mountains, the rocks, the precipices, the caverns, the islands, and the jagged coastlines of the earth, and the conviction grew in him that "the world which we inhabit hath been broke and dislocat'd." That insight led him to his solution.

When the earth was created out of a chaos of "little particles" and water "fixt together and floating in confusion," the heavier elements sank to the center. There they formed a hard symmetrical core. The water separated and surrounded the center, while the limitless leftovers of creation, the fine dusts, filled the air above. Slowly, though, the airborne particles began to settle down upon the waters. As they mixed with the "oily liquor" they coalesced and hardened into a thick, smooth skin. This even orb of an earth was without mountains and without seas, "for all the mass of Waters was enclos'd within."

Not a wrinkle, not a scar or a fracture marred the young globe's "beauty of youth," and even the air above was calm and serene. It seemed to Burnet a perfect world "well suited to a golden age" and to the "first innocency of Nature."

But the sun, beating down relentlessly on this flawless fresh earth, gradually dried and cracked the smooth skin and heated the waters that lay below. As time went on, the cracks grew wider and the vapors produced by the underlying super-heated waters pressed "to break out." At a time chosen by Providence for punishing a sinful people "the whole fabric broke and the frame of the earth was torn into pieces, as by an earth quake." Great fragments of the crust toppled into the watery abyss. The displaced waters, rising in a mountainous wave, swept across the surface, carrying with them "Woods, Buildings, living Creatures" and all. This was the deluge, the mighty deluge. Only a broken, ruined, wild, and disordered world remained.

Burnet urged any doubters to take a look at the globe. The lines where the earth had split were self-evident, he argued. There lay the Atlantic and Pacific oceans and the Mediterranean Sea.

Along the edges where the broken, twisted chunks of the crust had fallen were the shallows and shoals, the gulfs, the cataracts, the pits within pits, the rocks on rocks, and the ragged islands that looked so much like "countries torn up by the roots and tossed into the sea." The seas had been born and they were a wild and multifarious confusion.

"The best apology that can be made for Nature in this case," said Burnet, ". . . is to confess that the whole business of the Sea-Channel is but a ruine, and in a ruine things tumble uncertainly and commonly lie in confusion.

In his travels on the Continent, Burnet had crossed the Alps and the Apennines. As he gazed over their great heights and expanse, he was deeply moved. Thoughts of the infinite came into his mind. And yet his conscience forced him to admit that the mountains also were a disordered, aimless anarchy.

Burnet, like most scholars of the day, did not engage in close field studies. Nevertheless, he examined the mountains carefully enough to see that they were of one continued substance with the body of the earth. They were not, as some maintained, laid upon the earth as a tombstone; nor did they stand as a statue on a pedestal. They also were products of the great collapse. When the arched sections of the crust crashed into the abyss they piled up in an area necessarily narrower than their own width. It was like an arched bridge falling into a narrow stream below.

" 'Tis absolutely certain," wrote Burnet, "that it could not all fall flat or be under water: now as all those parts that stood above the water made dry land or the habitable Earth, so such parts of the dry land as stood higher than the rest made the Hills and Mountains."

The upended protruding pieces of the crust were more than enough to account for all the mountains of the earth, Burnet reasoned. And if the mountains appeared in clusters and ridges, was this not the general posture assumed by fallen material from any collapsed structure?

Burnet's first thought that this was a broken earth seemed everywhere substantiated. This was in truth a shattered globe, a ruin.

Burnet set forth his theories in a book that first appeared in 1681. It was written in Latin and only twenty-five copies were issued. But interest in it was intense, and in 1684 the Cambridge University clergyman wrote a fuller and more popular English version:

THE THEORY OF THE EARTH

CONTAINING AN ACCOUNT

OF THE

ORIGINAL OF THE EARTH

AND OF ALL THE CHANGES

WHICH IT HATH ALREADY UNDERGONE

OR

IS TO UNDERGO

TILL THE CONSUMMATION OF ALL THINGS

Burnet's unique theory at once aroused strong opposition, particularly from the theologians. The clergyman, whose main object was to buttress the Bible, was accused of "striking at the roots of religion." What alarmed the critics was Burnet's theory of the creation; if the earth had come into being as he said, far more than the six Biblical days would have been required. Some

also questioned whether there could have been as much alteration of the earth's surface as Burnet claimed. So much change,
said one objector, was "hitherto never dreamt of."

The majority, however, believed with Burnet that the Flood
had remade the surface of the earth and had piled up the mountains. It was "certain" that the mountains were linked to the
Flood. For centuries men had found sea shells buried in their
stone. Most students assumed that they were the shells of animals that had perished in the Flood, though others insisted that
they were "productions formed in imitation of life."

John Ray (1628–1705), another Cambridge University clergyman who was to be deeply involved in the dispute about the
earth and the Flood, knew too much about the form and structure
of living things to think that the fossils could be "stone cast in
animal molds." He was a skilled naturalist. Ray saw that some of
the fossil shells he picked up in deep-lying mountain strata were
exactly like the shells he gathered on the beaches. Others were
the remains of fish that he knew lived only in the deep seas.
Still others, like the perplexing cornua ammonis, the "serpent
stone," differed from all other known species of shells; a naturalist was bound to call it a different species.

But if the fossils were the remains of living creatures—a fact
that Ray had no wish to deny—how had they come to be buried
in deep strata and in the mountains? The problem disturbed Ray
both as a naturalist and as a clergyman.

As a devout Christian, Ray did not question that the fossils
had somehow been deposited in Noah's Flood. If, however, the
Flood had lasted for only the ten months and thirteen days that
Ray calculated, the animal bodies would not have settled in deep
strata but would have been spread thin across the earth. Instead
he often found them "amassed in great Lumps" and lying thick in
beds of sand. The deep-sea fossils and the unknown species also
had to be accounted for. To say that the "stone serpents" had
come into existence and then disappeared was worse than offering no explanation at all. Such a conclusion would undermine

the tenet that all species had descended from those Noah had saved in the ark; it would be an unbearable heresy.

But Ray felt keenly that the issues raised by these problems could not be avoided. To do so, he said, would simply place a weapon in the hands of atheists. Ray therefore worked out a hypothesis to explain all these incongruous facts. He presented it first in a series of sermons, and then, to "make amends" for the natural-history books that he, a clergyman, had published, he put his argument into a book. The edition which came out in 1693 was entitled: *Three physico-theological Discourses, concerning, I. The primitive Chaos and Creation of the world. II. The general Deluge, its Causes and Effects. III. The dissolution of the World and the future Conflagration.*

Ray saw no reason to question the testimony of Hesiod and other "ancient heathen writers" that the world was created out of chaos. Genesis had confirmed it: "And the earth was without form, and void."

If in the Creator's great wisdom the terrestrial globe had been made "partly of solid and more ponderous parts" and partly of fluids and lighter materials, "surely the most solid and ponderous must needs naturally subside and the fluid and lighter get above."

Like Burnet, Ray envisioned an early water-covered earth. Unlike his fellow student of these fundamental questions, he was uncertain about what had happened to disrupt this early perfect symmetry. Ray thought it likely that great internal fires in the hard core of the globe might well have thrust great blocks of the "ponderous" matter high above the surrounding waters.

Think, he suggested, of the incredible effect of gunpowder: "It rends Rocks and blows up the most ponderous Walls, Towers and Edifices. . . . Why then might not a proportionable quantity of such materials set fire together, raise up the Mountains themselves, how great and ponderous soever they be, yea, the whole Superficies of the dry land (for it must all be elevated) above the Waters?"

Ray granted Burnet's observation that the earth which resulted looked like a veritable "heap of rubbish and ruins," and
that there were no "greater examples of confusion in Nature
than the Mountains, singly or jointly considered." And yet as a
lover of nature, Ray could not quite yield to so derogatory a
dismissal.

"The present Face of the Earth, with all the Mountains and
Hills, its Promontories and Rocks, as rude and deformed as they
appear, seem to me," he wrote, "a very beautiful and pleasant
Object . . . and far more grateful to behold than a perfectly
level Country, without any Rising or Protuberancy."

On his collecting expeditions Ray often studied the movements of water through the ground, the seepages, the springs,
the streams flowing through caves. He became convinced that
all the surface waters and the seas were connected through the
ground network with the waters of the abyss. It seemed to Ray
that the ebb and flow of waters through the network might be
compared to the human circulatory system.

In this way, he argued, excess waters were safely drained
away and the springs and rivers replenished with a constant in-
flow from below. So well did the system work that the half-
ocean of rain that Ray estimated fell on the earth each day
could be absorbed with little or no variation in the world's water
levels. An equilibrium was maintained.

Then suddenly came the forty days and nights of Noah's
downpour. The balance was upset; the abyss was overfilled. Impelled by the relentless pressures built up, the waters burst
forth "At those wide Mouths and Apertures made by the Divine
Power breaking up the Fountains of the Deep." The waters also
forced their way outward through all the natural outlets, and
with a tremendous surge overflowed the earth.

Swept along in the outpouring waters were the fish and other
creatures of the seas. Perhaps some that were washed up from
the depths belonged to species that man would never again see.

That could account for the "serpent stones" and other fossils so notably unlike all species living in Ray's time. Ray thought that lesser floods might also have washed fish away from their habitats into connected waters, perhaps even into waters that flowed out in the higher parts of the mountains.

Many dilemmas had been solved by the gentle Cambridge naturalist and clergyman. Cuvier, the great French scientist, pointed out later in the *Biographie Universelle* that Ray had presented "a system of geology as plausible as any which had previously appeared or was produced for a long time afterwards."

Plausible though they might be, Burnet's and Ray's theories of the Flood and the earth could not satisfy John Woodward (1665–1728), professor of physics in Gresham College. A noted collector of fossils shells, he was the founder of the famous Woodwardian Collection.

On his busy trips about England, Woodward "searched" all places "as he pass'd along." He paid particular attention to "Grottos, or other Natural Caverns, Mines, Quarries, and Colepits"— in fact, to any digging. He would meticulously observe all plants, shells, or fluids that he could see from the "surface quite down to the bottom" and enter his findings in a notebook that he "carry'd along for that purpose." What especially impressed him were the stratified beds in which the fossils lay.

"By far the greatest part of the Terrestrial Globe consists of [Strata] from its Surface downward to the greatest depth we ever mine or dig," Woodward reported. "Upon my Observations of this I have ground'd all my general Conclusions concerning the Earth . . . and the Vicissitudes and Alterations that it hath undergone."

Woodward, a positive man, was certain that the fossils were "all remains of the Universal Deluge, when the Water of the Ocean, being boisterously turn'd out upon the Earth, bore along with it Fishes of all sorts, Shells, and like moveable Bodies."

About what happened next Woodward differed decidedly with his fellow students of the earth. All of the facts, he believed, indicated another order of events.

While the waters lay upon the earth, Woodward maintained, "Stone and all other solid Minerals lost their solidity, dissolving into their constituent particles." The dissolved bits of earth, chalk, and "all the rest" mixed with the "bodies" in the water in a vast "common and confus'd Mass." As the Flood subsided, the suspended particles and "bodies" began to settle, each according to its specific gravity.

The heavy shells of periwinkles and scallops and the weighty particles that would form marble went to the bottom first. The lighter chalk and the little shells of the echini gently drifted down together, forming a thick deposit atop the marble. The still lighter particles and bits, like the carapaces of lobsters and the branches of trees and shrubs, were the last to be deposited and hence made the top layer—a layer that would soon rot and turn into the fertile soil of the earth.[5]

Through this ordered, selective process, the doctor argued, the strata were laid down "plain, eaven, and regular." An earth as smoothly layered as an onion was taking shape. It was not to endure. Before the last vestiges of the Flood had disappeared, forces "seated within the Earth exerted themselves." There was a "mighty Revolution," the most horrible and portentous catastrophe nature had ever known. The "elegant and habitable" earth was quite unhinged; it was shattered into pieces and tumbled into a "heap of ruins." Strata heaved up to great heights became the mountains; those that were only crumpled and buckled, the hills. In the chaos other sections collapsed into depressions—this was the origin of the valleys and the "channel of the sea." Occa-

---

[5] In 1697 John Arbuthnot reported in his book *An Examination of Dr. Woodward's Account of the Deluge* that he had tested this settling theory. He tossed oyster shells and an equal weight of metal powder into some water. The oyster shells sank first. And Ray pointed out that he had found lighter and heavier shells mixed indiscriminately in the same strata.

sionally the sinking of large segments left a piece of land standing alone—an island.

"The whole terraqueous Globe was . . . at the time of the Deluge put into the Condition that we now behold," Woodward announced in 1695.

A ruined world, yes. And yet Woodward, like Ray, believed that good had been created out of chaos. Out of the "highest confusion and disorder" had come "the most consummate and absolute Order and Beauty," the world as it is.

Woodward promised that in a later and larger work he would explain how the stones had dissolved while trees and shrubs remained intact, and that he would tell more exactly how the cataclysm had come about. Somehow this larger book was never written.

At about this time, the last part of the seventeenth century, knowledge had suddenly moved forward with one of the tremendous leaps that come at rare intervals in man's study of the universe. In 1687 Sir Isaac Newton had published his *Principia*, which he had subtitled "The Frame of the System of the World." The frame of the system, the laws of motion and the movements of the earth and universe, had been discovered with unchallengeable accuracy.

Within a few years man's whole view of the earth and its relation to the universe was changed. And suddenly too there was new hope of solving the basic questions about how the earth came to be; if the laws of gravitation and the dynamics of the solar system could be worked out, surely it should be possible by applying the laws of mathematics to accomplish as much in the study of the earth.

Newton's successor as Lucasian professor of mathematics at Cambridge, William Whiston, proposed in his turn to solve this greatest of the remaining moral and physical problems and to do so in the light of the new knowledge. His theory of the origin of the earth and of how the Flood descended upon it and remade it was set forth in a book that epitomized the thinking of the seventeenth century generally, rather than that of its great light Newton.

Whiston's book, published in 1696, was called:

A NEW THEORY OF THE EARTH

FROM ITS ORIGINAL, TO THE

CONSUMMATION OF ALL THINGS

WHEREIN

THE CREATION OF THE WORLD IN SIX DAYS,

THE UNIVERSAL DELUGE

AND GENERAL CONFLAGRATION

AS LAID DOWN IN THE HOLY SCRIPTURES

ARE SHEWN TO BE PERFECTLY AGREEABLE TO

REASON AND PHILOSOPHY

In the *Principia* Newton had established the rules for calculating the orbits of comets, and had proved that the gravitational pull of the moon and the sun produced the tides in the oceans of the earth. Here Whiston saw the solution to his problem—a solution that he submitted in manuscript to Newton.

Earlier attempts to explain the Flood had erred, Whiston argued, because they had been based on the mistaken philosophies of Aristotle and Ptolemy, both of whom had assumed that the universe revolved around the earth. The "new and wonderful" discoveries in astronomy had not only shown how wrong such theories were, but how right were the "genuine contents of the Holy Books themselves."

Drawing upon Newton's astronomy as he saw it, and upon mathematics, "ancient testimony," and other material, Whiston "proved" that the deluge was brought upon the earth by a comet that had briefly flashed into the earth's orbit.

"On the first day of the Deluge," wrote Whiston, "it passed just before the Body of our Earth. If we consider . . . that the outward regions of its [the comet's] Atmosphere are plain Vapours, or such a sort of Mist as we frequently see with us; and the Tail a column of the same Vapours rarified and expanded to a greater degree . . . and that withal such a comet is capable of passing so close by the Body of the Earth as to involve it in its Atmosphere and Tail a considerable time, and leave prodigious quantities of the same Condensed and Expanded Vapours on its Surface; we shall easily see that a Deluge of Waters is by no means an impossible thing; and in particular that such an individual Deluge as to the Time, Quantity, and Circumstances which Moses describes, is no more so, but fully accountable, that it might be, nay is almost demonstrable that it really was."

The cloudburst began when the head of the comet approached the "terrestrial Paradise." Since the ark lay slightly to the east of the Garden of Eden, Noah and his train had time to get into the ark before the comet's waters sluiced down and the great tide it induced swept across the face of the earth.

Whiston interpreted the Biblical statement that the waters at the "utmost height" stood fifteen cubits above the highest mountains to mean that they rose about three miles "perpendicular above the common surface of those Plains which adjoined the Ark, or about fifty Miles higher than the usual height of the Common Surface of the Earth before."

The Cambridge mathematician was willing to concede that the "primitive Earth," the antediluvian earth, had possessed mountains and valleys somewhat similar to those of the world of his day. But when the deluge engulfed the earth, he said, the top layers of the earth were loosened, separated, and divided, and so "floated in the Waters."

On this point Whiston was in close agreement with Woodward, and he also believed that the huge mass of material suspended in the waters settled according to the law of "specifick gravity" and thus formed "the several Strata or Layers of which our present upper Earth does Consist." In this way the "upper Earth" was "acquir'd at the Deluge, the ancient one. having been covered with fresh Strata at that time."

Since the deluge, said Whiston, "there neither has been, nor will be any great or general Changes in the State of the World, till that time when a Period is put to the present Course of Nature."

Burnet had explained the earth's seemingly unexplainable confusion of heights and depths and land and water as the disordered result of the cracking of the surface and the flood that collapse produced. Ray in his turn had attributed the chaos of the surface to the bursting of vast underground reservoirs, overfilled by the forty days and forty nights of unending downpour. Woodward had insisted upon a different order—the dissolution of almost everything in the Flood and the later disruption of the Flood deposits. Whiston traced the havoc and irregularity to the deluge unloosed by a comet.

The earth, in short, was as Burnet had said, "a ruine." Only a cataclysmic universal flood and an utter upheaval could have produced the monumental confusion. And, the seventeenth century argued, such a wild tortuous disarray as the earth's surface was exactly what might be expected when the fountains of the deep were broken up and the windows of heaven opened. One proved the other, and vice versa.

Each of these major theories of how the Flood and the post-Flood world came to be had a certain plausibility and logic; they were earnest efforts to answer man's continuing questions about the outer form and inner workings of his world. Nevertheless, there were always discrepancies, always facts that remained outside the nicely rounded, imaginative explanations. And soon there was graver difficulty.

If Newton's law of gravity were applied, the crust could not have formed as Burnet said. The hypotheses of Ray, Woodward, and Whiston fared no better when they were examined by critics with a knowledge of physics and astronomy. According to physical law, the earth and comets could not have behaved as had been assumed.

The most devastating blow in words, if not in scientific disproof, came from the French naturalist Buffon. Speaking of the theories of Burnet, Woodward, and Whiston in the first pages of his *Natural History,* he wrote: "The whole of these hypotheses are raised on unstable foundations; have given no light upon the subject, the ideas being unconnected, the facts confused, and the whole confounded with a mixture of physic and fable; and consequently have been adopted only by those who implicitly believe opinions without investigation, and who, incapable of distinguishing probability, are more impressed with the wonders of the marvellous than the relation of the truth."

But the world at large did believe implicitly. For the next one hundred and fifty years, at least, few questioned that the surface of the earth as they knew it had been shaped by the Flood: the mighty universal Flood envisioned by the seventeenth-century scholars, not the limited valley flood that was to be discovered many years later by Woolley. Theirs was a Flood-made world. The Flood explained everything; it was the science of the earth.

By the time Woolley dug into that unsuspected water-laid silt so far below the surface of Mesopotamia and proved the existence of a great though not universal flood in the days of the Stone Age, men had already learned that the face of the earth had been sculptured by other forces. The Flood no longer mattered in the understanding of the earth. Its simultaneous discovery and limitation therefore produced no intellectual or scientific crisis.

What had mattered critically was the long legend of the Flood—the legend that grew out of the actual destruction of the valley in that overwhelming and unforgettable flood of the Tigris and the Euphrates, the relating of that story through all of history, and its expansion in the seventeenth century into full-rounded theories of the earth. Few legends have had so profound an effect on men's ideas.

But even as Burnet, Ray, Woodward, Whiston, and the others of the seventeenth century constructed their theories of how the

Flood had made the world, they tried to take some account of the facts of the earth as they had observed them. They had studied fossils and strata and attempted conscientiously to fit them to their theories. They had begun to observe the earth in order to understand the earth. The stage was being set for the second act.

The first act in men's discovery of their earth had been one of high drama, of gods, reason, and the consummate catastrophe of universal flood. The second was to be no less astounding.

Part Two

AN UNSUSPECTED PAST

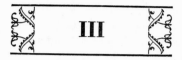

III

GUETTARD

A PAST OF FIRE

"It was a long time before men came to understand that any true theory of the earth must rest upon evidence furnished by the globe itself." [1]

A RAUCOUS LAUGH greeted the roughly dressed young Frenchman who was showing his handful of stone "apples" and "pears." He had his pockets full too. He had just told the Normandy villagers gathered around him that the stone "fruit" was not fruit at all but the fossilized bodies of animals that once had lived in a sea covering their land. People made signs with their hands that he was crazy. Everyone knew that the stones were fruit that had fallen from the trees and turned to stone in the earth. And the talk about Normandy having been under the sea only proved how demented he was.

On this occasion Jean Étienne Guettard did not argue. He went on his way and returned to the careful study of the earth which had brought him to Normandy and which in the end would make him one of the world's first geologists. By painstakingly examining the earth, instead of plying his imagination, Guettard would upset other old beliefs about the earth, although those whose legends were destroyed would not believe him any more than had the Normandy villagers. He would, more impor-

[1] Sir Archibald Geikie: *The Founders of Geology*. London: MacMillan and Co.; 1897.

tantly, demonstrate a promising new way to seek the answers to men's persistent questions about the baffling outer form of the earth, its rocks, its fossils, its volcanoes.

Guettard, of course, did not set out upon such a career. He was born at Étampes, a little town about thirty miles southwest of Paris, on September 22, 1715. When he was still very young his grandfather, the local apothecary, began to take him along on plant-collecting trips about the area. The child was happy and absorbed in learning to identify the plants and to distinguish their parts. He played at nothing else.

His grandfather had intended Jean to follow him as the village apothecary. When the time of decision came, Guettard's knowledge of plants was so remarkable that it had come to the attention of the directors of the Jardin des Plantes in Paris. These famed gentlemen urged him to go on with his studies. Medicine offered the most promising approach to his interests, and he therefore became a doctor.

As a young man without family connections or money, Guettard was glad to attach himself to the suite of the Duke of Orléans, an enthusiastic naturalist. He traveled with the Duke and supervised his natural-history collections. The powerful nobleman liked Guettard's love of science, his indifference to everything else, and his frankness. In turn, working with the Duke gave Guettard an opportunity to carry on his nature studies. At the Duke's death his son kept Guettard in charge of the collections and gave him a very small pension and modest quarters in the Palais Royal. That was enough for his simple needs.

Guettard had been interested in parasitic plants almost since his childhood. A study that he carried on with the old Duke classified them and revealed their true nature, whereas botanists before Guettard had been satisfied "simply to observe" these unusual plants. The work won him admission to the Académie Royale des Sciences in 1743.

In his wanderings about France, Guettard had noticed how often the distribution of plants depended on the occurrence of certain minerals and rocks. He began to trace this dependence from one district to another, and gradually became more and more interested in what was then called "mineralogy." Guettard may be considered a geologist in the fullest and truest sense of the word, though the words "geology" and "geologist" would not be coined for another half-century. He not only studied the distribution of rocks and minerals all over Europe, but he sought to determine the natural laws that would explain what he saw. In sharp contrast to most of the students of the earth who preceded him, he did not resort to conjecture; he shied away from it.

Some rocks that Guettard was studying were abundant in certain sections, but disappeared in adjoining regions only to crop up again in other places. Perhaps then rocks were not just indiscriminately spotted around. If there were some order in their occurrence, Guettard understood that it should be possible, once the breadth and direction of any band was known, to predict what rocks would be found along the band's course, even if it should pass into another country.

For Guettard this was a beginning, an insight that would lead him far. He started to make maps showing the distribution of rocks, minerals, and the fossil shells that he saw in so many places. With tiny symbols for chemicals and fossils and with cross-hatching and other devices he charted three great bands of rock which ran across France and suddenly came to an end at the English Channel.

Was it possible that they might re-emerge in England? Guettard did not have the means to go to England to see, so he ransacked French editions of whatever books on English natural history he could find. Although the information available to him was less than satisfactory, it was enough to show that his bands continued on across the southeast English counties. His surmise had been right! It was a stirring discovery for the scientist who had worked so laboriously over his facts and who had plodded so many miles collecting them.

Guettard reported in a memoir to the Academy, and both his paper and his unusual map were printed in the *"histoire"* or proceedings of the Academy for 1751. In the annual summary of the important work of the year, Guettard's contribution was cited as a significant new application of geography which, ignoring political boundaries, had sought to group the different regions according to the nature of the substances that lay below the surface.

"The work of M. Guettard," the proceedings said, "opens up a new field for geographers and naturalists, and forms, so to speak, a link between the two sciences which have hitherto been regarded as entirely independent of each other."

Guettard eagerly plunged into an effort to map the mineral formations underlying all of France and pleaded with the Academy to sponsor a similar atlas for all of Europe. With the assistance of the noted chemist Lavoisier, and traveling more than forty-eight hundred miles, he managed to complete sixteen sheets of the proposed French map. But the effort was a prodigious one, and it proved beyond the strength of one man. Guettard was forced to turn it over to a successor, who later published the maps.

The making of a mineralogical map had been discussed in England earlier, but Guettard's maps were the first to be published. The Marquis de Condorcet, the perpetual secretary of the Academy, in his warm, accurate *"éloge"* of Guettard, pointed out: "He was the first naturalist who saw the necessity for mineralogical maps and who dared to conceive this and to execute a part of it." He was thus the forerunner of the great geological surveys of later years.

As Guettard traveled widely, working on his maps, he collected a vast amount of information which he could not include on them. From time to time he would bring together data about a particular region and present it to the Academy. He was one of its most prolific members—and one of the most disputatious. Few other Academicians were involved in so many open quarrels.

Guettard did not argue for the sake of arguing. But he was remarkably well posted on the resources of France and on the many divisions of science. When he heard a false or pretentious statement he bluntly attacked it. He was equally unsparing of friend or foe. His friends forgave him, for they understood and appreciated the honesty that lay behind his attacks, and, as Condorcet said, "such frankness at least inspired confidence; one knew what to hope for and what to fear."

A colleague once thanked Guettard for giving him his vote in an Academy election. Guettard answered with his unusual outspokenness: "You owe me nothing. If I had not believed that it was right to give it to you, you would not have had it, for I do not like you."

In his plain, simple clothes and with his direct manner Guettard stood in great contrast to the elegance and suavity of some members of the Academy. His appearance did not belie his position and beliefs. He suspected all grandeur and éclat; to him the first seemed only a thinly veiled device for tyranny and the latter a deception.

On the other hand, he was unfailingly kind to the underdog. And when he was convinced that real merit and a love of freedom were present, he could accept and like someone guilty even of social rank or of the elegance he despised. Condorcet himself was one such friend. Chrétien de Malesherbes, president of the Cour des Aides and minister "maison du roi" to Louis XVI, was another—a close friend with a love of science and liberty that equaled Guettard's own. Moreover, Condorcet had often heard Guettard speak with the keenest interest and warmth of some scholar with whom he was warring on a scientifie issue and whom he seemed to despise.

The Academy and the men in the government respected this able, plain-duckling member. His services were often in demand. France had become disturbed because her porcelain, which she considered superior to that of the Chinese in color and beauty, was not so durable. It was decided that the trouble lay in the materials used. Guettard was assigned to search for materials equal to those used by the Chinese, and he found them. At the request of the government he also experimented with the firing of different sands and clays, and worked out a table showing the French porcelain-makers exactly the treatment required for each material.

Many of the fossils sent to Paris for study and identification were routed to Guettard, for he had become an authority on them too. He had collected thousands of fossils and had charted huge fossiliferous strata on his maps. His training in natural history aided him in identification. In some slate sent to the Academy from Angers, Guettard observed numerous casts and impressions of seaweeds and crustacea. He very sagaciously compared the latter to modern crabs and prawns. He wrote exact detailed descriptions of many of these unknown fossils and made excellent drawings of them for presentation to the Academy.

Guettard, with his knowledge, could not question that the fossils were the remains of sea creatures; everything that he saw made it undeniable. Nor could he overlook the miles-long deposits of fossil-bearing rock that stretched over much of France. He could come to only one conclusion.

He reported to the Academy: "Shells and other debris of marine animals are often found at great depths and even on the inside of rocks. They can only have been brought to such places by the sea, and they are irreproachable witnesses that the sea once covered a large part of our globe."

The direct examination of the earth was leading to startling results. But the unbelieving people of Normandy, where Guettard made many of his early collections of fossil coral and sponge, were not the only ones to regard such talk as the vaporous outpouring of a half-wit or worse. At almost the same time that Guettard was making his detailed studies and demonstrating the marine origin of fossils, a Swiss naturalist, Bertrand, was insisting that fossil plants and animals were placed in the earth by the Creator for the express purpose of displaying the harmony of His work—by a matching of the productions of land and sea. Others held with similar fervor that fossils were created by the devil to deceive, mislead, and perplex man.

"It is difficult perhaps, to imagine ourselves in the position of naturalists about the middle of the last century to whom such opinions seemed perfectly logical, natural, and probable," said Sir Archibald Geikie in a lecture to American geologists in 1896. "But unless we make the effort to realize the attitude of men's minds in those days, we cannot rightly appreciate the acumen and sagacity of the arguments with which Guettard assailed these opinions."

Guettard assailed them not with argument but with facts. He brought in fossil shells to which other fossil shells were attached. He produced others to which fossilized barnacles still were clinging, and others into which sea organisms had bored. Fossil wormholes were a little too much for even the strongest believers in the harmony of productions. To cap his case Guettard showed that in innumerable instances fossil shells were broken and worn; often whole layers of rock were made up of the bits.

It struck the French naturalist as he studied such fossils that the beds in which he found them bore the closest possible resemblance to the floor of the sea in his own day. In the sea, barnacles were clinging to shells just as barnacles had clung to those ancient ones. Exactly the same accidents were happening to shells on the existing sea floor as had befallen the fossil shells. Shells were being broken, crumbled, and packed on the sea bottom, just as they once had been no one knew how many years before. Guettard set down these confounding facts in a memoir to the Academy.

"Of course nowadays such reasoning appears to us so obvious as to involve no great credit to the writer who elaborated it," said Sir Archibald. "But we must remember the state of natural knowledge more than one hundred and thirty years ago. As an example of the method of explaining and illustrating the former condition of the earth's surface by what can be seen to happen now, Guettard's memoir is unquestionably one of the most illustrious in the literature of geology, opening up, as it did, a new field in the investigation of the history of our globe, and unfolding the method by which this field had to be cultivated."

As he mapped, measured, and examined rocks, Guettard was impressed too by the wearing-down to which they were subjected. If shells were worn and shunted about by the movement of the sea, it was equally evident that the stone of the land was being worn, dissolved, and washed away by rains, rivers, and the sea. It was being carried down into the valleys, Guettard saw, and ultimately to the sea. Guettard had one personal experience that underlined what was happening.

When he was a child at Étampes he often played under a picturesque crag called the Rock of the Good Virgin. Its outlines suggested a woman with a child in her arms. Years later when Guettard returned to the crag he found that the rock had broken away and lay in a pile at the foot of the slope. Rocks that he had never seen as a child—Guettard had a remarkable memory of the country—had appeared. It looked almost as though they had grown out of the earth, and yet Guettard knew of course that they had only been exposed by the washing away of the soil that had hidden them. And new deep ravines had been cut in the little valley. All of this had happened in the short span of part of one man's lifetime.

In other places too Guettard saw and recognized the work of heavy rains and flooded streams. Not only were the rocks moldering down the sides of hills; the hills were being gashed by ravines and even deep defiles. Guettard determined that the landslides that sometimes dramatized the process were not due to internal fires or subterranean winds, as many people held, but to the penetration of water into the surface of the hill. He was thus one of the first to recognize the efficacy of sub-surface as well as surface water in changing the face of the country.

The sea, however, seemed to Guettard to be the most powerful destroyer of the land. All along the northwest coast of France stretched high chalk cliffs. The sea pounded at them, loosening a grain, a boulder, a whole face, and washing it away in the sweep of the waves. Guettard told the Academy that he was convinced the cliffs were the relics of a long chain of hills, the greater part of which had been gradually but relentlessly washed away by the sea.

Guettard made a further point that is obvious to anyone today but was radical and astounding in his time: the rocks and soil eroded away and carried off by the streams were not destroyed but redeposited along the banks of the rivers, at their mouths, and along the shore of the sea. Sometimes, he said, this broken, fine substance of the earth is carried far from its point of origin—a matter, he suggested, that might profitably be borne in mind by those seeking deposits of minerals and useful stone.

Plains watered by the rivers had often become one big sheet of gravel as the streams changed their courses time and again and flowed over every part of bordering alluvial tracts. At the mouths of the rivers the sediments came to rest, but only transiently, Guettard said, for they were liable to be dislodged soon again and carried farther along on their seaward course.

At the sea's margins Guettard had watched for and seen evidence that the materials brought down by the rivers, and by the sea's own depredations on the land, were ground into sand by the ceaseless and violent rolling of the waves. The sea, he also noted, eats at its own partly submerged rock. All of this churning detritus of the land and the sea, he added, was mixed with the remains of coral, shells, fishbones, and marine plants as it settled endlessly and silently downward to the bottom.

Little was known in Guettard's day of the sea bottom. He was doubtful that the sediments that he had traced from the hills and the shores and the beaches were piled into mountains on the floor of the sea. In a memoir to the Academy he wrote:

"It follows from all of these observations here recited, that the deposits laid down by the sea along its shore are sandy and loamy; that these deposits do not extend far out to sea; that, consequently, the erection of new mountains by the sea by the deposition of sediment is a process very difficult to conceive; that still more difficult to accept is the suggestion that sediment from our continent is carried into the seas of the New World. In short we are still very little advanced towards the theory of the earth as it now exists. All the systems which have been devised on this subject are full of difficulties which appear to me to be insoluble."

Others before Guettard had understood that the rains were eroding the earth. Ray, some ninety years earlier, had spoken of "rains continually washing down and carrying earth away from the mountains." A group of Italian geologists, who traditionally gave more direct study to the earth than their counterparts in other countries, also had called attention to the degradation of mountains. Nevertheless, Guettard's memoir "On the Degradation of Mountains Effected in Our Time by Heavy Rains, Rivers, and the Sea" was the first to go into the whole system of the denudation of the earth and the transport of its materials to the sea. Guettard also had glimpsed the key point that most sediments accumulated along the shores of the seas, not farther out. And yet they did not pile up into mountains. While Guettard was unable to explain this baffling phenomenon—it would be almost exactly a hundred years before it was explained —he was wise enough to say that he did not know and to recommend the whole problem as one for "accurate and prolonged observation."

It was in 1752 that Guettard and his fellow naturalist Malesherbes set out for the south to obtain additional mineralogical data for the map of France. Near Moulins they noticed with surprise that the mileposts were made of a black stone. Guettard examined it closely; he thought it was of volcanic origin. Amazed at this, for no volcanoes had ever been known in that part of France, he quickly inquired where it had come from. He was told: "From Volvic."

"*Volcani vicus!*" cried Guettard with instant recognition of the source of the name.[2] "There must have been a volcano there."

Guettard and Malesherbes decided at once to change their plans and make for the area from which the stone had come. As they went farther along the road more of the black stone appeared. At Riom almost the entire city was built of it. And then, a short distance beyond the city, the two naturalists, with a growing sense of excitement which they did not try to suppress, saw looming ahead of them an undoubted volcanic cone; it was Volvic.

"I recognized it as a volcano because it was so like Vesuvius and Etna and the pictures of Teneriffe that I had seen in engravings," said Guettard, who never before had looked upon an actual cone.

As they began to climb toward the incredible mountain they came to the quarry from which the black stone had come. It had been cut into a huge solidified flow of lava. Guettard could see how this once-moving tongue of flaming lava had spilled out of the granitic ridge above and spread for more than five miles into the plain below.

The two men, their breath coming hard—and not from the climb alone—continued upward. The base of Volvic was a pale rose granite, but not far above this they came upon huge masses of red and black pumice stone. And above it were rugged ridges and blocks of ropy, spongy slags and clinkery scoria; still higher, near the top of the cone, more pumice and ashy, cindery stuff.

And then at last, at the truncated top, Guettard and Malesherbes looked down into the smooth-sloped hollow of a crater. No hot vapors or tongues of flame licked up at them. It lay

[2] Literally, "seat of volcano."

quiet and silent, carpeted with lush green grass, but eloquent of its past.

Or eloquent to one who could understand. For centuries the shepherds had pastured their flocks on the grasses of the slopes; for centuries quarrymen had cut big blocks of lava for building roads and homes; for centuries the people of the district had looked proudly upon their beautiful mountain and called it by its revealing name. Yet apparently no one had suspected that Volvic was an extinct volcano and that this land had once been the scene of a deadly destructive eruption. "The eruption must have been as terrible as that of Vesuvius, to judge by the lava that was poured out," said Guettard, with an evident shudder.

Not far beyond Volvic lay the great bulk of Puy de Dôme, the highest mountain of Auvergne.[3] It was another ancient volcano. Even before they climbed it, Guettard and Malesherbes had no doubt; the sharp outline of the cone was unmistakable. As they climbed they found the same red and black pumice, the same scoria, the same type of crater.

From the heights of Puy de Dôme (*"puy"* means "peak" in the language of the province) the two discoverers counted from twelve to fifteen other volcanic cones spreading in an irregular chain as far as the eye could see. Down below, rivers ran quietly through green forests and beside small towns. It was a scene of peace and tranquillity. But standing on the seared cinder top of the then quiet volcano, Guettard thought again of what had once happened there and of the burning, inexorable torrents of lava that had rolled over the lovely valleys.

The two men pushed on to Mont Dore (or Mont D'Or, as Guettard called it) and the group of lesser volcanic peaks clustered around it. The 6,100-foot mountain had the same cone shape, but they did not find the masses of pumice and other burned rock which they had discovered at Volvic and Puy de Dôme. The slopes were much more extensively overgrown with forest and meadow. When they collected samples of the basalt

[3] This is the hill made famous by Pascal.

around the base they were even more puzzled; it did not look quite like the lava at Volvic or samples of stone from "burning volcanoes." Time did not permit probing deeper into this odd variation, but Guettard did not forget it and he would go back to it many years later.

As scientists, Guettard and Malesherbes were interested, of course, in the more profound question of what had produced these mountainous eruptions. The most widely accepted theory of the day was an ancient one: eruptions were only the bursting forth of great underground fires feeding on flammable materials deep in the earth.

Guettard accepted it, for he thought he saw supporting evidence in the neighboring countryside. There was plenty of the kind of material needed to stoke a subterranean fire. Near Clermont black bituminous materials could actually be seen near the surface, and the house of the Benedictines there was built of such stone. Guettard also saw coal and traces of pitch.

They considered it significant, too, that hot springs bubbled up near the base of Mont Dore and also at Clermont, which was only about six miles from the chain of puys.

"For the production of volcanoes," said Guettard, "it is enough that there should be within these mountains substances that can burn, such as petroleum, coal, or pitch and that from some cause these materials should take fire. Thereupon the mountain will become a furnace and the fire, raging furiously within, will be able to melt and vitrify the most intractable substances." The hot springs, Guettard reasoned, probably were heated by the same internal fires.

Guettard also was eager to determine, if possible, when the tremendous eruptions had occurred. All that he could learn, however, was negative. In 480 when the Goths were menacing Clermont, a local leader, Sidoine Apollinaire, had written to the Bishop of Vienna asking for the same public prayers that had been offered when an earthquake had shaken Vienna. He said nothing about any physical disturbances or natural catastrophes in Auvergne. From this Guettard concluded that the volcanic outbursts certainly had occurred before 480.

In all their investigations and inquiries, Guettard and Malesherbes made no secret of their startling discovery of the true nature of the peaceful mountains of the district. Guettard also keenly felt it his duty to warn the people of Auvergne that they were living on the thin edge of danger, for what had burned once might burn again. But to be told such horrendous things about the mountains with which they had always lived, and which had stood there impassively as far back as memory or records went, was too much. Guettard's words and warnings were received with disbelief and resentment.

"The security of the people of Riom is perhaps no better founded that that of the Catanois immediately after the eruptions of Etna in 1536," said Guettard. "But the people of Riom regard as a fable all that is said about the ancient ravages of this mountain, and they imitate perfectly the incredulity of the Catanois, despite the certainty that these mountains have burned and perhaps are still burning."

Soon after his return to Paris, Guettard gave the astounding news to the Academy. It was easier for the Academicians at their safe distance to believe that a quiet section of France had once been the seat of a volcanic holocaust and that the famed mountains of Auvergne were volcanoes.

The effect was profound. Guettard's report startled scientists not only in France but all around the world, for it said that by studying their mountains and other features of the earth they might discover a totally unsuspected history and gain a new understanding of the earth they lived on. Everywhere naturalists began new studies. Condorcet said in his *éloge* that they soon confirmed what Guettard had found. "M. Guettard made us see that country which is today peacefully cultivated was covered at several distinct and widely separated eras in the past with flaming torrents," said the Marquis. "Others before him had studied these same mountains and they had seen nothing. M. Guettard recognized what he saw."

Additional studies continued to come from this dedicated man to whom only science mattered. In the forty-three years that he was a member of the Academy, Guettard wrote more than two hundred memoirs. His style was heavy and cumbersome and these memoirs had few readers—a fact that Guettard would sometimes wryly comment on. His originality and bluntness did not come through in his writing.

Some of Guettard's memoirs were so long that they could not be printed in the proceedings, and he had to bring them out privately. In the proceedings, one such collection was termed "a treasury of observations which merit the keenest gratitude on the part of naturalists and physicians." The Academy continued to respect the scientific prowess of its doughty member.

When Guettard happened to encounter Condorcet on his way to deliver one of his *éloges,* he would growl at him: "You are going to lie again." And on more than one occasion he added: "When my turn comes I want only the truth."

Soon after the 1780's began, Guettard became subject to what were described as attacks of "heavy lethargic sleep." He continued, nevertheless, to come to the Academy alone and on foot, only taking the precaution to carry his name and address in his pocket in case anything should happen. As his illness grew worse he refused to dine with friends, for he said he did not want to trouble them with the sight of his death. Death came on January 7, 1786, at the age of seventy-one.

Condorcet paid him the rare compliment of speaking of his faults as well as his virtues. "I am going to render him the homage that he most desired," said the Marquis. "His disinterestedness was in his soul. He sought so little to appear better than he was that his faults struck those who knew him only slightly. His friends alone knew his virtues."

Condorcet then revealed that Guettard, a "man so severe, so difficult, and forced by circumstances to live an isolated life," had adopted the large family of a woman who worked for him. He had assisted her in raising her children and had even watched over the details of their education. Condorect recalled too that Guettard had never been able to see anyone in distress without coming to his aid, and that his sensibility extended to animals. He always forbade the killing of any animal for him or at his house.

The scientific judgment that Condorcet pronounced would have been more pleasing to the brusque, kind-hearted, and far-seeing naturalist:

"By his painstaking research he has done more to advance the true theory of the earth—upon which he has never permitted himself a single conjecture—than the philosophers who have racked their brains to devise brilliant hypotheses, the phantoms of a moment, which the light of truth soon remands to eternal oblivion."

With Guettard the study of the earth had taken a new turn. The value of a new way of getting to the truth had been proved, but the truth that was emerging was startling and shocking. The earth, it seemed, had a past, an unsuspected, perhaps a violent past, and yet one that so intimately affected the present that no man could ignore it. For better or worse—and many feared it would be worse—the past had to be faced.

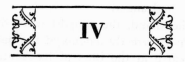

IV

DESMAREST AND WERNER
FIRE VERSUS WATER

"For it is as a very human adventure of quarrelsome individuals that the advancement of learning must be seen to be understood." [1]

DURING THE LAST QUARTER of the eighteenth century a furious scientific war raged in Europe. It was a war about the earth: about how it came to be, and what it was.

The immediate issue, as in many wars, was an odd one: was basalt, the dense black rock that scientists were finding widely spread over Europe, a product of volcanoes and fire or was it water-formed, a sedimentary stone that had settled down through ancient seas?

If the Vulcanists, those who maintained that basalt was forged in fire, were right, it meant that volcanoes had once been scattered over much of Europe and in a series of awful eruptions had poured their burning torrents of lava over great sections of the land. And in the prevailing state of knowledge no one could say that they might not do it again. A Europe that had always felt secure in the earth it lived on was confronted with the possibility that its security might be false and that its life and civilization could be wiped out in a new volcanic outburst. As in the twentieth century, when another scientific dis-

---

[1] James B. Conant: *The Citadel of Learning.* New Haven: Yale University Press; 1956.

covery created the chance that the earth might be shattered, there was unease and anger.

If, on the other hand, the supporters of the water theory, the Neptunists, had correctly diagnosed the nature of basalt, it meant that the earth at the time of its creation and perhaps much later had been covered by a universal ocean. This was a safer past, but it ran counter to much that science was learning about the earth.

A whole theory of the earth was involved in the bitter dispute. Also at stake was the question of how the earth was to be studied, of how fact and theory were to be tested and appraised.

The war was personified in two great naturalists: a Frenchman, Nicolas Desmarest, and a German, Abraham Gottlob Werner.

Desmarest was born at Soulaines, September 16, 1725, into a family too poor to afford school for even the brightest child. At fifteen he scarcely knew how to read. The death of his father at that time left a small sum of money, which was used to pay his tuition at the Collège des Oratoriens at Troyes. The over-age boy made such rapid progress that the school was glad to keep him even after his money was exhausted and, when he had completed his training there, to recommend him to confreres in Paris. For ten years Desmarest carried on his studies, all the while supporting himself by making translations of ancient authors. Then, suddenly, this obscure and poverty-stricken phase of his life was ended by a totally unexpected turn of fate.

In 1749 Buffon had startled France by the publication of the first three volumes of his *Natural History*. He maintained that the earth was originally covered by a deep ocean in which the mountains were built up out of sediments washed from the land.

"The bottom of the sea is filling up by degrees, the surface of the earth lowering to a level, and nothing but time is necessary for the sea's successively changing places with the earth," declared Buffon.

"Reprehensible and contrary to the creed of the Church," answered the Theological Faculty of Paris, the Sorbonne. Buffon was forced to recant: "I abandon everything in my book respecting the formation of the earth, and generally all which may be contrary to the narration of Moses."

Suddenly all France was debating the origin of the earth. In the fever of interest a society founded by the Duc de Chaulnes offered a prize for an essay on the question "Were France and England ever joined?"

Desmarest, whose interests had early settled on natural history, did some careful research and wrote an essay. He set up no hypothesis, but pointed to the similarity of the chalk cliffs of Boulogne and Dover, and to the chain of rocks that soundings had shown running from the French coast to the English. He also emphasized that Great Britain had formerly had many "noxious animals" that man certainly would not have transported to the islands. He concluded that an isthmus in the vicinity of the Pas de Calais must once have connected the two countries. It probably had been ruptured, Desmarest said, by strong sea currents of the kind that were now cutting into the French coast. The unknown young student won the prize.

One who read the essay with appreciation and delight was the noted French mathematician Jean d'Alembert. In it he saw a scientific treatment of a branch of research which, he maintained, Buffon and all the others had up to that time approached only with flighty imagination. D'Alembert insisted upon meeting Desmarest. The esteem of the famous geometer was, as Cuvier said later, "a fortune." Any protégé of his automatically became a protégé as well of Turgot, Malesherbes, Trudaine, and that group of scholarly statesmen who then held the reins in France.

Almost overnight the awkward, unpolished student from the country was being welcomed into the brilliant society that gathered around Vatelet, man of letters and financier. He was re-

ceived too by the Duchesse d'Anville and her son the Duc de
La Rochefoucault. France offered no more distinguished company.

"The transition was almost too sudden," said Cuvier, the perpetual secretary of the French Academy, "[Desmarest] did not
try to conform to his new position. His new friends found this
indifference more than philosophical, but they excused it when
they were assured that if fortune had not made over his manners, neither had it changed his character, and that if he retained certain village crudities in society he also conserved his
honesty. The contrast had its piquancy. Amid the elegance of
the grand monde his rough-hewn manners and untrained words
never obscured what was solid and learned in what he had to
say. Many affected to esteem him all the more for this."

About this time—the mid-century—the governments of Europe had wearied of ruinous war. In Cuvier's words, they had
decided that they would "find less trouble and more profit in
developing the industries of their people than in expanding
their territories." Desmarest's powerful friends decided that he
was the man to aid in this new movement. For the next twenty-
four years, from 1757 through 1781, he worked under a number
of ministers, making studies of cloth-manufacturing, cheese-mak-
ing, paper-manufacturing, and other industrial processes.

Desmarest would visit foreign countries to look for improved
methods. He would then carry this information to French manu-
facturers and work with them in improving their own methods.
He would also take back to the heads of the government in Paris
reports on the needs of various industries and regions. He was
in effect a one-man development bureau. Many of the industries
that acted upon his advice made fortunes out of it. "He was
perhaps the only one who did not think of profiting by his own
work," said Cuvier.

In a change of government in 1781, Desmarest lost his position, a reverse that he accepted calmly and philosophically. By
1788 he was not only back; the King had named him inspector

general of manufacturing of France. In another year, however, France was in turmoil; the Revolution had begun. One by one Desmarest's friends and protectors—Trudaine, La Rochefoucault, Malesherbes, and others—went to the guillotine or otherwise perished in the upheaval.[2] As an associate and friend of the aristocrats, Desmarest also was arrested and thrown into prison. It was only by a miracle that he escaped death.

When France had returned to order, Desmarest's services were once again needed. He was called back to assist in the building up of French industry and in the renewal of its manufacturing.

"For three-quarters of a century," Cuvier later told the French Institute (as the Academy was then called), "it was almost always under his eyes and often under his influence that French industry attained the marvelous development which, through frightful crises, sustained the wealth and well-being of the country."

As he traveled about the country on his work, Desmarest always made use of the opportunity to carry on his scientific studies. Putting on his old "rustic" clothes, and with only a little cheese and bread for provision, he would set out from wherever he happened to be. No mule track seemed impracticable for him to explore, and no rock inaccessible. He did not stop overnight at chateaus or inns, but was quite content with a shepherd's hut, or the ground, if need be. And he always talked to the men working in the fields, to miners, and men in the forges as well as to scholars. It was thus that he acquired an unequaled and detailed knowledge of the soil and rock formations of France. Many of his findings were reported in memoirs to the Institute or used in the colossal four-volume *Géographie Phy-*

[2] Malesherbes, the friend of Guettard as well as of Desmarest, and a lover of liberty, at first welcomed the Revolution. Only after it turned to excess did he oppose it. He was then proscribed and forced to flee. Later he was captured and thrown into prison. On the next day he was found dead.

sique that he wrote as part of the *Encyclopédie Méthodique* founded by Diderot and D'Alembert.

His studies and his intense interest in rocks were, in fact, never out of his mind, whether he was in a fashionable Paris salon or tramping the back roads of the provinces. One night *"chez la duchesse d'Anville,"* an English visitor held the notable company spellbound with the first account that had reached France of Cook's narrow escape on his first voyage. His ship had run upon a rock and been saved only when a piece of the stone broke off and stayed in the hole it had torn in the hull. Excitement over the story ran high; exclamations and questions filled the room. In a moment's quiet, Desmarest's calm, husky voice was heard: "Was the rock basaltic or calcareous?"

His friends also liked to tell the tale that he was so absorbed in rocks that he would have broken up the finest classic statue to find out what kind of stone had been used in it. The little fiction carried so far that when Desmarest went to Rome on a visit, museum directors were afraid to admit him to their galleries.

In 1763 while he was in central France studying the paper industry of Auvergne, Desmarest went to visit Volvic and the quiet volcanoes of the vicinity which Guettard had discovered. France had not yet recovered from the shock of that disturbing discovery.

At the foot of Puy de Dôme, Desmarest came upon an amazing sight: the face of a low cliff which was nothing but a row of six-sided pillars, one abutting another, and looking exactly like a gigantic post stockade. They formed the tongue end of a long thick flow of lava that had rolled down from the mountain above. Enthralled, Desmarest was reminded of what he had read about basalt in other countries, and particularly about the fantastic rows of pillars off the coast of Ireland, the Giant's Causeway.

He could not tear himself away from the black regular columns and the huge piles of smaller broken pieces that had accumulated below them. Each piece was as sharp-planed as though it had been squared by a skilled workman. During the next five years Desmarest followed down one solidified lava flow after another. At the end of each were the astonishing posts, thousands of them, perhaps millions. He was convinced that basalt, the black rock of which they were formed, was a lava that had cooled under circumstances that had somehow produced the unbelievably regular fissures. Modern research was to prove him exactly right.

To check his hunch about the Irish basalts, he sent to Ireland for engravings of the Giant's Causeway and for samples of the rock. Desmarest was not a man to jump to hasty conclusions.

Not until 1765 did he give his surprising findings to the Institute. The effect was startling because basalt had not previously been identified as volcanic. Guettard had been puzzled by the basalt he saw at Mont Dore, which differed from the solidified lava at Volvic and Puy de Dôme. Later he had concluded that it had not come from the volcano but was a stone that had been formed in water. He may have been influenced in reaching his judgment by the fact that basalt was known to occur in other parts of Europe where there was no sign of volcanic activity. Some observers who had been mystified by the strange black columns had suggested that they were jointed bamboos which somehow in the course of time had turned into stone.

"From the first moment when [Desmarest's] opinion was made public," said Cuvier, "it excited a sort of fermentation among the mineralogists."

It also excited other people.

Desmarest had not only said that "the prismatic basalt belongs to the class of volcanic products," but after studying his Irish specimens and engravings he further declared: "In the Giant's Causeway, and in all the prismatic masses which present themselves along the cliffs of the Irish coast; in short, even among the truncated summits of the interior, we see the operations of one or more volcanoes which are extinct like those of Auvergne.

"I am fully persuaded that in general these groups of polyg-
onal columns are an infallible proof of an old volcano whenever the stone composing them has a compact texture, spangled
with brilliant points and black or gray tints."

Here was a bold advance in theoretical as well as observa-
tional geology. It raised an urgent question. Did this volcanic
basalt occur in other places, had other unsuspected volcanoes
been in action in Europe? At this suggestion, research that had
already been spurred on by Guettard's work was pushed forward swiftly.

Desmarest, paying little attention to the furor, continued his
own studies in Auvergne. He had persuaded local officials that
the whole of the volcanic district should be mapped. Working
at first with the local surveyor and later alone or with others,
Desmarest in the next ten years covered most of the area foot by
foot. The map he was drawing up showed the area with surpassing completeness, including the volcanoes, their lava flows,
all the different kinds of rock, their condition, and the valleys
through the district.

As he climbed about the old Auvergne flows Desmarest was
especially impressed by the extraordinary differences in the
condition of the various lavas. Some of them were black, cindery, rugged, and still as barren of grasses and overgrowth as
when white-hot flames had played over them. Others had lost
their covering of loose pumice and scoria and were clinging
to the sides of valleys in positions that seemed impossible for
any lava flow. Still others lay in smooth sheets on the tops of
plateaus and ridges, with no cone near and no obvious source
from which they could have come.

Thinking deeply about all of this contradictory evidence,
Desmarest found the one principle that could explain it. All
of the odd differences could be explained, he saw, if the lavas
were of different ages, if they had erupted at different times.

What was being exhibited in Auvergne and elsewhere
throughout Europe, he concluded, were the different stages of

volcanic decay. He defined each with an exactitude and clarity that should have eliminated all doubt about volcanic materials—if his work had reached those who were concerned. An active or recently extinct volcano, said Desmarest, was distinguished by its cone and crater, by the cinders scattered over its slopes, and by the rough streams of lava extending like gigantic fingers into the surrounding valleys. But in even a short time, he pointed out, the loose frothy stuff began to wash down to lower levels and the lavas were trenched by rains. Before long, valleys were cut. If new eruptions then came, as they often did, the new currents of molten rock would again creep down to the lowest levels and fill the valley bottoms of that time.

Desmarest defined the second age of a volcano as that in which the cone had gone, and the streams of lava had been cut into entirely separate patches by the erosion of valleys. Gradually the lavas that once had covered the floors of valleys were turned into high tablelands, which in their turn were cut and crevassed by the endless wearing of water. To visualize the ancient continuity of lava sheets Desmarest suggested a feat of imagination: Imaginatively fill up the valleys and thus restore the plain over which the molten rock once flowed; you can thus see the ancient flows as they were in their youth.

The third and oldest age, said Desmarest, was marked by a complete absence of all signs of volcanoes. Often the lava was overlaid by sedimentary strata, for lakes and seas might have moved in to cover it.

"The labours of Desmarest marked the rise of a new era in the investigation of the past history of the earth," wrote Sir Archibald Geikie. "They showed how patient detailed research could solve some of the most transcendently interesting problems of geology, and how the minute and philosophical investigation of one small area of the globe could furnish principles of universal application."

But much of Desmarest's highly enlightening work was reported to the Institute only after a considerable delay, and was not printed for many years after that. He also held back most of his master map, hoping always to perfect it. The decisive effect it might have had in the raging debate about basalt was therefore lost.

In the meantime the research launched by his original report and by Guettard's memoirs was producing striking results. Montet announced the finding of basalt near Montpellier; Raspe reported it at Hesse; Arduino did a memoir on the volcanic origin of basalts near Verona; basalts were found in the Hebrides, on the Rhine, at Vivarais and other places in France. This stone, which all of the scientists accepted as unquestionably volcanic, turned up in place after place in Europe, and people realized "with a sort of fright" how extensive volcanoes had been, and that there was nothing, as Cuvier said "to prove that they would not some day burst forth again."

It was at this uneasy moment that a wholly unexpected development came. From Germany and from the greatest figure of the day in natural history came a pronouncement: "I hold that no basalt is volcanic, but that all of these rocks . . . are of aqueous origin." The year was 1787, though Abraham Werner had reached his conclusion more than ten years before.

The words struck like one of the ancients' thunderbolts. They produced what Cuvier described as an "upheaval" among the numerous naturalists who had devoted years and unsparing effort to seeking out and describing extinct volcanoes and their basalt. All that they had done, their judgment, and even their good faith were being called into question by an authority they could not ignore. They were angry, shocked, upset, and dismayed—and they were determined to fight. Some replied ironically, some with sharpness, some thundered back.

In a very short time the mineralogical world was divided into two strong factions, the Vulcanists and the Neptunists, and the battle was on. The non-scientific world looked on with an anxious sense of participation. Had Europe been falsely warned that it was living on a former volcano and perhaps a future one?

As incredible as the Werner decree sounds to anyone familiar with the French discoveries in Auvergne, it seemed not only believable, but an evident truth, to those who did not know of the French work and who were generally familiar with the surface and rock of Europe.

The strange black symmetrical pillars that made up the face of many a high cliff had long aroused the curiosity of scholars and others. In the sixteenth century Agricola had revived the old Roman name, "basalt," for this dark stone. It formed the eminence on which the old castle of Stolpen in Saxony had been built, and its regular colonnades were to be seen in many other places in the valley of the Rhine.

The basalt in Germany nearly always formed the cap on the hill—the vertical pillars were exposed only along the edge. But nowhere in any of these areas was there any sign whatsoever of volcanoes or that volcanoes had ever dominated the landscape. No cones were to be seen, and no craters, nor was there any trace of the cindery rock that everyone knew volcanoes spewed forth. What was more, the basalt often lay on top of limestone, coal, and other rocks of undoubted "aqueous" origin, and sometimes there were even strata of water-formed rocks covering the baffling black stone. Not unnaturally it was believed that all of this stone, and basalt as well, had formed in the same way—under water.

Werner's whole experience and his theory of the earth undeviatingly pointed to the same conclusion.

The man whose single statement precipitated one of the fiercest wars in geological history was born at Wehrau on September 25, 1749.[3] His ancestors had been engaged in the iron industry in the central part of Germany for more than three hundred years, and his father was the inspector of a large foundry. Almost the first toys with which Werner played and certainly the ones he preferred were pretty, many-colored, and

[3] Cuvier gives the date of Werner's birth as September 25, 1750, but K. A. Blödie, who had access to family records, says in the memoirs of the Mineralogical Society of Dresden that it was September 25, 1749.

variously shaped pieces of rock. He kept these cherished bits all his life and they became part of his famous collection, a part that he often showed to friends.

After the ordinary schooling, Werner worked for five years with his father at the foundry. All the while his interest in minerals increased, and in 1769, at the age of twenty, he enrolled in the Mining Academy at Freiberg. He took to the work there with a remarkable enthusiasm and in addition spent every free moment visiting the mines of Saxony. His knowledge of mining and minerals was so marked that he was promptly offered a place in the Saxon Corps of Mines. He reluctantly refused in order to enter the University of Leipzig.

At the university Werner studied mineralogy and mining law, and worked with his growing collection of minerals. Arranging, rearranging, and classifying them and studying their properties fascinated him. By the time he was twenty-five he was ready to publish a little three-hundred-page book on their external characteristics. It came as a revelation to the mining industry.

Up to that time minerals had been thought of as an unmanageable hodgepodge; no one had been able to suggest any way of grouping or classifying the vast numbers of stones. Werner showed that they might be classified according to cleavage, hardness, brilliance, feel, and similar characteristics. To each group with similar properties and to each subdivision he assigned ponderous German names. Cuvier complained half playfully, half earnestly, that the names were "semi-barbaric" and that anyone except a scientist accustomed to the chains of scientific terminology would have balked at them.

The meticulous little manual was one of the few things Werner ever wrote. Cuvier, in his pique at the names, suggested that one reason may have been Werner's fear of his own terminology and his desire to escape "the shackles he put on others."

Werner's classifications ignored the chemical composition of minerals, of which very little was known. Nevertheless, mineralogists, using his "hard or semi-hard," "cold, very cold, pretty cold," "indeterminate curved lamellar," and "not particularly difficultly frangible," and the like, were able to bring some order out of the old chaos. Cuvier hastened to add extremely high praise: Werner had done as much for the ordering of mineralogy as Linnæus had done for botany.

The brilliance of this achievement won Werner an appointment as professor of mineralogy at the Academy of Freiberg, a post that he was to occupy for the remainder of his life. Almost at once it became apparent that he was endowed with another form of genius: he was a master teacher. Within a few years European students were flocking to the obscure little academy founded for the training of German miners. A few years more, and they were coming from all parts of the world. Many learned German for the sole purpose of attending Werner's lectures. And the classes included not only young students, but men of established reputation in the study of the earth.

Freiberg was the center, the fountainhead, the authority, the oracle; it was creating, the scientific world believed, a new precise science of the earth.

Two factors contributed to building up this predominant influence. The first was Werner's personality and the deep ineradicable effect he had on all those who studied with him. The second was the imaginative sweep of his teaching, which stirred the minds and hearts of all who heard him.

Nothing was too much for Werner to do for his students. His classes grew so large that when everyone crowded around to see specimens he was showing, some had only a partial view. He divided the class into two sections and repeated the lecture in its entirety. His time, his strength, his purse, his home, all were theirs.

Nearly always a few students were invited to dine with him, and Werner, with his love of classification, arranged the seating of his dinner table with as much care as he gave to the arrangement of the rocks in his collection. His mineral collection had grown to a great size, and students who shared his feeling about it were often permitted to work in his study. They knew how to handle and how to appreciate a glistening piece of stone. Werner was often distressed by distinguished visitors who asked to see the collection. After they had left he would tell his students: "He may be a great general, but he does not know how to handle minerals."

Werner also built up a fine library on mineralogy, though this may have been as much for the pleasure of cataloguing the books as for reading them. Books coming in from the outside, as well as letters and manuscripts, had a way of interfering with the complete concentration and even-mindedness that Werner was determined to preserve for his work. The overflowing mail too often demanded answers and attention. He finally found it less trying not to open this influx at all, which also relieved his conscience of the guilt of not replying. Over the years Werner became increasingly averse to letting the outside world intrude into his placid, ordered life. A manuscript that a European scientist had sent on a round of other scientists disappeared. A frantic search at last uncovered it in Werner's study, buried deep in a pile of hundreds of other unopened letters and packages.

Werner's renown grew to such a point that the French Institute elected him one of their foreign associates. It was an honor that had been accorded to the great of Europe for more than a hundred years. But no reply came to the Institute's letter informing Werner of his election. Cuvier said that it was extremely doubtful that he would ever have learned of the honor if he had not chanced one day to see some mention of it in an almanac.

The Institute was understanding, though. They had heard that at about the same time their letter went unanswered, Werner's sister, who lived in Dresden, sent a special messenger to obtain his signature on an important family document. Werner kept the man waiting for more than two months. During all of this time he paid the messenger's expenses at the village inn.

The thought and attention that Werner was thus free to lavish on his students were repaid in the same generous measure. They cherished him as a father and delighted in catering to his little foibles. What was more, they followed in his footsteps and carried his doctrines around the world. It was through their writing, their work, and their defense that Werner's theories were presented to the world and attained their tremendous influence. In this respect the mild, pleasant-faced German professor was often compared to Socrates, another master teacher whose influence on his students was profound and whose thought survived principally in their writing.

Werner's mineralogy was far from a narrow study of rocks. Trim, neatly dressed, punctilious, he would smilingly walk into his classroom and place several pieces of stone or metal on the table before him. Perhaps his samples might include a piece of granite, a chunk of coal, some limestones.

Touching them almost reverently, he would explain: here is recorded the history of the earth and of life. As he demonstrated the "aqueous nature" of the stones, Werner would picture the universal primeval ocean in which they had been formed. Chemicals awash in its waters gradually had settled to the bottom, where, according to Werner's account, they formed the granite and other primitive rocks that make up the base of the earth. But great tempests sometimes swept through these early waters, and the primitive rocks were in part torn up and new strata formed from their debris. These were the transition rocks.

Werner pictured more sediments drifting down in a subsequent period of quiet to make the "floetz" rocks, the limestones, the basalts, the coals. Last of all came the alluvial series, the loams, the clays, the gravels, and the peats. That this was the way in which the earth's surface came to be was "proved" by the strata visible in Germany and elsewhere in the world.

It was a precise, clear world that Werner was expounding. When you stood on granite you knew you were at the root of all things. When you looked up at the limestone beds of a mountain you were seeing one of the last gifts of the ancient sea.

"It is obvious," said Werner in a twenty-eight-page pamphlet, "that we know with certainty that the floetz and primitive mountains have been produced by a series of precipitations and depositions formed in succession from water which covered the globe.

"We are also certain that the fossils which constitute the beds and strata of mountains were dissolved in this universal water and were precipitated from it; consequently the metals and minerals found in primitive rocks and in the beds of floetz mountains were also contained in the universal solvent and were formed by precipitation.

"We are still further certain that at different periods, different fossils have been formed from it, at one time earthy, at another time metallic, and at a third time some other fossils."

Werner did not seriously face the problem of what became of the water. He spoke of its having gradually disappeared, though at times he suggested that celestial bodies approaching the earth might have withdrawn part of it.

Eventually, in Werner's eloquently presented scheme of things, the earth stood forth, wonderfully varied, rich, and complete. Its mountains, its valleys, and its stones then shaped the civilizations that arose upon it.

The verdant, sheltered valleys of Greece and Italy nourished the arts and philosophy, Werner explained. The sandy wastes of Tartary and Africa enforced a wandering pastoral life. Rome drew much of its grandeur from the travertine of which it was built. Paris was made distinctive by its white limestone. Michelangelo and Bramante could not have built as they did, had they lived in Paris.

In short, the earth was the base of all—of all civilization, all culture, all art, and all science. The sweep of Werner's concepts and their grandeur were unforgettably moving.

"At an age when one passes easily over difficulties," said

Cuvier, "his students rushed into a career which he had shown them was so vast and so fertile that it seemed to hold the key to nature itself."

If virtually all of the stone of the earth, and certainly its base, had been deposited in a great universal sea, it followed indubitably that basalt too was an "aqueous" rock. Werner visited Stolpen with its basalt cliff and thoroughly examined all the countryside to see if he could detect any evidence of the volcanic action that some claimed. He saw "no trace of it." In certain other parts of Germany where basalt occurred, Werner conceded that there were a few hills with a "pseudo-volcanic" appearance. His studies showed, however, that they had been raised by fire burning in the underlying coal fields.

In Werner's majestic order, there was no early place for volcanoes. If there was only water at first, volcanic action could not have been under way, and it could not have played a major role in building up the surface of the earth. Fire could not burn in water. Werner regarded existing volcanoes as purely modern and purely accidental phenomena—fires accidentally set.

The famed Freiberg professor never ventured out of Germany to see any of the "burning mountains." From his studies, however, it seemed highly probable to him that Vesuvius and Etna, like the German "pseudo-volcanic hills," had been produced by the combustion of underground seams of coal. The coal, Werner said, might have been set afire by spontaneous combustion. If basalt looked suspiciously like the lava poured out by modern volcanoes, Werner insisted that this was because aqueous basalt had been "melted" by the furiously hot coal fires burning beneath it.

It was at this point that Werner issued his basalt pronouncement and that the basalt war began.

Soon afterward J. K. W. Voigt, of Weimar, made public a study saying that the very examples cited by Werner—the German basalts—were of volcanic origin. Werner replied and was answered in turn. But the controversy was becoming too disruptive of his equanimity, and he retired from the fray. His students, however, willingly and devotedly carried on for him. Literally they were willing to go through fire for him: they descended into live volcanoes to collect some of the data they believed to be essential to his case.

In France, Desmarest also remained largely on the sidelines. The battling was done by those who had carried on his work—not as disciples, in this case, but in the general pursuit of scientific investigation.

The Vulcanists offered to show the Wernerians flows of basalt descending from a crater that still was clearly visible—this was at Vivarais. They brought out new and even more specific descriptions of the basalt at Auvergne; they showed that basaltic columns had been formed by the lavas of Etna wherever they rolled down to the edge of the sea.

The Neptunists loftily replied that all of this was a mistake; Werner had declared basalt a chemical precipitate from water. But as more specific defense became necessary and as they were confronted with actual samples of columnar basalt taken from volcanic flows, the Neptunists took the position that rocks "altered by heat" were of course different "from those that constitute the great mass of the crust of the globe."

Gritty, cindery pumice was submitted. The Wernerians only became more extreme: "It was formerly the general opinion that pumice was a volcanic product . . . it is now ascertained to be an aquatic product . . . it alternates with Neptunian rocks like basalt and porphyry . . . it has never been observed to flow from a volcano."

Facts, proofs, arguments, pleas, and challenges to visit Auvergne had no more effect than if they had been hurled against a wall of basalt. In this impasse some conciliators suggested that there might be two kinds of basalt, one the product of water and the other the product of fire. The compromise was contemptuously rejected by both sides. The controversy continued bitterly through the last years of the eighteenth century and into the nineteenth.

In 1797 a wealthy and able young pupil of Werner's, Leopold von Buch, set out on his travels. He had his first view of the Alps and went on to the volcanic district of Italy. And his Wernerian faith held firm. In a report he wrote: "Every country and every district where basalt is found furnishes evidence directly opposed to all ideas that his remarkable rock has erupted in molten condition." In the spring of 1802, however, he went to southern France and saw with astonishment the wonderful crater and cone of Puy de Pariou.

"Here," he admitted with irrepressible awe, "we find a veritable model of the form and degradation of a volcano, such as cannot be found at either Etna or Vesuvius. Here at a glance we see how the lava has opened a way for itself at the foot of the volcano, how with its rough surface it has rushed down to the lower ground, how the cone has been built above it out of loose slags which the volcano has ejected from its large central crater."

Remembering the German basalts and all that he had learned at the feet of Werner, he could not yet concede that basalt "had flowed out as lava." But he stood "perplexed and embarrassed" before the magnificent volcanic spectacle of Auvergne, and he wrote to friends: "Opinions are in opposition which only new observations can remove." The evidence of the eyes was having its effect.

A year later a young Frenchman who had studied with Werner submitted a treatise on the German basalts to the French Institute. In it Jean d'Aubuisson upheld the Neptunian thesis with almost religious fervor. The two French scientists who re- viewed it added a bit of wise and friendly advice: "In a field where the two parties dispute foot by foot, every step should be justified by an observation and marked by a fact. Citizen d'Aubuisson has never seen either active or extinct volcanoes. Living until now in the midst of aqueous formations, we should like him to visit places where fire has manifested its empire. We especially desire that he should see the basalts of Auvergne, which another disciple of Werner [Von Buch] has just visited. That Citizen d'Aubuisson knows how to observe is shown by his published works . . . and the interest of his observations cannot be recognized in a manner more useful to science than by encouraging him to continue them."

D'Aubuisson promptly took this excellent advice. He had just started his visit to Auvergne when he came upon a basalt that lay on top of a twelve-hundred-foot-thick strata of granite. If basalts were aqueous rocks altered by the heat of coal fires, how could the heat have been transmitted to them through twelve hundred feet of granite? This painful question stabbed at the young Frenchman. Furthermore, according to the Wernerian system, coal, a recent deposit, could not have occurred under primitive granite. D'Aubuisson was staggered. Shaken, he climbed to the top of the puys and followed the great lava streams down into the valleys. He could no longer doubt.

"The facts which I saw spoke too plainly to be mistaken; the truth revealed itself too clearly before my eyes, so that I must either have absolutely refused the testimony of my senses in not seeing the truth, or that of my conscience in not straightaway making it known. There can be no question that basalts of volcanic origin occur in Auvergne and the Vivarais. There are found in Saxony and in basaltic districts generally, masses of rock with an exactly similar ground mass, which enclose exactly and exclusively the same crystals, and which have exactly the same structure in the field. There is not merely an analogy, but a complete similarity; and we cannot escape the conclusion that there has been an entire identity in formation and origin."

No capitulation could have been more complete, and it came with a regretful heart from a man whose personal admiration for Werner would never lessen. Von Buch too in later studies completed the big change-over that had started in his first days in Auvergne. Ultimately he too became a Vulcanist.

Desmarest watched the battle swing toward him with a considerable degree of impatience. Not infrequently some Neptunist would come to consult him. Desmarest would wave aside discussion of the issues and repeat as often as necessary the same words: *"Allez et voyez."*

It sometimes happened that those who took this advice and went to see made studies that brought out the same dramatic facts about Auvergne which Desmarest had published many years before. Some of the studies, including those made by Von Buch, were excellent, though none of them approached the thoroughness of the great map of Auvergne on which Desmarest still worked. With his once powerful patrons gone, he lacked the money to publish it, but he felt that others were taking over his territory. "The truth is he really had legitimate ownership of the greater part of the observations made after him," said Cuvier.

Aside from this disappointment, Desmarest was experiencing a useful and ripe old age. He had little money, but that troubled him not at all. He said and meant it: "When I have bread and cheese I do not need money or position to visit the mountains and factories."

His life was one of complete regularity. He arose and went to bed at the same hour every day, and every Sunday went to visit a friend who lived at Auteuil. When the friend died he continued to go, and because he had always walked he still made the trip on foot until he was eighty-five. It was only in the last five years of his life that he could be persuaded to take a carriage.

Desmarest had not changed his manners when as a young prize-winner he was suddenly introduced into the most glittering society of France; neither did he change the style of his clothes. In the nineteenth century his wig and coat were exactly the same as they had been sixty or seventy years earlier. He wanted no pretense.

This unchangingness of manner—perhaps it was a kind of honesty—did not extend to the domain of the mind and ideas, and least of all to science. All of his life Desmarest was the adviser and protector of inventors, men constantly working with the new. He would suggest how they might make a change to overcome some difficulty, and he would help them in finding a buyer or sponsor for their work.

The Institute also continued to give great weight to his advice. Desmarest did not speak often and then only on subjects he knew, but the Academicians, many of whom had been born after he had entered the Institute, listened with respect to his slow, rasping voice. What he had to say was always full of sense.

Death came on September 20, 1815. Desmarest had rounded out his ninetieth year without having suffered the infirmities of age or serious illness.

It is doubtful that Abraham Werner knew he was losing the controversy over basalt and that his precise theory of the earth was being overturned. Correspondence that might have broken the news to him lay unopened on his desk. He had long since ceased to read the scientific journals. He continued to live his life in gentle, scholarly contemplation, surrounded always by new groups of worshipful students and friends. His geologic certainty was never disrupted.

Only one rude happening broke through this insulation and disastrously upset the calm of his inner self. Werner gave the same deep devotion to Saxony and its prince that he gave to his students, and the disasters that came to both in the Napoleonic wars could not be concealed from him. Unable to bear the tragedy, he suffered a physical collapse that nothing could relieve. Full of his sorrow, the great German teacher and mineralogist died on June 30, 1817.

·　·　·

Time was required to prepare the remarkable *éloges* with which the French Institute preserved for history the accomplishments and lives of its members. Special sessions also had to be set for their presentation.

Thus it came about that Cuvier, as perpetual secretary, read on the same day, March 16, 1818, the *éloges* of both Desmarest and Werner. In the final honors accorded them by the leading scientists of Europe, the two men who had stood at opposite poles on the great geologic question of the latter eighteenth century at last stood together.

Speaking both to science and to history, Cuvier said of Desmarest: "The academy saw in him the monument of another century, one of those scholars, now become all too rare, who were solely occupied with science and not concerned with ambition.

"Among his confreres are some who have equalled him, though none who surpassed him in enlightenment or the gifts of the mind, but he had the good fortune to discover and state a great fact; his name will endure."

Turning to Werner, Cuvier continued: "It is to his irresistible influence that the scholarly world owes the men who have removed many of the obscurities that still cloaked the physical world. The Karstens and Wiedemanns in the laboratory, the von Humboldts, the von Buchs, the d'Aubuissons, the Hermanns, the Freieslebens, at the summit of the Cordillera, in the midst of the flames of Vesuvius and of Etna, in the deserts of Siberia, in the depths of the mines of Saxony, of Hungary, and Mexico . . . have brought him honor by their work, and one can say of him what before could only be said with truth of Linnaeus, that everywhere nature was interrogated in his name."

Nature had been interrogated by both men, Desmarest and Werner, and she had given back a disturbing picture of an earth once widely subject to volcanoes. The examination of the earth was yielding strange results.

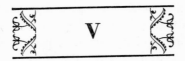

HUTTON

NO SIGHT OF BEGINNING OR END

D R. JAMES HUTTON strode into the weekly dinner meeting of the Oyster Society with even more exuberance than usual.

The other members of this small, distinguished Edinburgh dining club saw immediately that the tall, lithe physician had something special to show them. They gathered around—Dr. James Black, the noted chemist who discovered carbonic acid; John Clerk, authority on naval tactics and inventor of a method of breaking the enemy's line which produced many a famous English victory at sea; Adam Ferguson, author and secretary of the commission Lord North sent across the Atlantic to settle the dispute embroiling Great Britain and her American colonies; John Playfair, professor of natural history at the University of Edinburgh; Sir James Hall, chemist and Laird of Dunglass; and a few others who in the last quarter of the eighteenth century were adding luster to the young corps of Scottish science.

With a fine flourish Dr. Hutton produced a piece of granite. It was, as he said, a "singular specimen." Against a quite uniform "sparry" ground ran several nearly parallel rows of oddly arranged crystals. Ordinarily the crystals that are characteristic of this hard rock are flecked all through its feldspar background.

"They look like writing set in type," said Hutton, turning his specimen so that the light sparklingly caught the face of the crystals and further demonstrated the unusual uniform direction.

The doctor added that they actually looked more like ancient Hebrew characters than like modern print. And so they did, as they were later drawn by Clerk and published in the *Transactions of the Royal Society of Edinburgh.*

It was not, of course, with any fanciful resemblance that Hutton was concerned; that was simply an amusing coincidence. What interested him profoundly was that such an arrangement of crystals could have come about only if the granite had been "congealed from a fluid state." The alignment of the shining flecks proved that the rock had once been melted and had re-formed under elongating pressure.

At the time—the late 1770's—Desmarest and the Vulcanists were fighting to prove that basalt was a volcanic rock, a product of melting and fire. Few, if any, had ventured to suggest that granite also might have had an igneous origin. On the contrary, Werner, the leading figure in natural science, was insisting with all of his great authority that granite had been formed when chemical materials had precipitated out of the primeval ocean. Granite was one of Werner's prime examples of an "aqueous" stone.

From many very keen observations Hutton had concluded that great masses of molten material had welled up from below and "congealed" into granite and similar rocks—a fact that his "singular" specimen beautifully demonstrated. From such facts the doctor was also forming a new and different theory of the earth. It was a theory concerned not so much with the origin of things as with the changes the earth had undergone, in so far as distinct marks of such changes could be discovered. Hutton wanted to know what had happened to the earth and what was happening to it, and out of his gentlemanly research came the fundamental principles of modern geology. The earth, Hutton showed, was a product of change. Its surface had not always been what it was in his day.

Hutton was well equipped to work on such a theory of the earth. He had been born in Edinburgh on June 3, 1726. As the son of a well-known citizen, the city treasurer, he in due time entered the University of Edinburgh. It was while he was attending a lecture on logic that his always alert interest was caught by a passing reference to the fact that gold could be dissolved only by two acids mixed together (aqua regia), though baser metals yield to a single acid. Hutton felt rather than understood the import of this phenomenon, but it decided him then and there to study chemistry.

Before he could do more than acquire a few books, his family, thinking that he should enter business, obtained an apprenticeship for Hutton in the office of a "writer of the signet"—a legal business. While he should have been busy copying legal papers the seventeen-year-old amused himself and the other clerks by chemical experiments. It was soon evident that law and business were not for him.

Medicine seemed to be more in line with Hutton's interests. In 1744 he returned to the university to begin studying it, and in the next six years continued his work at Edinburgh, Paris, and Leyden. He took his Doctor of Medicine degree at Leyden in 1749.

When he returned to Edinburgh the next year Hutton found that medical practice was held tight in the hands of a "few eminent practitioners." There seemed to be no place for a young physician, he wrote with some anxiety to his friend John Davie. The two of them therefore began some chemical experiments, and soon were working intensively on sal ammoniac, a salt they made from coal soot. Since there was a demand for this product, they established a manufacturing plant that rapidly showed signs of the substantial success it was to become. Hutton was a full-fledged partner and ultimately the business made him wealthy, but he still wanted nothing to do with commercial affairs and left its running entirely to Davie.

Hutton had made up his mind: he would turn to agriculture. He had inherited a small property in Berwickshire, and, as his friend and biographer Playfair said, agriculture was certainly an appropriate choice for a man who was both independent and unambitious.

But Hutton, with his scientific bent, had no intention of becoming an ordinary farmer. His first step was to go to Norfolk, where farming practice was considered most advanced, and work there for two enjoyable years. He then crossed over to Flanders to study garden culture. Only after this preparation was he ready to return to Berwickshire and turn his acres into a model farm, practicing all the "new husbandry."

Hutton remained on the farm for fourteen years. At the end of that time it was in excellent order and the problems that had absorbed him were largely solved. He was ready to move on to an interest that had been taking more and more of his time and thought.

While he was in Norfolk, Hutton had started to study the earth. To the east, to pique his curiosity, lay the Crag with its heaps of seashells and to the west the Wash, where well-marked strata of red chalk stood out oddly against the prevailing white chalk. A long history lay revealed in both places, Hutton sensed, and he saw too that it was related to the changes that were going on around him—the little rill that ran muddy after a heavy rain, the rocks crumbling away with the frost. He formed the habit, Hutton wrote to a friend, of looking into "every pit or ditch or river bed."

These habits did not change during the years in Berwickshire. While he saw to the tilling of his fields, Hutton never ceased thinking about these phenomena and their cause. He realized with growing vividness that the earth with which he was working would end someday on the bottom of the sea, and the thought came to him that there the lands of the future were being formed.

In 1768 Hutton gave up country life and moved to Edinburgh to devote himself entirely to scientific pursuits. He was immediately welcomed into the city's top scientific and literary circles. Some of the members of this group were old friends. The others swiftly became new ones, for the doctor had a genius for friendship. His interest, his enthusiasm, his unalloyed enjoyment of a new idea, of good conversation and good company, drew people to him. His comfortable Edinburgh home was managed by his three sisters—he never married—and his time was entirely free to be spent as he wished.

Most of the day was used for his scientific studies. Late in the afternoon he went out for a long walk that always brought before him some of the problems with which he was working. If he turned to the east he went by Arthur's Seat and Salisbury Crag, both monuments of ancient volcanic flows. If he walked west the ravines of the Water of Leith presented an active demonstration of the erosive power of running water. Within the city itself was Castle Rock, a fine example of molten materials that had thrust up through the crust of the earth. Scotland was an excellent laboratory and showplace of the earth.

The doctor would stop at some friend's home for tea, and he always spent his evenings with friends. Sometimes the conversation would turn to his own work, for his friends were keenly interested and their assistance was always at his command—Black to help with problems related to chemistry, Clerk to make any sketches that might be needed. Often, though, the doctor was full of other things that were happening: perhaps some improvement his friend Watt had made in his steam engine, or perhaps Cook's discoveries in the South Seas. The doctor was an ardent reader of "travels." His "warmth, fire, and expression of animation" in such conversations were unforgettable, Playfair said.

The doctor, as they always called him, also loved a little fun. He and his close friend Black once launched a continuing discussion in the Oyster Club over the culinary merits of snails. The two insisted with all the scientific resources they could muster or invent that it was completely unreasonable for people who fed on the testaceous creatures of the sea—i.e., oysters—to reject those of the land. "Vulgar prejudice," the two declared with great conviction. When they were unable to sway the other devotees of the shellfish of the sea to their way of thinking, they announced that they at least would not be bound by such narrow-mindedness.

Snails were ordered. A great smoking stew of them was brought to the table. Looking at the dish boldly though with internal misgivings, they took big servings. Each managed to get down a small mouthful. Finally Black could endure the ordeal no longer. "Doctor," he asked, "do you not think they taste a little—a very little—queer." At this Hutton broke into a roar of laughter: "D—— queer, D—— queer," and with a sweeping gesture of surrender, he ordered: "Tak them awa', Tak them awa'!" [1]

The whole group had been members of the Philosophical Society. Science, however, was emerging as an entity of its own; it no longer fell comfortably under the head of philosophy. An organization was needed where scientific materials could be presented, discussed, and printed. The Huttonian group thus took the lead in the formation of the Royal Society of Edinburgh, incorporating it under royal charter in 1783.

Hutton by this time had distilled the great mass of facts which he had collected into a definite theory of the earth. He had been in no hurry to write it down—he was not working for fame or priority—and he might have delayed indefinitely had he not been persuaded that it was his duty to present it to the new society. At one of the first meetings the doctor gave a brief outline and sketch of his system. It was printed in the first volume of the *Transactions* of the society, 1783—6.

What stirred the society was the fact that Hutton looked at all that had happened and was happening on the earth as part of a connected, coherent, continuous whole. He saw five main stages in the process:

1. By far the greater part of the materials that compose the exterior crust of our globe bore marks of having been formed

---

[1] This anecdote is told in John Kay's *Kay's Edinburgh Portraits*. The "D——" was left blank and I would not presume to fill it in.

out of materials or organized bodies of more ancient date. All
the sedimentary rocks, including many of the mountains of Scotland, had come from the dissolution of still older rocks or from
the destruction of animal or mineral bodies. And ultimately all
of this wastage of former continents had come to rest in the sea.

2. All of the rocks of the earth, with the exception of those that
were non-stratified, thus originally existed in the form of loose
materials: the sands, the muds, the shells, the bones, the silts, the
mucks of the floor of the sea. There by pressure and the effect of
subterranean heat they were slowly converted into stone; sand
was made into sandstone; the limy remains of billions of sea creatures became limestone.

3. But this smooth layered pavement of the sea did not remain forever flat. Through the operation of tremendous forces,
the greatest of which probably was the unlimited expansive
power of heat, the layered stone was burst asunder and upthrust
into new lands and new mountains. The principal thrust had
come from below, but under the laws of "mechanical philosophy"
it was known too that a force which produces parallel motion
might also result in "angular motion." And thus the once level
strata were often broken, tipped, tilted, and sometimes, in this
crunching process, turned on end and pressed into great sinuous
folds.

4. In addition, enormous masses of molten material had
poured up from below or rolled forth from volcanoes. This ir-
rupting molten material—which cooled into hard unstratified
rock—might have been a factor in the disturbance of the stratified rocks. It might have been one of the instruments of their
elevation.

5. The moment any material had emerged from the sea,
whether it was a bed of soft clay or a peak of the hardest quartz,
decay began. Its wearing down started upon that instant, and
it was then only a matter of time until water and a multitude of
agents would resolve it into earth and return it once again to
the dominion of the sea.

In this series of changes, in these great natural revolutions, said the doctor, "we see neither the beginning nor the end."

Hutton later underlined the point that he had made in those never-to-be-forgotten words: "The raising up of a continent from the bottom of the sea is an idea too great to be conceived easily. . . . In like manner destruction of the land is an idea that does not easily enter into the mind of man in its totality, although he is daily witness to part of the operation. Whenever we see a river in flood, we must acknowledge the carrying away of part of our land to be sunk at the bottom of the sea; . . . whenever we see a storm on the coast we are informed of a hostile attack upon our country; attacks which must in time wear away the bulwark of our soil and sap the foundations of our dwellings. Thus great things are not understood without the analyzing of many operations. . . ."

Hutton did not shirk the analysis. Aside from his perceptive picture of the timeless, endless cycle of nature, his first radical departure from accepted belief lay in his contention that the loose, fine sediments of the sea were consolidated into rock by heat and pressure.

The Neptunists, who could not admit to internal heat in the earth, objected that if such heat had been present the volatile materials in the sediments would have been driven off, if indeed the sediments had not first been entirely consumed by the heat. Instead of limestone, they said, there would have been only burned-out lime, and instead of coal, charcoal.

Hutton argued in answer that gases were retained in sedimentary rocks because the enormous weight of the superincumbent ocean prevented their escape. The heat, he said, could not drive off gases as it would have done at sea level.

Sir James Hall later supplied unexpected support for Hutton's point. Hall packed carbonate of lime, similar to that lying on the floor of the ocean, into gun barrels, tubes bored through solid iron, and every other sort of container that he could devise for excluding the air. He hermetically sealed the tubes and applied the highest temperatures he could obtain. The carbonate of lime was in this way fused into a substance closely resembling marble. It was as Hutton said. If the gases could not escape, limy materials were converted into marble by heat.

Hall also succeeded in producing sandstone from sand. After pouring a layer of sand into an iron vessel, he filled it up with brine. Then he applied the hottest possible flame. The sand glowed red-hot, and yet the brine remained so cool that Hall could dip his hand into it. In the end, on the bottom of the vessel there was a layer of sandstone. Heat had turned loose sand into sandstone, again much as the doctor had conjectured that it did on the bottom of the sea.

"The truth of Hutton's principle has been established by direct experiment," said Hall.

Hutton long had studied the folding and fracturing in his native mountains. It was a sight of which he never tired. But if he was right about how this had occurred and about the cyle of deposition and uplift, he knew that it should show up most dramatically at the juncture of older and newer rocks. There you could see how one had been deposited atop the other and how this relationship had affected both. Hutton was always eager to apply every test to his theories, and he, Playfair, and several other friends went to the coast to look for such points.

Fine weather permitted them to keep their boat close to the rocky coast near Dunglass. A high point that looked promising soon came into view and they made for it. The tide was out. As they drew near they could see a nearly vertical bed of schist, a hard glassy rock, and lying horizontally over it a thin strata of red sandstone. Farther back from the water the sandstone rose into a high cliff.

They all hopefully scrambled ashore. In a moment there was a shout, a shout of elated discovery from the doctor. The upturned tops of the schist penetrated at a number of places into the level beds of sandstone. And the lowest part of the sandstone actually was made up of round and angular bits that had originally worn from the schist.

"One who was seeing this for the first time would never forget it," said Playfair. "Here was palpable evidence of one of the most important and extraordinary facts in the natural history of the earth. What clearer evidence could we have had of the different formation of these rocks and of the long interval which separated their formation?"

While Playfair and the others listened with a feeling of awe and wonder, the doctor sketched for them the history revealed by the upended schist and its covering sandstone.

The sediments from which the schist was formed had once stretched smooth and even on the bottom of the sea. Immeasurable forces had thrust the bed upward, breaking it, and turning it almost on end. Then through long ages rain and snow had rounded off its tops and piled the broken bits and sand in its crevices and around it—the latter formed the coarse angular sand that they saw between the hard schist and the sandstone above. And then again a change had come; the schist sank below the oncoming waves of the sea.

Sand, a fine reddish sand, had settled down upon it, covering the angular bits, filling in the small depressions and holes, and ultimately covering high and low points alike, much as a great snowstorm fills in the low places on the ground and covers all irregularities with its own smooth surface.

Another stirring in the depths had once more lifted the sand-topped schist, but this time gently, slowly, with no fracturing or twisting. Once more the ancient stone stood above the sea. And once again the sea and the rains had taken up their work; they had cut into this mass of rock along the Dunglass shore, laying bare its long and turbulent history.

"The mind seemed to grow giddy by looking so far into the abyss of time," said Playfair. "While we listened with earnestness and admiration to the philosopher now unfolding to us the order and series of these wonderful events, we became sensible how much farther reason may sometimes go than imagination can venture to follow."

This was truly a staggering kind of history the doctor was tracing. To a world that dated its beginning from 4004 B.C. and believed that no mountain or shore had been changed since the Flood, the enormously long changes to which the doctor was pointing were shocking and alarming. They would have required hundreds of thousands of years at least. They indicated that the earth had changed, and changed drastically enough for land to become sea and sea to become land, perhaps several times.

Many, of course, were familiar with the different strata and realized that they had been differently formed. But Hutton was the first to show the coherent story that lay behind the sequence, and to demonstrate that nature could serve as her own interpreter. That was why the imagination scarcely ventured to follow.

As Hutton had traveled about Scotland he had been impressed too by the great masses of rock that were not stratified—there were whole mountain chains of it. In other places the unstratified rock had thrust up into high vertical slabs that the doctor called dykes. In still other places it was spread wide in thick overlays.

It seemed to Hutton that this unstratified rock gave every sign of having once been molten. If molten materials deep in the bowels of the earth had forced their way through to the outer crust and there congealed, would not such piles and masses have appeared on the surface?

Was it not significant too that such rock took many different forms? The doctor distinguished basalts—which he called whin-stones—and other dark rocks that bore a close resemblance to lava, and a large group of rocks—granites—that were filled with crystals of quartz and mica and other materials. Hutton suspected that this might have had something to do with how they had cooled.

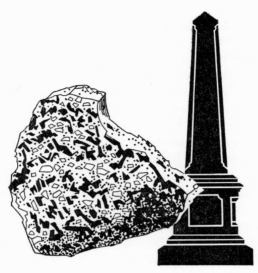

GRANITE—CRYSTAL-FLECKED AND HANDSOME IN THE PIECE OR IN MONUMENTS.

At about this time a report spread about a strange accident that had occurred at the Leith glassworks. Through an oversight a large mass of ordinary green glass had been allowed to cool slowly. To the amazement of everyone, it lost all the properties of glass; it became opaque, hard, white, crystalline. Hall's quick mind at once applied this peculiar conversion to what Dr. Hutton was saying about granite. He decided to investigate the phenomenon for himself.

The Laird of Dunglass obtained a piece of the "accident stone," heated it with a blowtorch, and cooled it rapidly. To his delight, it immediately reverted to glass. Hall rushed to the doctor with his remarkable results, but Hutton was suspicious of them. It seemed to him that the scale of nature's processes was so grand that no small-scale reproduction of them in the laboratory could possibly produce reliable results. He did not believe, he said, that you could learn what went on in the depths of the

earth "by kindling a fire and looking into the bottom of a crucible." The doctor reflected the prevailing opinion. It was not that
man had not thought about experimenting, but that it seemed
too puny a process to be trusted.

Hall could not agree, but because of loyalty and devotion to
the doctor he would not go on with his experiment. "I considered myself bound," he explained, "to pay deference to his opinion in a field which he had already so nobly occupied and I ab-
stained during the remainder of his life from the prosecution of
the experiments which I had begun in 1790."

After the doctor's death, however, Hall resumed his work.
One after another he put basalts from Scottish mountains, lavas
from Vesuvius and Etna, and other volcanic stones into a rever-
beratory furnace in an Edinburgh ironworks. By melting them
and cooling them rapidly he converted them into perfect glass.
And then Hall reversed the process. Into his furnace he put
some of the glass he had made, and cooled it slowly. From this
experiment came substances closely resembling the original volcanic stone. The demonstration was complete and undeniable.
Hall also "made" different kinds of granite by fusing the stone
and cooling it at varying rates. At different temperatures different crystals formed.

All of this, of course, was later. Even into the 1790's the idea
that granite could once have been molten continued to seem
outrageous to most naturalists. Hutton was convinced that the
only way he could prove his point would be to prove it in nature.[2]

If he was right in thinking that the molten material had
flowed in among the earlier stratified rocks, they should be
marked by the violence of the intrusion and by its searing heat.
If such marks could be found, they would confirm his case. The
doctor began a search.

----

[2] Desmarest did not agree that granite was an igneous rock. But in an
article in the *Géographie Physique* he praised the value of Hutton's work
and said: "It is to Scotland that Hutton's opponents must go to amend his
results and substitute for them a more rational explanation."

He soon succeeded in obtaining a sample of coal from a field bordering a big flow of basalt. Where the coal came in contact with the basalt it was charred and burned.

And just outside Edinburgh was picturesque Salisbury Crag, the ninety-foot precipice to which the doctor often walked. It stood upon a base of sandstone, and topping its huge bulk was another layer of exactly the same kind of sandstone. The intruding lava had wedged in between the two layers and separated them by its own mass. It would have been difficult, the doctor argued, to find a more explicit demonstration of how a hot intrusion from below could break through and disrupt existing strata.

How, Hutton asked, could such a formation be explained by Neptunian theory? Could a column of water standing in that particular place have deposited a ninety-foot-high block of basalt while other kinds of stone were settling out all around it? And could the column of water suddenly have changed and left behind the sandstone that capped the crag?

Further proofs also were needed to establish the original molten condition of the granites. The sample of granite with its parallel rows of crystals—the specimen Dr. Hutton so triumphantly showed to the Oyster Club—remained a prime example, but it was not enough.

If granite had welled up in semi-liquid condition, as the doctor thought it had, surely it would have forced its way into cracks and fissures in any rocks with which it came in contact. Hutton decided to search for such "veins." The likeliest place to look seemed to be in the highlands, in the granite country southwest of Aberdeen. There the granite chain of the Grampians met the schist that made up the lower ridges of the same mountains.

The project was often under discussion at Edinburgh gatherings, and the Duke of Athol, who owned a shooting lodge in the heart of the country, invited Hutton, Clerk, Playfair, and several others to join him there in the hunting season. His lodge stood on the River Tilt, a small impetuous stream that had cut a deep glen through the mountains.

On the first day of their arrival they decided to start up the stream and go however far might be necessary to find places in which they could observe the junction of the schist and granite. "Little did we imagine," Hutton said later, "that we should be so fortunate as to meet with the object of our search almost upon the very spot where the duke's hunting lodge is situate and where we were entertained with the utmost hospitality and elegance."

The glen, as they soon saw, was a scene of great beauty and boldness. The rocks rose sheer and bare, entirely free of the heath and moss that mantled the country above. They had gone only a short way when a mighty shout came from the doctor. He was pointing to a large vein of red granite that coursed through the face of the black schist.

When they could tear themselves away from the dramatic sight, they went on up the glen. There was soon another shout from Hutton; another vein of red branched through the dark basic stone. And this exultant scene was repeated four more times in the distance of a mile. The veins of red streaming out from their granite base were so striking that even an unskilled observer could interpret what had happened.

"The sight filled [Dr. Hutton] with delight," said Playfair, "and as his feelings were always strongly expressed, the guides were convinced that it must be nothing less than the discovery of a vein of silver or gold that could call forth such strong marks of joy and exultation."

The veins spoke in unambiguous terms of a molten invasion and of its violence and strength. The molten rock, intruding from below, had pushed into every opening and into the cracks that its own movement had made in the rocks above. In time, of course, the red granite had hardened in the invaded black rock. To see the tree-like veins, to discover them as he had reasoned that they might be, was one of the great moments in the doctor's life and in geology. No one before Hutton's time had been bold enough to imagine a series of subterranean intrusions of molten rock. Hutton not only imagined them, but with those red veins in Glen Tilt he proved their existence.

Having found this illuminating junction of granite and schist in the north, Hutton was eager to see if the same phenomenon would occur in the granite country of the south. Accompanied by friends, he went to the lonely moorlands of Galloway. In a little bay on the seaside he found place after place where the intruding granite had broken into older schist. It had not only fractured the hard schist and pushed it into many fantastic positions, but here, too, the fluid granite had forced into every small fissure or opening in the abutting strata.

There was "every mark of the most fluid injection among the broken, distorted strata," Hutton reported. Part of the group traced the line of separation between the granite and the schist around a tract eleven miles by seven. Innumerable veins of granite, ranging from tiny hairlike intrusions of no more than a tenth of an inch to wedges fifty yards and more in width, ran all through the schist. If the granite had not once been molten, it could not conceivably have got into those cracks.

Hutton also visited Arran, the mountainous island that lies in the mouth of the Clyde. Along its bare, lofty precipices and glens countless veins of granite had entered the dark schist. The doctor laboriously but triumphantly carried home one specimen of "some hundredweight," a block of schist through which ran a large conspicuous vein of granite.

The evidence was overwhelming and yet at first it had very little effect. Outside of the Edinburgh group, not much attention was given to Hutton's first (1785) report on his theory of the earth or to his later investigations. Not until several years afterward did the attack begin. When it came it was bitter. "The party feeling excited against the Huttonian doctrines . . . will hardly be credited," said Sir Charles Lyell many years later.

One of the blows came from the poet Cowper:

Some drill and bore
The solid earth, and from the strata there
Extract a register, by which we learn
That He who made it, and revealed its date
To Moses, was mistaken in its age.

In 1793 Hutton suffered a severe illness and had to undergo a painful operation. While he was still recuperating at home he received a copy of the *Transactions of the Royal Irish Academy.* In this volume Richard Kirwan, a well-known Irish chemist and mineralogist, made a full-scale attack on *The Theory of the Earth.* Kirwan, a follower of Werner, not only tore into all of Hutton's major premises, but vociferously accused the doctor of atheism. By denying that this world had a specific beginning, he said, the doctor was trying to revive the heathen doctrine of an "eternal succession."

Up to this point the doctor had resisted suggestions that he make a fuller exposition of his views. But at last he was aroused. The next day he began a full revision of his first report, adding the proofs, the evidence, and the arguments that he had not had available earlier or had not used. The first two of the resulting volumes were published in 1795. A third volume remained in manuscript.

Unfortunately Hutton did not write so well as he talked. His conversation was logical, lucid, and forceful, and he had an apt word or story to illustrate every meaning. On paper, however, he involved himself with one proviso after another until his sentences became mazes exceedingly difficult to thread. Even more disconcerting was his habit of tacking on a conclusion unrelated to what had gone before. The doctor's agile mind had made the transition; his readers could not. "His peculiar style and arrangement rendered his theory less intelligible and less known than deserved," explained Playfair. "It gave rise to mis-interpretation."

In the winter of 1796 Dr. Hutton suffered a recurrence of his first illness. Although he was in pain, he went on with his reading and writing, and chatted as entertainingly as ever with the procession of friends who came to his bedside. But this time there was no recovery. Hutton died on March 26, 1797, at the age of seventy.

Few scientists have had warmer friends. Hutton's friends not only mourned his loss; they undertook to preserve the memory of his rich, outgoing life and to make the world aware of his unique contribution to science.

Hall went on with the experiments he had postponed in deference to Hutton's prejudice against them, and used his significant findings to enhance Hutton's theories.

In order that the world might more fully appreciate the Huttonian theory, Playfair decided to write a full exposition of it. He spent five years of devoted work on the book he called *Illustrations of the Huttonian Theory*. It was published in Edinburgh in 1802. Playfair said modestly that his aim was to present the doctor's work in "more popular and perspicuous words."

In truth he did far more. He set forth Dr. Hutton's work with what Sir Archibald Geikie called "a precision of statement and felicity of language that has no superior in English scientific literature." And thus it came about that James Hutton's magnificently scientific theory of the earth lives in some of the most luminous scientific prose ever written.

Hutton had sternly guarded himself against formulating any principle that could not be supported by observation. To explain nature, he held, "no powers are to be employed that are not natural to the globe, no action admitted of except that of which we know the principle, and no extraordinary events to be alleged in order to explain a common appearance." This and Hutton's further point, "Chaos and confusion are not to be introduced into the order of nature, because certain things appear to our practical views as being in some disorder," stood in sharpest contrast to the speculations of antiquity and the seventeenth century. Reliance on gods, on reason unconfirmed by fact, and on imagination would thereafter be much more difficult in the study of the earth.

But the earth disclosed by Hutton's careful examination was no less wondrous. Who among the dreamers would have imagined an earth in which there was no sight of either a beginning or an end?

*"And Noah removed the covering of the ark and looked,
and behold, the face of the ground was dried."*

The desolate earth that was left, as it was pictured
by the French artist Paul Gustave Doré.

PLATE I

Six-sided pillars of basalt—
"The Organs"—near Issoire
in Auvergne, France. Were
the strange columns formed
from lava or were they laid
down in water? The seven-
teenth century furiously debated the question.

The Puy de Sancy, highest
of the beautiful mountains
of Auvergne. The discovery
that they were extinct volcanoes shocked the world.

PLATE II

The glacier of Zermatt, one of those studied by Agassiz. The rocks curving down the face of the ice and tumbling from its sides are median and lateral moraines.

Rocks polished and marked by the passage of a glacier. Such evidence showed Agassiz that glaciers and ice sheets had once spread over much of Europe.

PLATE III

Louis Agassiz, Swiss-born naturalist, whose studies of glaciers proved that the world had passed through an ice age.

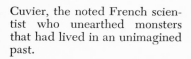

Cuvier, the noted French scientist who unearthed monsters that had lived in an unimagined past.

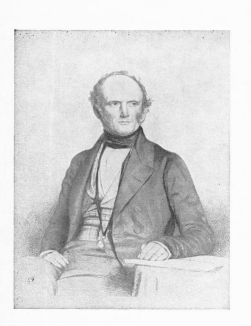

Sir Charles Lyell, English geologist who showed that the face of the earth had been shaped by the slow operation of natural forces and not by the Flood.

PLATE IV

A new volcano erupts from the depths of the Pacific Ocean, about six miles from the Bayonnaisa reefs, about one hundred and fifty miles south of Tokyo.

Another volcano is born, this time on land. Parícutin in Mexico grew from a crack in a cornfield in 1943 to a cone 1,500 feet high before it became quiescent in 1952. Lava rolled three miles down the valley.

PLATE V

Seething, burning lava in Crater Lake, Kilauea, Hawaii. When this photograph was taken the molten rock was broken up into three arms, one of which is shown in the foreground.

A glowing, white-hot stream of lava from Mauna Loa in the Hawaiian Islands cascades down a cliff into the sea. At this point the flow is about fifty feet wide.

PLATE VI

ipple marks in stone. A pattern set as water rippled over a shallow bed of
and and mud endures and testifies to the stone's shallow-water origin.

A larger rhythm in nature. Stratified pre-Cambrian limestones in southwest Africa. The steps or strata were deposited in recurring cycles.

PLATE VII

Strata that once lay flat were forced up and folded. Cross-section of a fold, Oslo Fiord, Norway.

More dramatic folding. With their loops, swirls, and inclines these folded sedimentary rocks near the Ugab River in southwest Africa look like old, roughly grained wood.

PLATE VIII

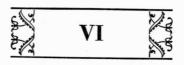

CUVIER

MONSTERS AND REVOLUTIONS

Paris was shocked, interested, incredulous, fascinated. In the fashionable salons, at the university, in the streets, everyone was talking about the fantastic elephant bones that M. Cuvier was digging from the very soil of the capital. Elephants, M. Cuvier had told the Institut National, had once lived in France and roamed the Paris countryside itself. It was almost too much, and yet it was an irresistible prospect. Everyone rushed out to see.

And the elephants were only a beginning. Soon the amazing M. Cuvier was unearthing even stranger denizens of a past that no one, or certainly very few, had suspected or even imagined. There were lizards as big as whales, lizards that could fly almost like birds, mammoths covered with long hair, hippopotamuses, rhinoceroses, bears, wolves, and other odd and often huge creatures that bore only a slight resemblance to living animals.

Cuvier, almost like a sorcerer, reconstructed them from their bones, often from only a few fragments of fossilized bone. His magic was almost as astounding as the singular, unnatural creatures themselves and the incalculably ancient worlds to which Cuvier said they had belonged. For Cuvier was telling his already staggered contemporaries that some of these ancient animals had lived in a time when the seas washed over the Paris basin, some in eras that were warm and tropical, and some in the years that had elapsed since the Flood, which Cuvier called the last great revolution that the world had undergone.

"Is Cuvier not the greatest poet of our century?" exclaimed Balzac with admiration and enthusiasm. "Our immortal naturalist has reconstructed worlds from blanched bones. He picks up a piece of gypsum and says to us 'See!' Suddenly stone turns into animals, the dead come to life, and another world unrolls before our eyes."

The man who was unveiling this unknown and astounding past was himself not only the most famous scientist of his age, but one of its most remarkable men.

Cuvier was born on August 23, 1769, in Montbéliard, the chief town in the little principality which then belonged to the Duke of Würtemberg and only later became a part of France. As the child of a sturdy Huguenot family he was christened Georges Chrétien Léopold Frédéric Dagobert Cuvier, but was thereafter called only Georges. His grandfather had been the town clerk and his father, who had not married until he was fifty, had served in the French army. His mother, a woman completely and tenderly devoted to her young son, undertook the easy task of assisting with his first education—easy because from the outset this was a prodigious child. Together they worked happily at his lessons, and at reading and drawing.

Cuvier was a triumph in school, and at fourteen, an age when boys' interests usually lie elsewhere, he not only organized some of his friends into a reading circle, but had the influence to keep them interested and working at it. He had already come upon Buffon and had developed a deep enthusiasm for natural history. Following Buffon's lead, he drew and described the plants and animals that he found around him.

The Cuvier family had hoped that Georges would become a Protestant pastor. This plan was circumvented, however, when he came to the attention of the Duke and was invited to attend the famed school that the Duke had established in the principality—to put larger nations to shame, some said.

More than eighty masters instructed the four hundred students in the usual academic subjects and in the arts as well. The more advanced students had their choice of five courses: law, medicine, government administration, military arts, and commerce. Cuvier chose government administration because, as the curriculum was organized, it gave him an opportunity to study natural history. One of the professors had given him a copy of the *Systema Naturæ* of Linnæus. All during his school years, and for nearly six years afterward, it was his natural-history Bible and almost his only guide, for he had few other natural-history books. At this select school Cuvier again carried away all the honors.

Cuvier expected that after his graduation he would obtain a government position. But at this time his father's small pension was severely cut, and he had to find immediate employment. He took a post as tutor in a Protestant family living in Normandy. It seemed a necessitous but unfortunate choice for a nineteen-year-old of such extraordinary promise. In the end, it proved quite the contrary, although perhaps Cuvier would have risen from any place and any degree of obscurity. In Normandy, Cuvier for the first time met the sea and the richness of its life. He plunged ardently into a study of its multitudinous creatures, dissecting with rare skill, drawing, analyzing, keeping a careful record of his work. And in the earth of Normandy, he, like Guettard, found many fossils. Cuvier was fascinated to discover how much they were like the sea life that he was studying.

He thought of the manuscripts he was compiling as only for his own use, and wrote to a friend: "They doubtless contain nothing but what has been done elsewhere, and better established by the naturalists of the capital, for they have been made without the aid of books or collections." In reality, however, his mind was free of preconceived notions, and his senses were absorbed in the direct handling of the actual materials hauled from the sea or dug from the Norman earth; as a consequence, his manuscripts were full of fresh new facts and techniques that had not been thought of, much less established, by the naturalists of the capital.

At Valmont, near where Cuvier was employed, a local society had been formed for the study of agriculture and science; Cuvier had been elected its secretary. Another member was M. Tessier, a scientist who had fled to Normandy to escape death in the French Revolution. He quickly recognized the amazing value of Cuvier's work, and put him in touch with some of the leading naturalists of France. They also were impressed by the studies of the young man in the provinces. Tessier was so enthusiastic about the rare talent he had discovered that he wrote his friend M. de Jussieu: "You will recall that it was I who gave Delambre to the academy; in another generation this also will be a Delambre." Cuvier saw the letter and, among all the honors that came to him, never forgot it.

In 1795 Cuvier was invited to Paris as a professor in the central school of the Panthéon. Before the year was over his *Tableau élémentaire de l'histoire naturelle des animaux,* proposing a new zoological alignment of animals, was a brilliant success, and along with Daubenton and Lapécède he was named to the zoological section of the newly re-established Institut National. Thus, in one year Cuvier had advanced from the unknown young Normandy tutor and secretary of an unheard-of local society to become a professor in Paris and a member of France's most distinguished scientific body.

Two years later, when Daubenton died, Cuvier, then only thirty, was appointed to the chair of natural history of the Collège de France. Another three years brought the death of Mertrud, and Cuvier was named his successor as professor of comparative anatomy at the Jardin des Plantes. The next year, 1803, he was elected by unanimous vote secretary of the academy of sciences of the Institut National.

It is doubtful that there had ever been a more meteoric rise in the history of French science. At the incredible age of thirty-four Cuvier occupied three of the most distinguished scientific posts of France and of the world. What was more, he was to hold them with ever growing fame and an unchallengeable security for the remainder of his life. Napoleon appointed him an adviser on public education, a counselor for life of the university, and a counselor of state. When Napoleon fell and other scientists closely associated with the Empire went down with him, Cuvier was unaffected. The restored monarchy not only continued him in his offices, but made him a baron and a peer of France. Cuvier outrode all storms with the solidity and certainty of a mighty mountain.

There was an unassailable quality to this human Everest which others recognized and accepted, and generally with less resentment or jealousy than might have been expected. Cuvier made an ineradicable impression on all who met him; they could not forget his lucid and eloquent lectures, his startling memory, his unique methods of work, or his remarkable appearance.

A great mane of coppery red hair crowned an enormous head and framed a face that was all crags and angles. His nose and chin were jutting bony outcrops, but people always noticed his blue eyes also. They shone with a quiet intelligence that no one could mistake. Even when he was young and not yet a national celebrity, artists and sculptors could not see him without itching to paint or model him, and during his life many—including David and perhaps a dozen others of national reputation—did. They made not one but numerous studies of this extraordinary head.

Not all of the many paintings, cartoons, busts, and plaques adequately show the great size of Cuvier's head, but that is a matter of practical and scientific record. His hats always had to be made in extra-large sizes; one of them, far too large for almost anyone else, still is kept in the Muséum National. An autopsy disclosed that Cuvier had a brain of 1,850 grams, five hundred above the average of 1,350.

An efficiency that, like everything else about this exceptional man, has few scientific parallels enabled him to carry on his science and research, to produce a steady stream of books, to teach, to fulfill superbly all his numerous public advisory duties, to read all the major scientific publications of the world, to carry on a world-wide correspondence with scientists, and to prepare the historic *éloges* in which he immortalized deceased Academicians.

When young Charles Lyell went to Paris in 1828, a friend, Gideon Mantell, asked him to get from Cuvier some casts for which he had been "begging in vain." Lyell had previously met Cuvier and attended his weekly soirees; he found him quite willing to oblige. Lyell obtained not only the requested casts but casts of "everything." In carrying out this mission he was admitted to Cuvier's "sanctum sanctorum"—his workrooms—and found them so astonishing that he hastened to write the whole story to his sister Marianne.

"In every part," he said, "it displays that extraordinary power of methodizing which is the grand secret of the prodigious feats which he performs annually without appearing to give himself the least trouble. But before I introduce you to this study, I should tell you that there is first the museum of natural history opposite his house, and admirably arranged by himself, and then the anatomy museum connected with his dwelling.

"In the latter is a library disposed in a suite of rooms, each containing works on one subject. There is one where there are all the works on ornithology, in another room all on ichthyology, in another osteology, in another *law* books! &c, &c. When he is engaged in such works as require continual reference to a variety of authors, he has a stove shifted into one of these rooms, in which everything on that subject is systematically arranged, so that in the same work he often takes the round of many apartments.

"But the ordinary studio contains no book-shelves. It is a longish room, comfortably furnished, lighted from above, and furnished with eleven desks to stand to, and two low tables, like a public office for so many clerks. But all this is for the one man, who multiplies himself as author and, admitting no one into this room, moves as he finds necessary or as fancy inclines him, from one occupation to another. Each desk is furnished with a com-

plete establishment of inkstand, pens &c., pins to pin MSS. together, the work immediately in reading and the MS. in hand,
and on shelves behind all the MSS. of the same work. There is a
separate bell to several desks. The low tables are to sit to when
he is tired. The collaborateurs are not numerous but always
chosen well. They save him every mechanical labour, find references &c., are rarely admitted to the study, receive orders, and
speak not.

"Brongniart, who in imitation of Cuvier has many clerks and
collaborateurs, is known to lose more time in organizing this auxiliary force than he gains by their work, but this is never the case
with Cuvier. When I went to get Mantell's casts, I found that the
man who made moulds and the *painter* of them, had distinct
apartments so that there was no confusion, and the despatch
with which all was executed was admirable. It cost Cuvier a
word only."

It was during his first year in Paris that Cuvier found the fossil
elephants. He reported the discovery to the Institute in 1796.
The knowledge of dissection and anatomy which he had acquired during his solitary work in Normandy left no doubt that
they belonged to different species than the living pachyderms.
To the scientists this was as startling a thought as the idea of
elephants inhabiting the Paris area was to the lay public. It
meant that certain species had been lost. A search of the gypsum quarries near Montmartre—they furnished the material for
plaster of Paris—turned up more fantastic extinct species of the
past.

Cuvier was such a master of anatomy that he saw that each
bone or part had its specific place in an organized being. And
each kind of being therefore could be recognized as to its order,
genus, and species by any fragment. Using this principle, which
he had discovered, Cuvier could start with, say, a leg bone, a
piece of neck, and maybe a few other pieces, and reconstruct an

animal as it had been in life. He had tested his skill so often with similar small bits of living animals that he knew his method was reliable.

Thus, by his hands a vanished past was re-created. Animals long gone from the earth stood forth again in all their fantastic sizes, shapes, and attributes. This restoration disclosed that the animals were not simply an odd assortment of individuals; they belonged to orders, to species, and to other organized groupings exactly similar to those of the living animal kingdom. Furthermore, nearly all the different groups were represented: reptiles, mammals, birds, and all the others. Cuvier therefore was able to announce that not only individuals had disappeared from the face of the earth, but whole genera had been eradicated.

Cuvier was haunted by the implications of this astounding conclusion. How had the extinct species disappeared? How had they been succeeded not only by one new series, but perhaps by several, before the animals of the "present creation" appeared upon the earth? Cuvier was primarily a zoologist deep in studies of the living animal kingdom, but his work with the giant fossil bones led him inevitably to geology. If he was to understand the fossil animals, he had to know how they had been entombed, and all the facts that could be learned about their occurrence in the earth.

He was fortunate at this point in obtaining the co-operation of a man who had the knowledge of rocks and rock structure which he lacked. This was Alexandre Brongniart, director of the famous porcelain factory at Sèvres. Brongniart, through his research on ceramic chemistry and his revival of the lost art of painting on porcelain, had made Sèvres ware some of the finest in Europe. A distinguished naturalist also, he succeeded Haüy as professor of mineralogy at the Museum of Natural History.

Almost every week for four years, Cuvier and Brongniart made excursions into the country around Paris to study its geological and fossil structure. They focused their attention on the problem of determining the succession or order in which the strata and the fossils appeared.

The first results of their investigations were reported in a memoir presented to the Institute in 1808. They industriously continued their work, and in 1811 published a full-scale book, *Essai sur la géographie des environs de Paris*. This and an enlarged edition that came out in 1822 were complete with elaborate maps, sections, and plates of fossils.

The country around Paris, which came to be known as the Paris basin, was a fine field for their study. There were a clear succession of notably different strata and a tremendous wealth of fossils. Millions of marine shells alternated regularly with fresh-water shells and the bones of the monstrous, extinct terrestrial animals. And then there were strata that contained no fossils at all.

Cuvier and Brongniart could interpret this alternating wealth and paucity of remains. At times, they saw, the Paris basin had been filled by the sea. At other times the land had been generally dry, though dotted by lakes and drained by full flowing rivers. Then the sea had conquered again, and had once more retreated; and this cycle had been repeated a third time in the beds they studied. In the deposits of the sea eras, the remains of marine animals were found; in the stones that marked what had once been the bottoms of fresh-water lakes and rivers lay the bones of land animals. And there was no mixing of the two. The different eras were sharply set apart.

Underlying the Paris area and part of England was a great deposit of chalk, a soft limestone made up largely of the shells of tiny sea organisms known as foraminifers. The lack of any strong stratification in the thick white deposits indicated that the little shells had drifted down to the bottom in a tranquil sea. Huge reptiles, tortoises, and lizards also had lived in these mild waters. Their bones were scattered through the chalk in great numbers. Cuvier and Brongniart identified more than fifty species.

Just above, resting on the chalk, came a contrasting layer of clay. Search as they would, they could find no organic remains in it. The two investigators drew the inference that the clay had been laid down under very different conditions, and in water where the swarming special life of the chalk sea no longer existed.

In all probability a long interval of time had elapsed between the epoch of the chalk and the age of the clay, for occasionally a layer of chalk fragments lay at the base of the clay. There had been time for the top of the chalk to crumble before the clay settled down upon it. It had also had time to become hard—originally the chalk had been a fine ooze.

The next formation was one of sand and a shell-laden *"calcaire grossier"* or limestone. It was made up of a number of bands of limestone and marl—a crumbly mixture of clay and limy materials—which always followed one upon the other in the same order. In some places around Paris some of the bands disappeared, but wherever they were found the same alternating arrangement of limestone and marl always appeared.

"This constancy in the order of superposition of the thinnest strata for a distance of twelve myriametres [about seventy-five miles] is in our opinion one of the most remarkable facts which we have met with in the course of our researches," said Cuvier and Brongniart. "It should lead to results for the arts and for geology all the more interesting because they are sure."

They were sure because of the fossils.

"The means which we have employed for the recognition, among so many limestones, of a bed already observed in a distant quarter, has been taken from the nature of the fossils contained in each bed," said the two scientists. "These fossils are generally the same in corresponding beds, and present tolerably marked differences of species from one group of beds to another. It is a method of recognition which up to the present has never deceived us.

"It must not be supposed, however, that the difference in this respect between one bed and another is as sharply marked off as that between the chalk and the limestone. The characteristic fossils of one bed become less abundant in the bed above and disappear altogether in the others, or are gradually replaced by new fossils which had not previously appeared."

All of this was new; it was a new observation, a new interpretation, and a new key to the past. Many before them, of course, had seen and studied fossils. At the end of the sixteenth century in France, a potter, Palissy, had dared to say that the Paris fossils were shells deposited in a sea which had once engulfed that part of the world. He had been denounced for the heresy and for his presumption by all the learned men of France. But in the seventeenth and the early eighteenth centuries the scholars had felt compelled to explain the stubbornly present fossils. In England Burnet, Woodward, and Whiston had struggled with the problem; in Germany, Leibnitz; and in France, Buffon. Buffon had finally convinced the French scholars of the fact that fossils were the remains of once living creatures rather than chance concretions or freaks of some kind.

Lamarck had further underwritten this conclusion when he studied more than six hundred species taken from the Paris limestone, the *calcaire grossier*. But Lamarck had not known how completely all the divisions of the animal kingdom were represented in the fossils, and he had not suspected that certain fossils were always associated with certain strata, and that the strata could be identified by them. Lamarck had made his studies in the museum. Working in the quarries and walking over the countryside, Cuvier and Brongniart clearly saw and grasped this relationship.

They also saw that the shells in the lower part of the limestone were much less like living forms than those which occurred in the higher beds. The farther away from the present, the greater was the difference.

The gypsum series of beds that lay above the limestone were interesting; though they contained a succession of differing strata, yet they seemed to have been deposited in one sequence. It was from these strata that Cuvier had dug the bones of his fabulous extinct quadrupeds. Sometimes with the bones of the giant rhinos and tapirs they found fresh-water shells—there were none of the sea shells that filled the limestone below. Cuvier and Brongniart agreed with the conclusions of their predecessors: the gypsum had been formed in fresh-water lakes. Perhaps the animals had died in the lakes, or perhaps their bodies had been washed down into them.

At the top of the gypsum series stretched a thin band of marl which they could trace for a great distance. It was important because it separated the fresh-water deposits from a new marine series that overlay them. All the shells in the gypsum just below the marl were fresh-water varieties, and all those in the new series above, marine.

The next marine beds, however, were very different from either the marine chalk or the marine limestone below. This time they were made up of sandstone and of a sandy limestone in which no fossils were found. The seas that invaded the Paris basin this time were not like the earlier ones.

And then came some fresh-water limestone containing lacustrine, or lake, shells. The seas had drawn back from the sandy shallows of the preceding era, and lakes had again formed on the new land.

The top layer in some parts of the Paris area was the alluvium of valleys, and it was in this layer that they found the bones of the elephants and the trunks of ancient trees. Rivers once more had been running through the land, and in the silt that they had spread over their flood plains were the bones of animals that resembled and yet differed from those of the present day. This layer was the last, Cuvier and Brongniart assumed, before the creation of the world's modern animals.

Others later studied and elaborated the revealing strata of the Paris basin with its succession of deposits of sea, land, sea, land, sea, and land. The later work, however, did not alter the broad outlines of the picture drawn by Cuvier and Brongniart.

The two observant French scientists had done far more than mark out the formations in one section of one country. They had, as Sir Archibald Geikie said, "established on the basis of accurate observation the principles of palaeontological stratigraphy," and they had demonstrated how fossils might be used for the determination of geological chronology. Science had a new and accurate method of establishing the order and the relative antiquity of the fossil-bearing strata of the earth. And the past was beginning to emerge from the deep shadows that had concealed it for so long.

Surprisingly, though such coincidences are frequent in science, the same discovery was being made in England at virtually the same time. William Smith, who like Cuvier was born in 1769, was a self-taught surveyor who acquired an unmatched knowledge of the earth of England as he traveled about laying out routes for canals. Smith came to know rocks so thoroughly that by looking at the contours of a hill and the character of the country, he could accurately predict what its stratification would prove to be. His close examination of the strata had inevitably called his attention to fossils. "Each stratum contained organized fossils peculiar to itself," said Smith, "and might in cases otherwise doubtful be recognized and discriminated from others like it, but in a different part of the series. . . ."

Smith later worked out a great map of England—one of the classics of geological cartography—which showed the strata underlying England, and proved that "the same species of fossils are found in the same strata, even at a wide distance." By coloring the bottom of each separate formation a more intensive shade than its upper reaches, Smith made his map easily intelligible. "The method of knowing the sub-strata from each other by their various substances imbedded is easily learnt," he declared.

Smith had never had anything except his slender earnings to support his work, and he spent so heavily on his great map that

he was financially ruined. He was forced to sell both his house
and his rare collection of fossils. He was a simple earnest man
who did most of his work outside established scientific circles,
and it was only belatedly that recognition came to him. In 1831,
however, the Geological Society gave him its Wollaston medal.
His life was also made easier by the grant of a small pension.

By completely different routes, Cuvier and Brongniart in
France and Smith in England had awakened the world to the
importance of fossils in the geological record. They had supplied
an unexpected answer to the world's old questions about the
shells and strange bones in the rocks. But, as so often happens in
science, the discovery that these shells and bones had belonged
to a whole progression of vanished species only raised new and
troubling questions.

Cuvier had identified one hundred and fifty fossil species.
Ninety of them had no living counterparts; their kind had completely disappeared from the world. Eleven or twelve resembled
known species. The others belonged to living groups. Cuvier had
already noted that those which differed most lay buried in the
deepest formations. There was an order in this, too. In the chalk
with which his studies began there were no mammals; there
were only egg-laying animals. The mammals appeared only in
the higher-lying limestone, and those which were similar to living species only in the alluvial deposits at the top of the Paris
formations.

Why had whole species and even genera been wiped out?
Cuvier asked again. Why did different species appear in later
deposits?

Cuvier was a man noted for his rigorous adherence to facts.
His lectures on zoology stood out in sharp contrast to those of
many of his colleagues because he did not indulge in speculation. But this scientific approach broke down when he attempted to answer these two leading questions. To admit that
species had evolved, and thus man too, would have conflicted
fundamentally with all that he and the world believed about the

origin of life. Cuvier accepted what his eyes seemed to see and what his strong Huguenot faith dictated.

Looking at the strata and seeing how various species had disappeared never to appear again, he convinced himself that they had been destroyed in one of a series of revolutions through which the world had passed. It seemed to him that the record of the revolutions was written indelibly in the rocks.

"These repeated irruptions and retreats of the sea have neither been slow nor gradual," Cuvier wrote in his *Discours sur les révolutions du globe*. "On the contrary, most of the catastrophes which have occasioned them have been sudden. . . ."

He envisioned a world swept by great floods and wrecked by vast upheavals that wrote an end to most of the life and the existing land and seascape of the era. This was why strata and distinctive groups of fossils broke off abruptly and different deposits began; the world had changed.

The French scientific leader pointed to other strong evidence that this had been the order of the past. Not many years before, in the last quarter of the eighteenth century, Pierre Simon Pallas, working with a Russian expedition, had discovered elephants frozen in the ice of Siberia. Some were so perfectly preserved that even the hair and skin had survived. They were so numerous that a lively trade was carried on in the ivory.

Here was certainly further proof of the suddenness of the revolutions of the past. With clear logic Cuvier pointed out that if the elephants had not been frozen as soon as they were killed the carcasses would have been decomposed. "Eternal frost could not have previously occupied these places," he argued, "for they could not have lived in such temperatures. Therefore at one and the same moment in which these animals were destroyed the country which they inhabited became covered with ice." Ice thus had taken over the northern part of the world suddenly, instantaneously, without gradation. The ice age had gripped the world with the speed of a blizzard.

It seemed to Cuvier that there was equally strong proof that the world at other periods had been torn and rent by gigantic earth movements. "The breaking to pieces, the raising up, the overturning of older strata leave no doubt in the mind that they have been reduced to the state in which we now see them by the action of sudden and violent causes," he declared. "Life has often been disturbed by great and terrible events which are everywhere recorded."

Cuvier did not ignore the possibility that the vast changes so evident in the surface and life of the globe might have been brought about by the operation of forces presently altering the surface. But after examining this idea, he dismissed it as one not to be taken seriously. Where in the world were rain, running water, the seas, volcanoes, or even earthquakes wiping out whole species, throwing up mountains and remaking continents? "In vain," said Cuvier, "do we search for present causes sufficient to produce the revolutions and catastrophes the traces of which are exhibited in the earth's crust."

But if the past had been a series of world-shaking revolutions, and if all living things within their reach had been annihilated, Cuvier was compelled to find an explanation for the new and changed life that in its turn had taken over and left its remains in the rocks. How had the new population come to be? Cuvier found the answer to this puzzling question by postulating a new creation, a fresh creation to fill the places left vacant by the destruction of the earlier. Perhaps there had been several new starts. Cuvier spoke frequently in his essay about earlier creations having preceded the existing one.

Flourens, who succeeded Cuvier as secretary of the academy of sciences, listed this as one of Cuvier's great contributions to science. "The idea of an entire creation of animals preceding the actual creation, the idea of the destruction and loss of an entire creation was conceived as part of [Cuvier's] over-all plan," he said.

Cuvier actually did not go quite so far. "When I maintain that the stone banks contain the bones of several genera and the beds those of several species which no longer exist, I do not pretend that a new creation is necessary to produce the species existing today," he wrote. "I say only that they did not exist in the places where we see them at present, and that they had to come there somehow." He gave every indication, however, of thinking that the "somehow" was by a special act of creation.

Cuvier's theory of revolution brought him into sharp conflict with Lamarck and Geoffroy St. Hilaire, both of whom believed that species had evolved over a vast period of time from simple undifferentiated bits of matter. It was revolution versus evolution.

But the transitional forms that evolution presupposed were not to be seen in the stones, or so it seemed. On the contrary, anyone who journeyed out to the Paris quarries and valleys—Cuvier personally escorted scores of visitors from all parts of the world—could see the undeniable fossil proof that different species had lived in different epochs. One species did not merge into another; each was distinct and alone. The non-scientific also could look at the huge extinct animals that Cuvier had reconstructed and realize that they were unlike living animals. The Bible was cited as further proof of the theory of revolution, and revolution in the earth carried the day.

Cuvier's immense prestige, which had increased with the years, aided its triumph. His work in zoology and comparative anatomy had given new life to both sciences. Additional public honors had been pressed on him; he had been appointed president of the Conseil d'État and administrator of all non-Catholic religions. Many other posts he had refused, among them a lifetime appointment as head of the Museum and a place in the cabinet. He insisted on confining his public service to an advisory role; he would take no office that might interfere with his pursuit of science.

His personal life was quiet, a mixture of happiness and sorrow. His marriage to a widow with four children was happy, but three of their four children died in infancy or childhood. The loss of their remaining child, a twenty-two-year-old daughter, was an almost unbearable grief to him. He sought consolation by plunging even deeper into his work. With the years his hair turned to a silvery blond that was almost as striking as its former flaming red, but his energy seemed undiminished.

Perhaps he was feeling the strain of his high-pressured life when on the day before he was stricken he told young Louis Agassiz: "Be careful and remember that work kills." But perhaps not. He had been in the fullest health and was only sixty-two.

After his collapse as he walked to the tribune of the Chamber of Deputies, his condition and the paralysis that set in grew steadily worse. He died five days later, on May 13, 1832. The medical reports were not conclusive; physicians who have since studied them incline to the belief that he died of one form of the cholera that was then raging through Paris.

True to his habit of forgetting and neglecting nothing, Cuvier left a note for whoever might deliver his *éloge*. "I have written so many *éloges*," he wrote, "that there is nothing presumptuous in believing that someone will write mine, and knowing by experience what it costs the author of this sort of report to learn the details of the life of those of whom he speaks, I wish to save this trouble for the one who will have to do mine." He left a concise outline of the major facts of his life.

Flourens, performing the duty Cuvier had foreseen, spoke with great feeling and learning of the Institute's and the nation's loss, though he lacked Cuvier's masterful touch in making the individual as well as his work live in all their human dimensions and significance. "The history of M. Cuvier is nothing less than the history of science in the nineteenth century," he told the Institute.

This was true to an unusual degree. It was also true that the history of M. Cuvier was the history of part of the past and a key to the history of the future. Cuvier had disclosed a past peopled with unimagined and fantastically different animals. More than this, he and Smith had proved that by studying their succession the order of the past could be read with great certainty. Science had an effective and essential tool for timing the past, and a tool that would not be equaled in usefulness until the mid-twentieth-century discovery of absolute radioactive methods of dating the past.

"Vous avez trouvé ainsi, la théorie de la terre dans la terre même," said Cuvier. ("You have thus found the theory of the earth in the earth itself.")

And Cuvier was right, insofar as he was speaking of method. To understand the earth, men had to study the earth—and there was nothing more interesting or surprising. Cuvier also had removed any lingering doubts about the latter point.

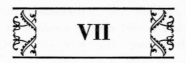

AGASSIZ

ICE!

EUROPE HAD BEEN TOLD, though not wholly convinced, that unsuspected volcanoes had once poured their burning lava over much of the land, that more floods of molten rock had broken through from below, and that strange, monstrous animals had formerly roamed the countryside. Then, as the nineteenth century rolled around, the already shaken and shocked were to hear that Europe and much of the world had at another era been covered by ice.

Fire, monsters, and then ice!

The more conservative, and those who believed that the earth they lived on was exactly as it had been since the Flood, felt increasingly outraged. The French Revolution had added to the sense of menace, until, as Sir Charles Lyell said, "the most resolute minds" were alarmed and the timid were haunted by a dread of innovation "as by the phantom of some fearful dream."

Science was creating an imposing dilemma.

The man who revealed that the earth had passed through not only one but several ice ages was one of the most dedicated, devout, productive, and warm-hearted of scientists—Jean Louis Rodolphe Agassiz.

Louis Agassiz, as he always was known, was born on May 28, 1807, in the picturesque parsonage at Motier, Switzerland. The balconied house with its steep-pitched roof looked out over the Lake of Morat toward the snowy, glacier-filled slopes of the Bernese Alps.

Through the carefully tended garden and orchard flowed a

clear, pure, little mountain stream. It spilled into a large stone basin just behind the parsonage, and there, when he was very young, Louis began to keep his collection of fish. It was his private aquarium.

Thus, at the very beginning the two principal interests of his life—glaciers and fish—were before his eyes and a part of his being. In the beginning, though, the fish came first. Louis and his brother Auguste were uncannily adroit in catching fish without the use of hook, line, or net. Their curious fingers shot into holes and under rocks and they could even seize fish in the open water, attracting them by little arts to which the fish seemed to respond with a kind of fascination.

At fourteen Louis was finishing his first schooling at Bienne. On a sheet of yellow foolscap he wrote his devoted parents about the books he would need and about his plans: "I wish to advance in the sciences and for that I need d'Anville, Ritter, an Italian dictionary, a Strabo in Greek, Mannert, and Thiersch. I have resolved to become a man of letters. . . . For this I should like to stay at Bienne till the month of July, and afterward serve my apprenticeship in commerce at Neuchâtel for a year and a half. Then I should like to pass four years at a university in Germany and finally finish at Paris, where I should stay for about five years. Then, at the age of twenty-five I could begin to write."

The boy's hopefully written plan turned out to be almost an exact forecast of what was to come. Only the apprenticeship was abandoned; it lost out to his intense interest in the study of natural history. At seventeen Louis entered the medical school at Zurich, for that seemed to offer the best route to the life of science of which he dreamed. Soon the professor of natural history had given the ardent young student the key to his library and Louis was spending hours copying the books that he could not afford to buy. In 1826, with a brilliant record behind him, he was ready to go to Heidelberg.

With Alexander Braun, a young German student of botany

and one of the close, warm, lifetime friends that he would make everywhere he went, Agassiz plunged into a day-and-night study of natural history. A few medical courses were reluctantly squeezed in. All the while he was collecting, experimenting, and studying the country on long walks, and on vacation trips.

In 1827 he and Braun moved on to the University of Munich, where Agassiz's room became known as the "Little Academy." Not only was it a center where all the most avid science students gathered and Agassiz sometimes gave lectures on zoology; it was also a menagerie of no mean proportions. There were fish, a large cage of birds, rare mammalia, reptiles, shells, and a herbarium of some three thousand specimens. Books filled all the chairs, and the white walls were used for scientific diagrams of every kind.

Soon Agassiz was secretly at work on a description of the Brazilian fishes brought back by Martius and Spix from their celebrated Brazilian journey of 1817. Spix had died before he could complete the publication of the material on the fish, and the professors at Munich had recommended Agassiz to carry on the work. The young Swiss hoped to establish his scientific reputation with this study and at the same time to appease and surprise his parents, who were becoming increasingly disturbed by his neglect of his medical studies.

To illustrate his folio on the fish, Agassiz had to have the services of an artist. Although he had scarcely enough money to buy his food, he employed an artist, Joseph Dinkel, who was to remain with him for the next sixteen years. Dinkel was added to the Little Academy, drawing at a stand-up desk near the two big windows.

Agassiz would have liked to give up medicine entirely; he felt only a repugnance toward practicing. But his parents firmly, though lovingly, insisted: "We will come to an understanding in one word," his father wrote. "Let the sciences be the balloon in which you prepare to travel through the higher regions, but let medicine and surgery be your parachutes. I think, my dear

Louis, that you cannot object to this way of looking at the question and deciding it."

Agassiz obediently and cheerfully yielded. After taking his diploma in the faculty of philosophy in 1829, he went on, crowding the work in whenever he could, to take his medical degree in April 1830.

In the meantime the first part of his *Brazilian Fish* had been published and promptly acclaimed by scientists all over Europe. While the busy student still was working at forced draft to finish this first undertaking, a collection of fossil fish was placed in his hands by the director of the Munich Museum. Fascinated, Agassiz mapped out a bold and grand project: he would study all the fish that had lived "at each of the geological epochs of creation," and trace their characters and their relations with fish now living. In some cases he had no more than a single tooth, a scale, or a spine as his guide in the reconstruction, and it was clear that he would have to reconstruct at least five hundred species.

The already distinguished but nearly penniless young doctor of philosophy and medicine returned to his parents' home, bringing innumerable crates of fish and an artist along with him. Although he took care of a few patients, virtually all of his time went into concentrated work on his fossil fish. After a little more than a year, in 1832 he saw that he would have to go to Paris to continue his work. With a tiny bit of money from his publisher and a loan from his uncle, he headed straight for the Museum of Natural History and its noted authority, Cuvier. Agassiz knew that Cuvier himself was planning a study of fossil fish, and he anxiously laid his work before the great French scientist. There were a few painful days of doubt. Then Cuvier invited him to his house for dinner. He had his secretary bring out his own portfolio of materials.

"I had indeed anticipated him," Agassiz wrote to his uncle. "He had intended at some future time to do the same thing; but [since] I had given it so much attention and had done my work so well, he had decided to renounce his project and to place at my disposition all the material he had collected and all the preliminary notes he had taken."

In the few months that remained before Cuvier's death, he gave the young Swiss every assistance. Nevertheless, the vast project was threatened with collapse; Agassiz had no income. The cost of materials, of keeping Dinkel and other artists at work, and of living on even the lowest of scales was running him deep into debt and overwhelming him with anxiety. At the very moment when he had decided that he could not go on, a letter came from Alexander von Humboldt, the famous naturalist and traveler. He had been watching Agassiz's work with growing admiration and he knew that worry and lack of money might kill it. He begged his young friend "to make use of the accompanying small credit. You would do more for me, I am sure." It was for one thousand francs.

"My benefactor and friend," wrote Agassiz with an outpouring of heartfelt gratitude, "it is too much. I cannot find words to tell you how deeply your letter today moved me. At what a moment has your help come. . . . I find myself rescued unexpectedly by a kind, helping hand and to have again the hope of devoting my whole powers to science—you can judge the state into which your letter has thrown me."

Soon afterward the city of Neuchâtel, only a few miles from Agassiz's birthplace, established a professorship of natural history and offered it to its already noted young compatriot. An important place in Paris opened at about the same time, but Agassiz chose to go to his native Switzerland.

Within a few years his courses of lectures had a large following, his children's classes were crowded, he had made headway in assembling a distinguished museum, and he was one of the best-known and best-liked figures in the small Swiss city. Stirred by Agassiz's infectious enthusiasm, all Neuchâtel was taking an interest in natural science.

All the while the young professor was working steadily on his fossil fish. By 1833 he was ready to begin publishing—if he could obtain the seventy subscriptions necessary to cover the cost of printing one hundred and fifty copies of the first folio. In a scramble for time and money, the first volume came out. Nothing previously in the field had approached this magnificently studied and illustrated work.

Recherches sur les poissons fossiles reclassified all fish, fossil and living. What was more, it pointed out for the first time the strange combination of reptilian and birdlike characters in the early geological fish. And, also for the first time, it showed how strikingly the embryos of the higher fish relive the history of their kind.

The book and its remarkable illustrations made it possible for science to trace the organic development of fish, "the progress of organization in one great division of the animal kingdom," through a "complete series of ages of the earth." [1]

On February 4, 1834, came a letter from Sir Charles Lyell. The Geological Society of London had conferred their Wollaston Award on the twenty-six-year-old Agassiz for his "magnificent work." The book was received with equal enthusiasm in other scientific circles. In the first happy hours of this brilliant success, Agassiz was married to Cecile Braun, the sister of his close college friend, Alexander Braun.

He also was invited to England and cordially received by all the greats of English science—Buckland, Lyell, Sedgwick, Murchison. They not only opened their collections to him, but permitted him to select two thousand choice specimens and take them to London for comparative study. The Geological Society set aside a room for his use in its headquarters, Somerset House. And the already enormous job of studying all fossil

[1] All the facts that might have made Agassiz an evolutionist were clearly set out in his own work. Nevertheless, he indignantly rejected all such implications; they would have conflicted with his earnestly held religious beliefs.

fish grew even larger. It would be a work of years, enough to consume all the time and energy of even such an extraordinary worker as Agassiz.

But two friends, Charpentier and Venetz, had been studying the Alpine glaciers and had announced that all of the erratic boulders that lay strewn in such great profusion over the plains of Switzerland and the sides of the Jura had been carried there by glaciers, and not by water, as everyone had always thought. The theory sounded improbable to Agassiz. Nevertheless, he went to see. He spent his vacation in the summer of 1836 climbing around the glaciers and the moraines—the ridges of rock dropped or carried by the glaciers—in the valley of the Rhone. In the winter of 1837 he went back again.

What he saw soon convinced him that Charpentier was right, but that he had been too conservative. Everywhere that Agassiz looked, he saw rocks polished and grooved exactly as the rocks were being polished and grooved by living glaciers. And there were ancient moraines exactly like the tumbled piles of rock then accumulating along the sides and at the end of the glaciers over which he was climbing. The distant moraines and the telltale scratching could only mean that the glaciers had once spread out over a great part of Europe.

Agassiz had to know what lay behind these phenomena of nature. What could be more natural, he asked, than to inquire what had caused these great masses of ice, what modifications they had undergone, and what effects they had exercised and were exercising on the places around them? It seemed astounding to him that the thousands who had visited the glaciers had looked at them only with "astonishment and admiration" rather than with questions.

Had these great snowy tongues once been thicker? How thick were they even now? Agassiz and some friends strapped a hundred feet of iron rod to their backs and laboriously lugged it onto the glacier with the intention of making a boring. "As well might I have tried to sound the ocean with a ten-fathom line," he ruefully said.

Later they carried up two hundred feet of rod and tried again. Again they scarcely made a dent. Eventually Agassiz succeeded in transporting a thousand feet of rod, and then he satisfied himself, after many attempts, that this was about the thickness of the glacier of Aar.

Studying the old moraines, Agassiz also felt sure that glaciers moved. Some early observers had suggested this, but so uniform did the glaciers seem from year to year that many denied it. It was true that rocks seen at a certain point one year might be much farther down the glacier the next year, but did the fact that a rock had moved prove that the glacier had moved too? Neither did the occasional encroachment of a glacier on a valley mean anything, people said. That was only the effect of an unusually heavy accumulation of snow during a severe winter.

Agassiz decided to test the point by planting a row of stakes in the ice. If the glacier moved, they would move with it. If they remained where he put them, the advance of other objects on the same glacier could be traced to sliding or some other motion of their own. It was an excellent idea, but Agassiz had much to learn about glaciers. In a very short time all of his stakes lay flat on the ice.

He had discovered nothing about glacial movement; instead he had found that the surface wastes away each summer to a depth of about five feet. That was why his rods had lost their support and fallen; the snow that held them had melted. Agassiz realized that stakes would have to be driven at least ten to fifteen feet below the surface, and when he repeated the experiment in this way a few years later the results were dramatic.

At thirty-one Agassiz was as agile as in his student days— he would take a crevasse with a flying leap. Handsome, with almost classically molded features and an aliveness and daring

in every movement, he suggested a D'Artagnan. A traveler who
saw him with his friends in an inn one evening and heard them
call him Agassiz asked if he could be the son of the celebrated
professor of Neuchâtel.

In an address before the Helvetic Society in 1837, Agassiz
daringly announced to the world that it had passed through a
great ice age. Because of an oscillation in temperature, he said,
a sheet of ice similar to that covering the Arctic had extended
from the north pole at least to central Europe and Asia.

"Siberian winter," he declared, "established itself for a time
over a world previously covered with a rich vegetation and peopled with large mammalia, similar to those now inhabiting the
warm regions of India and Africa. Death enveloped all nature
in a shroud, and the cold, having reached its highest degree,
gave to this mass of ice at the maximum of tension, the greatest
possible hardness."

The erratic boulders, he further said, had been carried along
on the ice. Agassiz described them as "one of the accidents accompanying the vast change occasioned by the fall of the temperature of our globe before the commencement of our epoch."

A number of well-known geologists, including Von Buch,
were present at the meeting—and had expected Agassiz to speak
on fossil fish. Von Buch scarcely concealed his impatience with
the brash theory he had heard. Humboldt later said that the
German geologist was "in a rage about it." Humboldt himself
was disturbed both by what Agassiz had said and by the diver-
sion of his attention to glaciers. In one of the delightful letters
that he wrote to Agassiz, Humboldt urged him to concentrate
his efforts on his "beautiful work on fossil fishes." "In doing so,"
he said, "you will render a greater service to positive geology
than by these general considerations (a little icy withal) on the
revolutions of the primitive world."

Agassiz could no more be stopped by words than could a
glacier. He set out to track the footsteps of the ice in valleys and
mountains. During the next summer he examined all the glaciers

coming down from the majestic summits of Monte Rosa and the Matterhorn, whose crests form a gigantic amphitheater rising above the everlasting snow. He also visited the glacier of Aletsch, which flows from the Jungfrau. At the glacier of the Rhone he established headquarters, and from that point he and a party of friends started out to climb to the junction of the Finsteraar and the Lauteraar. They wanted to study glacial movement.

For four hours they climbed along the rough, rugged middle moraine. Suddenly they were amazed to come upon a cabin. They knew that a cabin had been built on the glacier in 1827 by a scientist-priest named Hugi, but it seemed impossible that this could be his. Hugi had placed his shelter at the foot of the great rock that formed the angle separating the two glaciers. That was far above where they found the little hut. But it was definitely Hugi's. Under a pile of stone they found a bottle containing papers recording not only the date and location of the cabin, but a later visit of the priest's. In twelve years the cabin had traveled more than four thousand feet.

The next summer, that of 1840, Agassiz established his first permanent station in the Alps. Along the middle moraine of the lower Aar glacier, which they had chosen for their continuing work, stood a huge boulder of schist. Its upper surface projected in such a way that it formed a natural roof. By building a stone wall along one side and rigging a blanket across the entrance, they made a hut where six people could sleep. A sheltered recess outside served for kitchen and dining-room.

This sturdy but far from luxurious shelter was promptly christened "Hotel des Neuchâtelois," and they carved the names of its builders in the stone. They had hoped to use Hugi's cabin for an additional shelter, but in 1840 it had crumbled. Its wreckage lay two hundred feet below the point where they had encountered it the summer before.

Agassiz, assisted by his pupil François de Pourtalès, was to handle the meteorological work on the Aar; another scientist was assigned to study the red snow, a common phenomenon on glaciers; another, the flora of glaciers; and another, glacial features.

One of their first projects was to drive again the stakes that had previously refused to stay in place. This time they hammered them eighteen feet down in a straight line across the ice. Positions were determined with reference to certain fixed points on the rocky wall of the valley.

The next year, when they returned, the straight line of the stakes had changed into a crescent, a graceful festoon looped across the face of the glacier. Not only had the stakes moved; those in the center had advanced faster than those at the sides. For the first time accurate data on the movement of a glacier had been established. The experiment was repeated in other years with similar results.

This experiment also helped to explain the crevasses—the gaping fissures, sometimes several hundred feet wide and often as much as a mile long—that were such a danger to both the ordinary traveler and the mountaineer.

Once it was conceded that the glacier moved, it followed that the huge mass of ice would be rent across whenever it flowed over a hill or any other big protuberance. That accounted for the transverse crevasses.

The lateral crevasses are produced, Agassiz saw, when the moving ice crushes into some promontory jutting out along the side of the valley through which it is flowing. As the glacier pushes around this obstacle, a long slanting crack opens, a crevasse that points upward and into the glacier. But this is a position the crevasse cannot long retain, for the glacier is moving, and its center is moving faster than its edges. The crevasse thus moves downward, almost like the hand of the clock. As a result, Agassiz pointed out, older lateral crevasses can always be distinguished from new ones, for they point down-glacier, "while the fresh ones point upward," toward the glacier's source.

Agassiz needed to know, too, about the upper limits of glacial action and about the places where glaciers were born.

Thus, he and his party began to scale the Alpine peaks, many of which had previously been considered unscalable.

On the August morning set for the ascent of the Strahleck, their guides awakened the Hotel des Neuchâtelois at three o'clock in the morning, an hour earlier than usual. And their hearts sank; they were walled in by a solid bank of fog. As their guide, Leuthold, cooked breakfast, he urged them not to give up. He was, it proved, an excellent judge of the weather; in a few minutes the sun lit up one by one the summits of the Streckhorn, the Finsteraarhorn, and the Oberaarhorn. The peaks stood out, glowing islands above the swirling gray below.

Three hours later they were at the base of Strahleck. Leuthold and Währen, the party's regular guides, had engaged three additional men, for the ascent was going to be a difficult one and an array of barometric instruments had to be taken along. In single file they began to climb, floundering in light snow up to their knees. The slopes were so steep and the going so difficult that the guides had roped them together. Only Leuthold and Währen remained detached; they stayed free to cut footholds in the ice and to warn of dangers ahead. At nine o'clock, after an hour of the most difficult climbing, they stepped onto a small plateau and the smooth unbroken snow of the summit of Strahleck.

The day was perfect. Above them arched the bluest of skies and at their feet lay the valley of Grindelwald. Before them were the masses of the Eiger and the Mönch, and to the southwest the Jungfrau towered above the chain of the Viescherhorner. They stood motionless, awed by the intense stillness, the solitude, and the "purity of aspect of every object," and by the beauty of the patterned world below and around them. Then their human elation broke forth. As Portalès, then seventeen, tells the story: "The guides began to wrestle and we to dance, when suddenly we saw a female chamois, followed by her young, ascending a neighboring slope, and presently four or five more stretched their necks over a rock as if to see what was going on.

"Breathless, the wrestlers and dancers paused, fearing to disturb by the slightest movements creatures so shy of human approach. They drew nearer until within easy gunshot distance, and then galloping along the opposite ridge, disappeared over the summit."

More than an hour was spent in making measurements. Then, after a little rest and some food, they roped themselves together again and began the descent, much of it a long slide.

Below the slopes of snow, said Portalès, "rocks almost vertical or narrow ridges covered with grass served us as a road and brought us to the glacier of the Grindelwald. To reach the glacier itself we traversed a crevasse of great depth and some twenty feet wide, on a bridge of ice, one or two feet in width and broken at the end, where we were obliged to spring across. Once on the glacier the rest was nothing. The race was to the fastest and we were soon on the path of the tourists."

They were in the village of Grindelwald at three o'clock in the afternoon, having a hard time persuading the townspeople that they had left the glacier of Aar that morning.

Soon after his return from the glaciers, Agassiz went to England. Dr. Buckland, Dean of Westminster and an admirer of Agassiz's work with fossil fish, had been extremely skeptical about his glacial theories. He had, however, succumbed to Agassiz's challenge "*Venez voir*" and had gone to Switzerland to see. He had been fully convinced. He was thus ready to listen sympathetically to the Agassiz contention that glaciers had once extended over much of Scotland and England.

Following a Glasgow meeting of the British Association for the Advancement of Science, the two left for the highlands on a "glacier hunt." As they approached the castle of the Duke of Argyll, Agassiz said to Buckland: "Here we shall find our first traces of glaciers." He was an accurate prophet. As they entered the valley they drove over an ancient terminal moraine.

They went on to the famous Glen Roy. For a number of years British and Scottish naturalists had been baffled by the

"parallel roads" of the glen—terraces stretching one above another like three roads built at varying levels. Some thought that
the "roads" had been created by ancient lakes; Lyell and Darwin attributed them to continental upheavals and subsidences;
others held that they had been formed in the Flood or in subsequent floods. Agassiz quickly saw that they were the work of
glaciers.

As he and Buckland climbed excitedly through the beautiful glen, Agassiz read its past and its present. A glacial lake
once had filled the valley. It had been formed by the melting
of its own glacier, when glaciers descending from more sheltered neighboring valleys had thrown a dam across its end. As
this barrier gradually yielded, the waters of the lake fell; the
terraces marked each of the levels at which they had stood.
There were innumerable proofs. The bottoms of both glens
still showed deep rectilinear scratches and furrows. There were
moraines and the rounded *"roches moutonées"* left by glaciers
everywhere.

The same unmistakable track of glaciers was to be found
elsewhere in Scotland and England. The Grampians, where Hutton had discovered the vast irruptions of molten granite, had
at another era formed a great center for the distribution of glaciers.

"A colossal ice field spread itself over the whole country, extending in every direction toward the lower lands and the sea-
shore," Agassiz reported. "In time . . . it was reduced to local
glaciers, circumscribed within the higher valleys and the more
mountainous parts of the country, until they totally disappeared,
as those of Switzerland would also have done, had it not been
for the greater elevation of that country above the level of the
sea. Scotland nowhere rises above the present level of perpetual
snow, while in Switzerland the whole Alpine range has an altitude favorable for the preservation of glaciers."

The proofs that Agassiz assembled were so detailed and so
precise that some noted scientists yielded to them. Soon after

they had been presented in London, Buckland wrote to Agassiz, who was then back in Switzerland: "Lyell has adopted your theory *in toto!!!* On my showing him a beautiful moraine within two miles of his father's house he instantly accepted it, as solving a host of difficulties that have all his life embarrassed him." Darwin also accepted the Agassiz theory, and always considered his first opinion of the origin of Glen Roy one of the worst mistakes of his life.

Humboldt also was coming around. He wrote to Agassiz: "Taught from my youth to believe that the organization of past times was somewhat tropical in character, and startled therefore at these glacial interruptions, I cried 'Heresy!' at first. But should we not always listen to a friendly voice like yours?"

SECOND STATION ON THE GLACIER OF AAR: AGASSIZ'S HEADQUARTERS.

The next winter—or, rather, in still wintry March—Agassiz went back to the glaciers. He wanted to compare summer and winter temperatures and to see if water still flowed from the glacier in winter. There were some who claimed that if glaciers did move, it was because their lower surface was melted by the central heat of the earth. Agassiz did not believe it, but characteristically he set forth to find out.

In the cold of March the glacier of Aar lay white and immobile. The rills and the cascades that coursed over its surface during the summer were still, and no water poured from beneath into the rivers below. Despite a careful search, Agassiz could find no running water except the pure limpid outpouring from springs that never froze over. Crevasses were also closed and only the bold black summit of the Finsteraarhorn stood out against the white world. The brilliance of the sun striking the glittering white surface was so intensely painful to the eyes and skin that Agassiz had to wrap his head in double veils. But it was easy for him to establish that in winter the glacier did not move.

The next summer was to be devoted to a study of the internal structure of the great moving fields of ice, and particularly to the action of water in influencing their movement. In addition to his usual collaborators Agassiz took with him the noted physicist Professor James D. Forbes, of Edinburgh.

The big drill they had brought with them penetrated deep into the ice. Once, after it had been driven one hundred and ten feet down, it suddenly dropped another two feet. The air bubbles that came rushing up indicated that the glacial cavern into which it had bit was not hermetically sealed.

But Agassiz was not satisfied with what he could learn from his instruments. He decided that he himself would descend into one of the so-called "wells" of the glacier. To make this possible they had to divert a stream that ordinarily cascaded into this seemingly bottomless hole; a new bed had to be dug for it. A large tripod was rigged over the "well" opening, and Agassiz, seated on a swing-like board, was lowered into the hole of ice, into the heart of the glacier. One of the party lay flat on the edge of the wall to direct the descent and listen for any warning cry.

Down Agassiz went, forty feet, sixty feet, eighty feet. At that point he shouted to them to hold the line. The icy tube in which he was descending suddenly divided into two compartments. He decided to go down into the larger of the two and signaled: "Lower away." But soon this narrow shaft divided into several narrower tunnels, much too small to accommodate a human body. Agassiz was lifted back to the eighty-foot level and called to be let down into the smaller half of the well.

Down he went again, so absorbed by the amazing blue bands that ran through the still luminous walls of ice that he was aroused to his danger only when his feet plunged into icy water. In instant alarm he shouted to be lifted, but from that great depth—he was then one hundred and twenty-five feet down in the glacier—his muffled cry was misunderstood. They lowered again. The scientist went down into the freezing water. His frantic cries then were unmistakable, and the surface crew desperately hauled him out of the water that could have frozen and drowned him.

Peril was far from ended. The ascent was more hazardous than the descent. Going down, Agassiz could slide around the great jagged ice stalactites that hung from the walls. Going up, he might have been caught by them; he had to steer his way precariously and gently around their sharp points. There was also the ever present chance that one of them, loosened by the friction of the rope, might come plummeting down upon him. A man could easily have been killed by a blow from such a weight.

Afterward Agassiz admitted: "Had I known all the dangers, perhaps I should not have started on such an adventure. Certainly unless induced by some powerful scientific motive, I should not advise anyone to follow my example." That might be considered a classic understatement.

Having plumbed the depths, Agassiz was determined to scale the heights to make further studies of the formation of glaciers in the upper parts of the mountains. The summer closed with his famous ascent of the Jungfrau.

Six scientists and six guides left the hospice of the Grimsel at four o'clock on the morning of August 27, 1841. Crossing the Col of the Oberaar, they descended to the snowy plateau that feeds the Viescher glacier. The snow in this amphitheater, walled in by the peak of the Viescherhorner, seemed to be a solid mass, and they moved over it confidently, though they had observed certain window-like openings in the snow. Stopping to examine one of them, they looked down into an immense vault filled with an eerily beautiful blue light. They were, in fact, walking on only a thick crust of snow.

A five-hour trek over deep snow and rugged névé brought them to a shelter used by earlier climbers. As they wearily and gratefully settled down to spend the night, Leuthold, again their chief guide, discovered that a ladder which he had left at the shelter years before and needed for the ascent was missing. He surmised that it had been carried away by a peasant living in the area.

A messenger was sent off immediately to get it. Leuthold was right in his guess but the peasant refused to give the ladder up. A second messenger had to be dispatched, and this time dire threats succeeded in obtaining the surrender of the ladder. By the time the second man returned, their next day's start had been delayed by two precious hours. They had intended to begin their climb at three a.m. It was then five o'clock. Leuthold warned them that unusual speed would be required, and urged anyone who felt that he could not endure a forced march to stay behind. No one did.

They skirted Lake Méril, with its miniature icebergs, and reached the glacier of Aletsch, where the real difficulties of the ascent would begin. In a semicircle around them rose the Jungfrau, the Mönch, and many a lesser peak. They halted for a short rest, and left behind them every possible encumbrance before moving on. For the last all-demanding lap they took only a little bread and wine, a few meteorological instruments, the ladder, and the essential axes and ropes. Roped together, they made their way up steep slopes, alternately wading through deep snow and crossing ice so slick a cut had to be made for every step. Crevasses yawned before them, but these were the least dangerous because they could be seen. What the climbers feared were the ones hidden by the snow.

ASCENT IN SINGLE FILE.

They stood at last before the summit of the Jungfrau, a perpendicular wall of rock rising in seemingly inaccessible isolation from all beneath and around it. To all except Leuthold this looked like the end; they could see no way up the precipices of snow, ice, and rock. Leuthold, however, had a plan.

He placed their ladder across a crevasse just spanned by its twenty-three-foot length. He and the other guides crept over and began cutting steps in the sheer wall of ice that rose on the other side. Then the rest of the party crawled across and slowly made their way up the steps.

At the top they abruptly found themselves on a terrace beyond which a more moderate slope led to the Col de Roththal.

But from this point on, every step had to be cut. The intense cold and a thick mist added to their difficulties. Leuthold kept the party near the edge of the ridge they were following because the ice there yielded more readily to his ax, but it took steadiness. The precipice lay before their eyes every minute—except when it was hidden by the fog. They could drive their alpenstocks through the overhanging rim of frozen snow and look straight down to the amphitheater below. One of the guides turned back; he could not stand the sight.

Finally they stood just below their goal, the summit. "We can never reach it," Agassiz gasped. It was a sheer wall. For answer Leuthold threw down every bit of equipment, caught his alpenstock over the top as a grappling pole, and went up. He stood on the summit, the unreachable summit, of the Jungfrau. So narrow was the apex of the immense mountain that there was only room for one at a time on its top, and then only when the snow had been trampled down.

One by one each of them scrambled up for his moment on that sublime peak. The fog rolling up from the southwest alternately revealed and concealed the wide land below them, but as the intense cold of the summit converted its water vapor into crystals of ice, the air filled with a glittering gold. They looked down upon the world through a haze of gold.

Huddled around the sharp top of the great mountain, they drank a little wine and made their measurements and observations. They could understand more about the atmospheric conditions that produced the glacier-making snows well below. Although not a moment was wasted, it was four o'clock in the afternoon before they could start back down the icy cliffs, groping for each of the more than seven hundred steps that had led them upward. In an hour they were at the Col de Roththal, and so exuberant at the success of the expedition that they wanted to rush forward. Leuthold had to hold them back with his constant, quiet *"Hubschle! nur immer hubschle!"* ("Gently, always gently!")

By nine o'clock that night, back at the glacier, they heard a yodel. An assistant who had been instructed to meet them was waiting with a big wooden pail of fresh milk. They hungrily drank until it was empty. Another three leagues lay ahead; it was near midnight before they reached the shelter from which they had started.

The full scientific report on this work and on the work that was done during the next five years was presented in two books, *Études sur les glaciers* and *Système glaciaire*. As Agassiz said in his preface, he had lived with the glaciers, striving "to draw from them the secret of their formation and advance." He had succeeded to a remarkable extent. With precision and clarity and an enthusiasm that shone even through tables of statistics, he made understandable to all the basic structure of glaciers, their external aspects, their movement, their color, crevasses, moraines, and other phenomena that had puzzled and resisted men up to that time. The *Études* was accompanied by an atlas filled with superb drawings of the glaciers, re-creating them for everyone to see.

"You have made all the geologists here glacier-mad," wrote Forbes from Edinburgh. "They are turning Great Britain into an ice house. Some amusing and absurd attempts at opposition to your views have been made by one or two pseudo-geologists; among others, poor ——, who has read a paper at the Royal Society here, maintaining that all the appearances you refer to glaciers were caused by blocks of ice which floated this way in the Deluge."

Murchison still was doubtful. At the London Geological Society he warned: "Once grant to Agassiz that his deepest valleys of Switzerland, such as the enormous Lake of Geneva, were formerly filled with ice and snow and I see no stopping place. From that hypothesis you may proceed to fill the Baltic, and the northern seas, cover southern England and half of Germany and Russia with similar icy sheets. . . ."

This, of course, was very nearly what Agassiz was doing. Murchison simply was too limited in what he predicted. Agassiz was about to expand his studies and his proof of an ice age to another continent.

America was calling to the famed Swiss scientist. His unmatchable *Fossil Fish* had at last been completed. He was eager to search for evidence of glacial action on the American continent. Furthermore, the lecture fees and other financial opportunities promised a way out of his always urgent financial difficulties. After sending his wife and their three children to his brother-in-law in Germany, Agassiz sailed for America in the autumn of 1846. He was to deliver a series of lectures at the Lowell Institute in Boston.

His ship docked at Halifax. "Eager to set foot on the new continent so full of promise for me," said Agassiz, "I sprang on shore and started at a brisk pace for the heights above the landing." Almost the first things that met his eyes were the furrows and scratches and the polished surfaces on the rocks, the line engraving of a glacier or ice sheet.

"I became convinced," he continued, "of what I had already anticipated as the logical consequence of my previous investigation. Here also this great agent had been at work."

It was an auspicious beginning. Agassiz was then forty-two; during the next twenty-seven years he was to become one of the leading figures and scientists of the United States. His lectures in all parts of the country drew great crowds and the newspapers printed them in full. His articles were a major feature of the young *Atlantic Monthly.* He became professor of zoology and organizer of the Museum of Comparative Zoology of Harvard University. Unofficially the museum was never called anything but the Agassiz Museum. His enormous project for a ten-volume natural history of the United States drew support and subscriptions from every section.

After the death of his wife Cecile, a grave woman who often had been overwhelmed by the ebullience and boundless projects

of her husband, he married Elizabeth Cary, who understood
him and his work. She turned a house that was largely a teeming
laboratory into a home, and even found for Agassiz the money
he needed for his huge scientific undertakings—his Harvard salary long was only fifteen hundred dollars a year. Mrs. Agassiz,
with her husband's enthusiastic assistance, opened a highly successful school for girls on the upper floor of the house the university furnished them.[2]

Harvard was an illustrious company in those years embrac-
ing the Civil War, and Agassiz was a central figure in it. He was
one of the members of the "Saturday Club." Oliver Wendell
Holmes, in his *Life of Emerson,* tells how Longfellow sat at one
end of the club table, "florid, quiet, benignant," and Agassiz at
the other, "robust, sanguine, animated, full of talk and boy-like
in his laughter." Among the other members were Hawthorne,
Motley, Dana, Lowell, and Whipple.

To celebrate Agassiz's fiftieth birthday, Longfellow wrote:

> *It was fifty years ago,*
> *In the pleasant month of May,*
> *In the beautiful Pays de Vaud,*
> *A child in its cradle lay.*

> *And nature, the old nurse, took*
> *The child upon her knee,*
> *Saying: "Here is a story-book*
> *Thy Father has written for thee."*

> *"Come wander with me," she said,*
> *"Into regions yet untrod;*
> *And read what is still unread*
> *In the manuscripts of God."*

Zoology, teaching, and lecturing came first during the
crowded American years, but wherever Agassiz went—and he

[2] After her husband's death Elizabeth Cary Agassiz wrote a fine biography of him: *Louis Agassiz—His Life and Correspondence* (Boston: Houghton Mifflin and Company; 1896). Much of the material in this chapter is
drawn from it.

traveled widely—he always continued his studies of glaciation. The marks of ice lay over a large part of the American continent. "With the exception of some higher points of the Alleghany range, the surface of this whole plain (east of the Rockies) is glacier-worn from the Arctic regions to about the fortieth degree of northern latitude," Agassiz reported.

He proved, too, that the ice had moved over the American continent in a continuous sheet that overrode mountains and plains. "The polished surfaces stretch continuously over hundreds and hundreds of miles; the rectilinear scratches, grooves and furrows are unbroken for vast distances; the drift spread in one vast sheet over the whole land, consisting of an indiscriminate medley of clays, sands, gravels, pebbles, and boulders of all dimensions so uniformly mixed together that it presents hardly any differences whether we examine it in New England, New York, Pennsylvania, Ohio, Michigan, Indiana, Illinois, Wisconsin, in Iowa beyond the Mississippi, in the more northern territories, or in Canada," Agassiz said.

On a journey to Brazil, Agassiz found the same unmistakable signs of ice under the lush tropical growth of the valley of the Amazon.

In a remote period of the past, he explained, the world had become colder and an enormous accumulation of snow had taken place around the northern and southern poles; it probably had piled up to a thickness of from twelve thousand to fifteen thousand feet. Pressure had transformed the snow into ice, and rains and melting had set the sheet into motion from the Arctic to the more temperate latitudes in Europe, Asia, and North America, and from the Antarctic to South America, the Cape of Good Hope, and Van Dieman's Land.

"But we need not build up a theoretical case in order to form an approximate idea of the great ice sheet stretching over the northern part of this continent," Agassiz continued. "It would seem that man was intended to decipher the past history of his home, for some remnants or traces of all its great events are left as the key to the whole. Greenland and the Arctic regions hold all that remains of the glacial period in North America. Their shrunken ice fields, formidable as they seem to us, are to the frozen masses of that secular winter but as the patches of snow and ice lingering on the north side of our hills after the spring has opened; let us expand them in imagination until they extend over a continent, and we shall have a sufficiently vivid picture of this frozen world."

People generally were as slow to accept this carefully filled-in picture of a world covered with ice as they had been when Agassiz made his first startling prediction of it. They were interested, however.

With all the enthusiasm that was characteristic of him, Agassiz in his sixty-sixth year was planning a series of articles to show that "however broken the geological record, there is a complete sequence in many parts of it." But at a family dinner on December 6, 1873, his sight suddenly grew dim. He was taken severely ill and died on December 14.

The boulder that marks his American grave came from the glacier of Aar. His unforgettable and influential discovery of the ice age, one of the great eras in the earth's history, is a monument even more enduring.

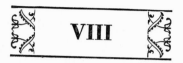

VIII

LYELL

THE CHANGED AND CHANGING EARTH

A T YARMOUTH IN 1817 they were getting ready to erect a monument to Lord Nelson. The pit for the base had already been dug at the time handsome young Charles Lyell wandered by. Then nineteen and on a holiday from Oxford, he was making use of his visit to the east-coast town of Yarmouth to "examine the geological wonders of the county." The excavation, with the fine cross-section it afforded of what lay below the surface, at once attracted his attention. Lyell was surprised to see that eight feet of sand lay atop the first strata of stony shingle.

A friend of his host's had just told him that there had been very little sand at that point thirty-five years before. Suddenly Lyell realized that the land on which he was standing had been built up at least eight feet in the preceding thirty-five years. He also saw that the sand of the near-by dunes and much of that around him had been blown in by the wind, and he reasoned that the sand would have started piling up as soon as there was a base on which it could accumulate. Probably that stony shingle on which it lay had emerged from the sea not much more than fifty years before.

It was an exciting, gripping idea. In the geological studies that he had just begun at Oxford, Lyell had been told that the continents, the seas, the mountains, the plains, and all the "monuments" of the earth had been part of the "original state" of the earth, or that they had been tumultuously formed in the Flood or some other cataclysm. Thus, they had come into being on one of the first days of creation or in a sudden convulsion surpassing in scope and violence anything known to the modern world.

But there he was, standing on land that had been built up a solid eight feet in less than fifty years. Perhaps there had been other slow changes in the earth. The young student began a systematic observation of the whole Yarmouth area, and he saw with a growing sense of discovery that it had all undergone marked changes, though the changes were so gradual, so imperceptible, that hardly anyone realized they had taken place.

As he examined the land, Lyell found unmistakable evidence that the city of Norwich, then situated about fifteen miles inland, had once been a seaport. And a search of local history at once revealed that this was true. The River Yare and the sea had laid down new land in front of the city until it was no longer on the coast.

The river was still at this work; you could see it silting up its channel. It had done the same thing many times in the past, and when one channel was blocked with sand and mud it had cut out a new one. In this way the delta on which Yarmouth stood had been built.

"All these ancient channels I found, and the doctor [Dr. Joseph Arnold, an able amateur naturalist] confirms them," Lyell wrote to his father. "However, Mr. Turner [Dawson Turner, his host] laughs in spite of facts and tradition."

Although Dr. Arnold had previously said little about it, he had come to almost the same conclusions about the Yarmouth region. When he found Lyell expounding these ideas, the taciturn naturalist "became a communicative and quite different person," Lyell noted. Arnold in his turn startled Lyell by advancing the opinion that the Strait of Dover, not far down the coast, had formerly not existed at all. He thought that England and France had once been joined by a narrow neck of land at that point, and that when this barrier existed the North Sea had "flowed much higher" over the whole eastern part of England. For good measure, he added the speculation that the strong north current probably had "burst open" the neck of land and thus united the North Sea and the English Channel.

"With this I was delighted," said Lyell.

At this moment in his young life Lyell had firmly grasped the basic idea with which he would ultimately change the world's concept of its own past. He had seen, as he tramped along the Yarmouth water front, that great changes could come about gradually through the work of rivers, winds, seas, and other forces operating in the present. No earthquake, no universal flood, no cataclysm any greater than the normal wear and storm of nature was needed to explain the landlocking of Norwich and the rise in the surface of the Yarmouth beach, or the even greater changes that the doctor had suggested.

Lyell also had learned another prime lesson that he would never forget and that became central to his work: go and see. In a letter to his father he approvingly quoted a statement that he had come across: "Local information from actual observation tends more to promote Natural History and Science than all that is done by the speculations and compilations of voluminous authors."

The Oxford student who was looking with such observant eyes at the earth had been born on November 14, 1797, at Kinnordy in Forfarshire, Scotland. Kinnordy was the Lyell family mansion, a big house with two symmetrical L-shaped wings and fine carved dormers. When Charles was still very young, his father, a distinguished amateur botanist, took a house in the south of England. The family lived there during most of the years when the boy was growing up.

Before he was quite eight, Charles was sent to school at Ringwood. The school had fine playing-fields and woods all around it, but, what was even more important in the eyes of the boys, it became a station for the volunteers called into service to defend England against the threatening and greatly feared invasion by France. The senior Lyell was a captain in the corps.

The invasion, of course, never materialized, and before Charles went home for his first holiday the British had won at Trafalgar. Bonfires blazed on all the hills around Ringwood, and Charles always remembered how every house was illuminated to celebrate the victory, and how all the candles were blackened on the outside in mourning for Nelson.

Charles was later sent to a more fashionable school at Salisbury. After an illness that his family feared might have affected his lungs, he was kept at home for three months. At the time his father had temporarily "exchanged botany for entomology," and he interested his son in studying insects. Even after Charles returned to school he could not resist catching any rare moth that flew into sight and pressing it in his dictionary.

This interest in entomology continued, and when Charles matriculated at Oxford at the age of seventeen he took some work in the subject. It was excellent preparation for his later study of fossils. In the meanwhile, however, he had come upon Bakewell's *Geology* in his father's library. What he read in it about the antiquity of the earth so aroused his imagination and enthusiasm that he decided to attend the lectures on geology given by William Buckland. The noted Oxford cleric-geologist was then at the height of his fame.

It was not long afterward that Charles went to Yarmouth and that his budding feeling for geology grew into what was to be a lifetime passion. The next summer, 1818, Mr. and Mrs. Lyell, Charles, and their two eldest daughters were off on a European tour that was to be another important step in the education of a geologist. Traveling by coach, they went south through France into Switzerland and Italy. At Chamonix, Charles had his first opportunity to visit a glacier.

The deep fissures and rents in the ice of the Mer de Glace had to be taken in a flying leap if you were going to get anywhere. This looked easy enough, for the snow appeared to be soft and fresh; in actuality it was frozen hard and packed with a multitude of water-filled holes. Landings were not what they promised to be.

"I saw," said Charles with his always alert observation, "that even in July this large body of ice creates frost enough in the night to encrust over the water which fills many of the chasms. Thus there are but a few months out of twelve that can melt the glacier at all, and in these not twelve hours perhaps out of twenty-four, and even the twelve hours must in the hottest month be partly occupied in doing over again the work which each night undoes."

After a nine-mile climb over the glacier it was a "wonderful transition" to reach the foot and sit down on grass "so richly strewn with our blue garden violets that the air was really perfumed." Charles and his guide ate their lunch, leaned back, and were soon asleep. When they awoke they climbed a precipice to the high Aiguille du Moine.

"From the foot of this rock you see a valley of ice extend up to the summit of Mont Blanc; around you are all his shapeliest points, ending in beautiful pinnacles of pointed rock. The picture is in short composed of the sublime and terrible—bare rock, ice, snow, and sky, and with a dead silence around."

Charles had a feeling for the beauty and grandeur of the earth; it was part of his desire to interpret and analyze. What was more, he was always able to convey his sense of the earth's beauty to others.

In December 1819, Lyell received his bachelor's degree at Oxford, and the following spring went to London to begin the study of law. It had not yet become clear what his occupation would be. Perhaps geology would remain only a side interest, although it certainly would be at least that. He was immediately elected a fellow of the Geological Society and joined the Linnean. But the reading required for the law soon proved too much for Lyell's never overly strong eyes. He was compelled to give it up—temporarily, he thought.

During the next three years he traveled widely on the Continent and in the British Isles, studying geology wherever he went. He carried with him letters of introduction to leading geologists and he made use of them. Cuvier received him so warmly that he felt free to attend the geologist's "soirées" regularly. He found them a "great treat," he wrote to his father. He also called on Humboldt, whose porter, Lyell amusedly reported, addressed his employer as "M. Hoombowl." Again Lyell was cordially welcomed.

After three years his eyes had improved so much that he was able to resume the reading of law and to go on circuit. This yielded no income, but there was another advantage in "ostensibly" following a profession. "It is wonderful how little mercy one's friends have on one's time, if one has no excuse deemed valid for declining unprofitable parties, or refereeships, or secretaryships &," he explained to his sister. The pursuit of the law enabled Lyell to keep his time relatively free for geology! But he was thinking of dropping the law part of this strange medley: "I am quite clear, from all that I have yet seen of the world that there is most real independence in the class of society, who possessing moderate means, are engaged in literary and scientific hobbies."

Lyell had such "moderate means"; he did not have to worry about earning a living. His wealthy father not only supplied him with a generous income, but was thoughtful about anticipating his needs. Nevertheless, Lyell felt that he would like to earn enough by his "own exertions" to defray the expenses of his geologic travels.

He had written several papers that had been favorably noticed, and he was considering adapting to geology an idea that had been successful in other fields of science, a popular book to be called *Conversations in Geology*. "It is what no doubt the booksellers and therefore the greatest number of readers are desirous of," he explained to a friend. He finally decided, however, that such a form would not be adequate for a subject "where so much is to be reformed and struck out anew, and where one obtains new ideas and theories in the progress of one's task, where you have to controvert, and to invent an argumentation."

Lyell was thinking of another kind of book, one that would take a historical approach to geology and marshal the evidence to show that "the external parts of the earth were not all produced in the beginning of things, in the state in which we now behold them, nor in an instant of time."

To test his theory and collect material, he planned a trip abroad with the noted Scottish geologist Sir Roderick Murchison and his wife. They would go to Auvergne, where Guettard and Desmarest had shown that tremendous volcanic changes had occurred. The Scots met in Paris and set out for Clermont in a "light open carriage with post horses." Their stops were frequent, but no matter how thoroughly they searched they found no sign of volcanic pebbles until they reached Auvergne.

On their first day at Clermont, Murchison, Lyell, and Lyell's secretary took a *patache*, a one-horse cart, to the puys. They were not looking particularly for proofs of volcanic action—that had been thoroughly established. Rather, they were interested in changes that had come about since the volcanoes had poured out their lavas. Almost at once they came upon a perfect proof of such a change.

A great tongue of lava that had rolled down from one of the cones had piled up in the bed of the River Sioule and dispossessed the water of its course. But not for long had the river been vanquished. Its waters had soon begun to cut their way through the lava dam; Lyell and Murchison traced the excavations.

Their guides, seeing their interest in the lava's interference with rivers, offered to show them a still more remarkable example a little farther down the river. Desmarest's map, with which they were working, showed no volcano in the place the guides were indicating, and they thought the whole thing a fable to sell them a little more service. Nevertheless, they decided to see.

"You can imagine our surprise when we found a set of volcanic phenomena entirely unknown," said Lyell, "a volcanic cone, with a stream of basaltic lava issuing out of both sides and flowing down to the gorge of the Sioule."

Here the contest of river and lava had been even more dramatic. The cascading lava had built a high and deep dam completely across the river's narrow gorge. They could see what had happened then. At first a large lake had formed behind the lava barricade; then slowly the river had started to carve out a new passageway between the lava and the hard gneiss cliff.

"In the progress of ages," said Lyell, "the 150 feet deep igneous rock was cut through and the river went on to eat its way, 35, 45, and in one place 85 feet into the subadjacent beds, leaving on one bank a perpendicular wall of basaltic lava towering above the gneiss.

"This is an astonishing proof of what a river can do in some thousand or hundred thousand years by its continual wearing."

By cutting through the lava dam, the Sioule gave the most graphic demonstration possible of how a river can make its own course, even through the hardest stone. The Sioule, then, had cut its own gorge, and was not following a gorge dug by the Deluge —Noah's Flood. No deluge could have descended the valley without carrying away the crater and ashes above.

Hutton and a number of others had understood this, but it was not the general belief in the first half of the nineteenth century. When Murchison and Lyell reported their findings to the London Geological Society, a sharp debate was provoked. The seventy persons present at the meeting—the first in the society's handsome new quarters in Somerset House—split into warring factions. Lyell, who was not present, was told that Buckland, his former professor, was "furious" in his attack.

Before continuing the trip Lyell wrote happily to his father:

"The whole tour has been rich, as I anticipated, in those analogies between existing nature and the effects of causes in remote eras which it will be the object of my work to point out. I scarcely despair now, so much do the evidences of modern action increase upon us as we go south (toward the most recent volcanic seat of action) of *proving* the positive identity of the causes now operating with those of former times."

On the coast of the Maritime Alps, Lyell came upon another proof of his point. The Magnaçon River was then carrying down to the Mediterranean Sea exactly the same kind of debris it had deposited in those waters for illimitable ages in the past. Evidence as easy to read as the levels on a gauge showed that this was the case.

During eight months of the year there was little water in the Magnaçon. But when the spring floods rushed down from the Alps they brought with them a huge load of gravel and left much of it in the sea just beyond the river's mouth. During the dry months shells, sands, and other normal deposits of the sea settled down on the gravels dumped by the spring floods. And with the next flood came more coarse gravel. For countless ages this alternate piling up of gravel and sand had been going on.

Through some changes in elevation which had occurred, a part of this layered sea bottom had been upraised and had become a part of the coast. In time the river had cut a fifteen-mile-long valley and gorge through the one-time sea beds. The walls of the gorge thus plainly revealed the pattern for all to see, the gravel conglomerate and fossiliferous limestone alternating in the eight-hundred-foot-thick cliffs.

The fossil shells in the rock helped to develop the picture of what had happened in the past. Local collectors had found more than two hundred species. About one fifth were living Mediterranean species, most of them exactly like the shells still found on the offshore bottom during the dry part of the year. In his letter

to his father telling of this remarkable discovery, Lyell underlined the words "living Mediterranean species." Their presence
proved a continuity from past to present.

On a tour of Scotland, Lyell, Buckland, and Sedgwick had
come upon a similar deposit of sandstone alternating with conglomerate. Lyell had argued that the gravel had been brought
down by the rivers, but both Sedgwick and Buckland had objected. Sedgwick had said to Lyell: "You who wish to make
out that all is now going on as formerly, help me to conceive a
sea deep enough and disturbed enough to receive in any length
of time, such a series of strata of conglomerate and sandstone
as you have shown me in Angus."

These words came back vividly to Lyell as he gazed up at
those eight hundred feet of Mediterranean gravels and fossils.
"Now here," he wrote triumphantly, "we have just such a series
as that in Forfarshire, only very much thicker and in the intervening laminated sands are numerous perfect shells. . . .

Measurements that Lyell thought accurate had shown that
the sea just off the mouth of the river was about three thousand
feet deep. It was therefore easy for him to see how eight hundred feet of deposits could have accumulated. He thus did not
have to deal with the problem implicit in Sedgwick's point, that
of how thick deposits could have been piled up in shallow offshore waters. The deep Mediterranean took care of the difficulty
for Lyell. The real answer would come a little later. But Lyell
was entirely right in seeing that the Magnaçon was building up
the same kind of deposits in the present that it had in the past.

At Parma, Lyell called on Professor Guidotti, a "gentleman-
like and agreeable" scholar who had the finest collection of
fossil shells in all of Italy. The professor was as fascinated by
what Lyell told him of how the shells had come to rest in the
mountains as the young Scot was by his shells. For three days
they "exchanged their respective commodities" from six o'clock
in the morning until late at night. The professor then presented
Lyell with a set of fossil shells "identical with those now living

in the Mediterranean," and Lyell mapped out for him a trip that would show the wonders he had been describing. Lyell went on south and the professor left immediately on the Lyell tour.

Between Sienna and Viterbo the rain came down in torrents; it did not in the least stop Lyell and Murchison. They halted their gig repeatedly to jump out and examine the country, for they were riding through a "theatre of extinct volcanic action." Ash, pumice, and cinders were stacked high in layer after layer; whole hills, in fact, had been formed in this way. Often the volcanoes had cast their burned and molten products over limestone formations filled with shells like those Lyell had seen in the professor's collection.

"Some geologists pretend that there are proofs that the volcanoes began before these strata had done forming, which may be true of some; but I have seen none yet, although I have been from morning till eve immersed in matters relating to times beyond the Flood," said Lyell with light amusement.

He arrived in Naples after two "fagging days" of travel, but he set off at once for the nearby island of Ischia. In three days of active work he found shells two thousand feet high on the old volcano on the island, which, he pointed out in his journal "had not been dreamt of here." Among them were thirty different species.

Elated, Lyell wrote to his sister Eleanor: "I will let the world know that the whole isle of Isk, as the natives call it, has risen from the sea 2,600 feet since the Mediterranean was peopled with the very species of shell-fish which now have the honor of living with, or being eaten by us—our common oyster and cockle amongst the rest."

Here was more evidence that the land had risen in relatively modern times. Lyell could scarcely wait to go on to Etna to see if a similar phenomenon had occurred there. The pirates of Tripoli controlled the Mediterranean so completely, though, that service to Sicily was greatly reduced, and Lyell had a long wait for a government steamer. On his arrival, his attention was drawn first to the islands of Cyclops, which according to legend, the giant Polyphemus had thrown at the Trojan fleet. They still stood where the giant's arm was supposed to have heaved them, but their basaltic columns and their clay topping were wasting rapidly away. Lyell estimated that in another ten thousand years they would be gone.

Lyell saw with the keenest interest that the same type of clay covered the mainland at the foot of Etna. The peasants told him that it contained fossils, which they called *"roba di diluvio"* ("things of the flood"). Certainly the fossils were there. Some seven hundred feet up Etna, Lyell found alternate beds of lava and fossil sea shells, many of them again easily identifiable as modern Mediterranean species.

"This was exactly what everyone in England, and at Naples and Catania told me I should *not* find, but which I came to Sicily to look for—the same which I discovered in Ischia . . . ," said Lyell. He put a man and a boy to work digging for the fossils while he made an ascent of Etna.

Before he could start out the next day Dr. Giuseppe Gemellaro, who lived on Etna and had written about its formations, came to call. He was at a loss to understand Lyell's excitement about the fossils on the volcanoes. Such shells had often been brought to the doctor, but he had paid no attention to them; he supposed they had been taken from the sea to strengthen walls. "A good joke," exclaimed Lyell, "as I found them for miles and in strata more than one hundred feet thick! He is not a little annoyed at seeing how much importance I think it."

To Lyell the fossils were a visible measurement of the great though gradual changes through which the volcanic land had passed. No one eruption had produced all the volcanoes. The presence of the shells indicated that there had been long eras when lakes or the sea had washed over their lower levels, and that when new eruptions came they came at different times, in different places, and in different degrees of violence, just as modern ones did.

On his climb of Etna, Lyell and his guide started in the middle of the night, making their way by moonlight over the lower slopes. At daybreak they had reached the timber line. On the advice of friends, Lyell had taken along a teakettle, and they stopped for a breakfast with hot tea. They made their fire from the boughs of chestnuts and oaks that were perhaps from one thousand to two thousand years old, and yet stood on "modern lavas of the volcano."

As they approached the cone, Lyell found his head aching and he felt nauseated. The guide told him that all visitors experienced such unease when they breathed the fumes of the volcano.

Clouds of steamy vapor all but hid the bottom of Etna's crater. But from his vantage point on the rim, Lyell could look down into the crater of the Val del Bue. Buckland had begged him to make a sketch of this view. The wind was so strong that the guide had to hold Lyell's hat while he drew, and the cinders on which he stood were so hot he thought his boots would be burned. But he worked away. All the while the sulfurous vapors curled up over the masses of ice which rimmed the crater. Lyell breathed so much of the noisome stuff that it was hours afterward, he said, before he could get the "horrid taste" out of his mouth.

Lyell had made his ascent on December 1. The next day the wind changed and a heavy snow fell; the mountain was transformed into a mass of ice and snow. Lyell was only too glad to hole up for a few days with his library of books on Etna.

He made a rugged journey over the rest of Sicily. The inns were "execrable beyond description," and the bread often required "all the digestive power" he had gained by being on horseback for ten successive days of eleven hours each. But all physical discomfort was a minor matter; Lyell was jubilant. Everything that he saw further confirmed the fact that this country was slowly rising from the sea. He estimated that the rise, of which men were so unaware and unbelieving, had amounted to four thousand feet "since all the present animals existed in the Mediterranean."

Lyell had another source of deep satisfaction. His book was taking shape in his mind, and he had even started to work on it. At Naples on his return trip he paused to write to Murchison, who had gone off on other interests of his own: "My work is all planned. It will not pretend to give even an abstract of all that is known in geology, but it will endeavor to establish the *principle of reasoning* in science; and all my geology will come in as an illustration of my view of those principles and as evidence strengthening the system necessarily arising out of the admission of such principles. . . ."

In words that have echoed through all the following years, he set down those principles: "No causes whatever have from the earliest time . . . to the present, ever acted, but those *now acting;* and they have never acted with different degrees of energy from that which they now exert."

Lyell was soon back in London and at Kinnordy, engaged in the double occupation of writing his book and defending his views. At the April 1829 meeting of the Geological Society a fight broke out over Lyell's contention that rivers cut their own channels and that this was evidence the earth was undergoing gradual change.

One well-known geologist arose to announce in ringing tones: "No river within the time of history has deepened its channel one foot."

Another turned to sarcasm: "Our opponents say 'Give us time and we will work wonders.' So said the wolf in the fable to the lamb."

This brought roars of laughter. But Lyell and Murchison fought so stoutly that they had one of the chiefs of the opposition admitting "three deluges before the Noachian," and Buckland conceded any number of "catastrophes."

The argument went on, for it reached to the roots of men's deepest beliefs about their world. At the June meeting the

Diluvialists, as those who supported the Biblical Flood were called, were ready with a paper asserting the impotence of all rivers that fed "the main river of an isle," and with data showing that the Thames itself was "scarce able to move a pin's head."

The devastating answer of the Fluvialists—the Lyell group—was to read a surveyor's report on a Scottish river. It had just swept away a bridge and buried a large tract under gravel.

Forced to account for all the varied physical features of the world, the Diluvialists later conceded four or more deluges. And realizing that they had been pushed into an untenable position, Sedgwick, their spokesman, granted that in the light of existing knowledge of floods it might be well to "doubt and not dogmatize" about Noah's Flood and its effect on the world.

"We have driven them out of the Mosaic record," Lyell rejoiced.

The young geologist's celebration of victory was a little premature. But over the next forty to fifty years the book he was then finishing would widely persuade both geologists and non-scientists that the world was not the unchanged and unchanging relic of the Flood.

The first volume of the *Principles of Geology or the Modern Changes of the Earth and Its Inhabitants* was published in 1830. The second volume followed in 1832. The book was a success almost from the beginning and within forty-five years would go through twelve editions. Lyell was thirty-three when the first volume came out. The building up of the material for the later editions and several closely related books, and their revision, would occupy him fully for the remainder of his life.

The basic principles that Lyell was setting forth had first been formulated by Hutton and Playfair. Lyell acknowledged his great indebtedness to them, and on the flyleaf of the *Principles* were these words from Playfair's *Illustrations of the Huttonian Theory:* "Amid all the revolutions of the globe the economy of Nature has been uniform, and her laws are the only things that have resisted the general movement. The rivers and the rocks, the seas and the continents, have been changed in all their parts; but the laws which direct those changes and the rules to which they are subject, have remained invariably the same."

But Hutton's theory had been dismissed on the Continent as mere speculation. In England it had received scarcely more acceptance. Until Lyell transformed these doctrines with his eloquence and his tremendous wealth of evidence, they had no real hold on men's minds. Lyell forced men to look critically, though painfully, at their old assumptions about the world, and then he convinced them of the fact of change. "It is impossible to exaggerate the service Lyell did to the cause of truth by striking boldly at the root of the fundamental postulates of his contemporaries," said Geikie. "He shook the old convulsionist faith."

Some of Lyell's influence came from the fact that he did not write technically. He spoke to all, and deliberately so. As he was correcting proofs for the first edition, he wrote to a friend: "I get on slowly, but with satisfaction to myself. How much more difficult it is to write for general readers than for the scientific world, yet half our *savans* think that to write *popularly* would be condescension to which they might bend if they would."

The *Principles* began with what Lyell called the progress of geology; it was a history of men's search for an understanding of their earth from the time of the earliest Egyptians to his own day.

Lyell then met head on the issues he was debating with his fellow geologists—the "prejudices" that "had retarded the progress of geology." They included:

► The early belief that every earthquake, flood, or storm was caused by "mysterious and extraordinary agency."

► The conviction that the earth was only a few thousand years old.

► Men's inability to imagine that the earth had been altered by slow, insensible changes, and the consequent assumption that only disasters infinitely greater than any known to the modern world could have produced such tremendous, awe-inspiring features of the world as mountain chains and deep gorges.

► Our failure as dwellers on the land to picture "the new strata which Nature is building beneath the waters."

► Our failure as dwellers on the surface of the earth to realize what is happening below us. Thus, fossils were assumed to be forms "created in the beginning of things by the fiat of the Almighty" rather than the remains of creatures like many of those still living in the seas. And volcanic rocks were thought to be a precipitate from a chaotic fluid or an ocean that rose periodically rather than ancient lavas.

► The theory that all the materials that went into the sedimentary rocks were stripped from the earth in the Flood, that "erratic" boulders were strewn about the earth on a deluge of mud, that the mountain chains were thrown up by terrific waves sweeping over whole continents, and that there had to be a universal ocean to account for the sedimentary rocks found all around the earth.

► The theory that the faults or cracks in the earth's crust and the evidences of violent movements and pressure were proofs of a prodigious holocaust.

"The real point on which the whole controversy turns," said

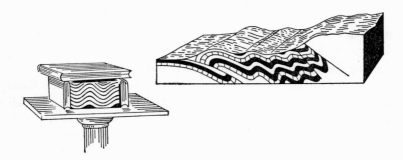

STRATA THAT ONCE LAY HORIZONTAL ARE CRUMPLED AND BUCKLED. LYELL DEMONSTRATES THE SAME EFFECT BY CRUSHING LAYERS OF CLOTH BETWEEN BOOKS.

Lyell, "is the relative amount of work done by mechanical force in given quantities of time, past and present."

To demonstrate that mechanical forces operating in the present could have produced the marvelous natural results that surround men, Lyell traveled the world to collect data. Soon after the *Principles* was published he married Mary Horner, daughter of Leonard Horner, a well-known geologist. She afterward accompanied him on nearly all of his trips and aided in his work in every possible way.

The Lyells made other visits to the volcanoes of Italy and France. They traveled along the coasts of Scandinavia, measuring the rise of the coast and making marks to guide future generations in detecting changes. They journeyed through the Rhineland and through central Europe. They also made three visits to America and innumerable trips to all the points of geological interest in the British Isles.

But Lyell did not rely alone on the evidence that he himself could collect. He made full use of the volume of information being brought in by other scientists who were applying the new technique of "interrogating" the earth. The remarkable geological reports brought back by Charles Darwin from the five-year voyage of the *Beagle* appeared in the *Principles* before Darwin's own *Journal*—or *The Voyage of the Beagle,* as it was called in the United States—could be published. The *Principles* had all the fascination of a book of travel and discovery, and this undoubtedly helped to make the two fat volumes favorite reading in England and elsewhere for nearly half a century.

Lyell seldom talked abstract principles, and always illustrated his points. When he wanted to discuss the rise and fall of coastlines he described the places in the world where such changes had actually occurred. The Temple of Serapis near Naples could be seen as Lyell saw it, with the upper parts of its marble columns perforated by the pear-shaped holes of marine bivalves. And the history of the ancient Roman temple became clear—its subsidence into the sea, the boring of the marine organisms into the parts of the columns not protected by silt, the subsequent re-elevation. What Lyell meant by insensible, non-violent change took on new meaning.

Reading Lyell, the layman and the scientist could under- stand how mountains could have arisen without a single awful convulsion, how valleys could have been carved by running wa- ter, how organic life might have changed without man's seeing the change.

Lyell was one of the first to show how plants and animals and insects had come and gone and changed with the changing world, and how their deaths had timed the world's geological history. He emphasized the organic or biological side of geology as well as the physical.

"The movement of the inorganic world is obvious and pal- pable and might be likened to the minute-hand of a clock the progress of which can be seen and heard," said Lyell. "The fluctuations of the living creation are nearly invisible, and resem- ble the motion of the hour-hand of a timepiece. It is only by watching it attentively for some time, and comparing its relative position after an interval that we can prove the reality of its mo- tion."

Lyell gave a wholehearted devotion to geology. Except for two years in the early 1830's when he held an appointment as professor of geology at King's College in London, he refused any position. His books, as he had hoped, brought in enough money to defray some of his special expenses, and the wealth he inher- ited relieved him of any further financial concern.

As much as was possible, Lyell also tried to avoid being sad- dled with scientific offices and duties. Nevertheless, he served two terms as president of the Geological Society and one as pres- ident of the British Association for the Advancement of Science. He was knighted in 1848 and made a baronet in 1864. He could not escape the honors and obligations that went with the posi- tion he had attained—that of the leading geologist of Great Brit- ain and perhaps of the world.

Although Lyell regretted the time he had to spend away from geology, he enjoyed it too. He was an affable man who liked good society and good talk. His London home in Harley Street was a gathering-place for all the leading statesmen and scientists. His close friend Charles Darwin, on the rare occasions when he went to London, always stopped in to sit with the Lyells at breakfast.

Lyell's life was singularly free of the problems and defeats that beset many men. Almost his only difficulty was his extremely weak eyesight. Tall, with handsome, sensitive features, he was slightly stooped from constantly bending forward to peer at the world he had so much difficulty in seeing physically, but which he mentally saw with such rare clarity.

In 1873 Lyell was badly shaken by the death of his wife. He lived for another two years and was working on the twelfth edition of the *Principles* when death came suddenly on February 22, 1875, at the age of seventy-seven.

Upon petition of the most noted scientists of Great Britain, the great geologist was buried in the nave of Westminster Abbey. On his gravestone of fossil marble from Derbyshire is carved:

THROUGHOUT A LONG AND LABORIOUS LIFE

HE SOUGHT THE MEANS OF DECIPHERING

THE FRAGMENTARY RECORDS

OF THE EARTH'S HISTORY

IN THE PATIENT INVESTIGATION

OF THE PRESENT ORDER OF NATURE

ENLARGING THE BOUNDARIES OF KNOWLEDGE

AND LEAVING ON SCIENTIFIC THOUGHT

AN ENDURING INFLUENCE.

O LORD, HOW GREAT ARE THY WORKS

AND THY THOUGHTS ARE VERY DEEP.

Other scientists and geologists may have made more original contributions, but to the world at large Lyell brought an understanding of time and change in the earth. It was a drastic, a revolutionary change in thought. For the majority Lyell wrote an end to 4004 B.C. as the date of the earth's creation, and to Noah's Flood as the definitive event in the history of the world.

"Never perhaps, did any science, with the exception of astronomy, unfold, in an equally brief period, so many novel and unexpected truths, and overturn so many preconceived notions," said Lyell. "The senses had for ages declared the earth to be at rest, until the astronomer taught that it was carried through space with unbelievable rapidity. In like manner was the surface of this planet regarded as having remained unaltered since its creation until the geologist proved that it had been the theatre of reiterated change and was still the subject of slow but never ending fluctuation."

This reversal of the evidence of the senses, this overturn of cherished concepts, nevertheless aroused little of the virulent, alarmed attack that the very suggestion of it had stirred up earlier—or that the scarcely more radical ideas of Charles Darwin aroused at about the same time.

The new, the startling, the incredible was for once accepted almost philosophically. Perhaps people could look back with a certain superiority and tolerance on the ignorance and the innocence of their ancestors, like the prophet in an allegory that Lyell liked to tell and that he used in the *Principles:*

"I passed one day by a very ancient and wonderfully populous city, and asked one of its inhabitants how long it had been founded. 'It is indeed a mighty city,' he replied, 'we know not how long it has existed and our ancestors were on this subject as ignorant as ourselves.'

"Five centuries afterward, as I passed by the same place, I could not perceive the slightest vestige of the city. I demanded of a peasant, who was gathering herbs upon its former site, how long it had been destroyed. 'In sooth a strange question!' he replied. 'The ground has never been different from what you now behold.' 'Was there not of old,' said I, 'a splendid city here?' 'Never,' he answered, 'so far as we have seen, and never did our fathers speak to us of any such.'

"On my return there five hundred years afterwards, *I found the sea in the same place,* and on its shores a party of fishermen, of whom I enquired how long the land had been covered by the waters? 'Is this a question,' they said, 'for a man like you? This spot has always been what it is now.'

"I again returned five hundred years afterwards and the sea had disappeared; I enquired of a man who stood alone upon the spot, how long this change had taken place, and he gave me the same answer as I had received before. Lastly on coming back again after an equal lapse of time, I found there a beautiful, flourishing city, more populous and rich than the city I had seen the first time, and when I would fain have informed myself concerning its origin, the inhabitants answered me 'Its rise is lost in remote antiquity; we are ignorant of how long it has existed, and our fathers were on this subject as ignorant as ourselves.' "

The second act in the discovery of the earth had opened with one crashing climax after another, with the discovery of volcanic eruptions, of the outpouring of molten rock "from the bowels of the earth," of fantastic monsters, of the invasion of ice. It was ending, however, with the realization that all of this had come about gradually, with an almost inconceivable slowness, and not catastrophically. Wonder could succeed alarm; "the charm of first discovery was ours," said Lyell.

And what prospects of further discovery lay ahead—what unlimited possibilities of understanding how the earth and its great features had come to be!

Part Three

HIDDEN CHANGE

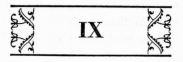

IX

LOGAN
AN ANCIENT CORE

AT THE SURFACE in much of eastern and central Canada lies some very peculiar rock. It is hard, dense, crystalline, and it is often streaked with differently colored bands that twist and swirl like the grain in a fine piece of walnut.

And it produces a distinctive kind of country, a low terrain of tundra, forest, and hummock. The tree-fringed hummocks stand like polished stone sets in a tracery of "glint" lakes.

But not until William Logan came back to Canada in 1843 and began an intensive geological study of the country did many suspect that these rocks were among the world's oldest, or that they formed the core, the nucleus, of the North American continent. In their greatest extension of about two million square miles they were later to be called the Canadian shield, for on the map they look like a great upraised shield.

Logan was born at Montreal on April 20, 1798, and christened William Edmond in the little St. Gabriel Street Presbyterian Church. The William was for his father, the son of a Scot who had moved to Canada in the 1780's and established a highly prosperous bakery and importing business. The Edmond was for his mother, Janet E. Edmond, who had come from Scotland to marry her cousin.

William did very well in school in Montreal, but his father wanted him and his brother Hart to have the opportunity of studying in Scotland. In 1814 they were sent to the Edinburgh High School, where many of the most famous Scotsmen of the day, including Sir Walter Scott, had been educated. William was so well prepared that he was assigned to the "Rector's Class," the fifth year in this six-year school. There were two hundred boys in the class, but soon William stood at their head; he was the "dux," a position that he held through nearly all of the next year too.

In the meanwhile, Mr. Logan, Sr., had decided to move his entire family to Edinburgh; his importing business and "counting house" were doing so well that he could afford "to live at ease." He bought a handsome house on Queen Street, looking out over "one of the finest views in the country": the west Lothians, the Port of Leith, the Firth, and the coast of Fife. Two younger sons also were enrolled in the high school, and soon they as well as their two older brothers were at the heads of their respective classes and capturing a disproportionate share of the prizes.

In 1816 William entered the University of Edinburgh. John Playfair, the friend and illustrator of Hutton, and Robert Jamieson, the noted follower of Werner, were on the faculty. William, however, took classes in logic, chemistry, and mathematics, and seemingly did not come under their influence. Although he took first prize in mathematics, he decided at the end of his first year to go to London to enter his uncle's large counting house.

During the next ten years the uncle shifted responsibility for a large part of the business to his able young nephew. Away from the counting house, William and his friend Alexander Gillespie worked at translating *Gil Blas* and at Homer and Cicero. He and a college friend also carried on what might be called a mathematical correspondence. They sent geometrical problems to each other, solving them and returning new ones. William also liked to play the flute, and was known then and throughout his life for his singing of a hearty version of "The Laird of Cockpen." He was also increasingly drawn into the very active social life that centered around his uncle's town house and country seat.

When his uncle became interested in a new process for extracting copper from the slags of Welsh coal mines, he asked William to go to Wales to take charge of it. Logan was glad to get away "from too much company, rich food and rich wines."

In 1831, equipped with his old clothes—he thought he was going to a good place to wear them out—his scientific books, and the best books he could obtain on mineralogy and geology, he set out for Swansea.

Before long he was writing to his brother James, who had returned to Canada: "The study of the ores of copper has gradually led me to that of mineralogy and geology, and of specimens in both departments I have become a bit of a collector." Logan was thus in his thirties before he was launched into what would be the main interest of his life.

He was working long, hard hours to put the business affairs of the new company into order. He also had to supervise the smelting and soon had to take over the direction of the coal-mining as well. "Here I am," he wrote to his brother, "out of the world altogether, and attending to nothing else but the making of copper and the digging of coal from morning to night."

While working with coal, he became interested in the Glamorganshire coal field in which the mines were situated. He bought a theodolite, compass, and other instruments and began the production of a geological map. He laid his measurements out with such care and exactness that when Sir Henry de la Beche, director of the Geological Survey of Great Britain, began a survey of the area, and William generously gave him the sheets, they were adopted without change as part of the Survey's own report. Logan's name was engraved on them to express the Survey's appreciation.

Although his start was late, once into geology, Logan was in with all of his heart. When he was detained in London on a lawsuit he made a study of the London clay, and on a business trip to Spain he took notes on the geological formations he saw.

In 1837 he was elected a fellow of the Geological Society and in the same year exhibited his map of the South Wales coal district at the Liverpool meeting of the British Association for the Advancement of Science.

By the 1830's it was generally admitted that coal was of vegetable origin, but just how it had accumulated was a moot question. Some maintained that the vegetable material had washed down into the seams in the rocks during Noah's Flood or perhaps in later, smaller floods. Others insisted that the coal vegetation had grown in great peaty swamps. Logan did not start out to settle the problem; he simply took note of an odd thing that he saw.

Under each of the coal seams that he mapped—and there were nearly a hundred—Logan saw that there was always a bed of bleached clay. The miners used the "underclay" to undercut the beds of coal. As Logan pointed out in a paper he submitted to the Geological Society of London, a miner "would as soon expect to live in a house without a foundation as to work in a coalseam which did not rest upon underclay."

The clay might differ in color and composition, but it was always filled with a tangled mass of long, slender fibrous casts "with a thin coating of carbonaceous matter." They came from a main stem or branch that lay in the plane of the bed; to the layman it looked exactly like the root of a plant. Later it proved indeed to be the root system of the trees that grew in the coal swamps.

"This fossil, the *Stigmaria ficoides*, taking for granted that the slender fibrous impressions belong always to it, so completely fills every bed of underclay that it is not possible to cut out a foot which does not contain portions of the plant," Logan reported.

What was more, the coal was never found unless the underbed was "wholly monopolized by these peculiar vegetable remains." They were virtual trade marks. Logan was easily able to conclude that one was essential to the other. It was also evident that if the vegetation which produced the coal grew from these roots, the coal had not "drifted" into the beds where it was found.

"To account for the unfailing combination by drift, seems to me an unsatisfactory hypothesis," Logan mildly said. "But what-

FROM FERN- AND PALM-FILLED ANCIENT SWAMPS—COAL.

ever may be the mutual dependence of the phenomena, they give us reasonable grounds to suppose that in the *Stigmaria ficoides* we have the plant to which the earth is mainly indebted for those vast stores of fossil fuels which are now so indispensable to the comfort and prosperity of its inhabitants."

Later microscopic study showed *Stigmaria* structures in the coal itself. Whole branches and trunks also were frequently found. Logan's theory was thus overwhelmingly confirmed; there no longer could be much doubt that coal was produced in swamps that once had occupied the coal sites.

Logan had always retained his interest in Canada, and now he was particularly eager to see if the clay and *Stigmaria* underlay the coal beds there and in the United States. When his uncle died he resigned his position with the Welsh smelter and sailed for Canada. As soon as possible he set out on a tour of the coal fields. He went first to Pennsylvania and the coal works at Mauch Chunk, where he stood on the edge of a "black precipice," marveling at the fifty-foot-thick seam of coal and at the open workings below him. They were "quarrying" coal! But his delight was aroused by another sight. Under the seam lay his underclay "in all its glory, crossed by fibres coated with carbonaceous matter, and presenting the character of the underclay of the South Wales seams!" Here the clay was a dark gray, but it was the same stuff. Logan happily carried away some "whacking" specimens.

He spent the next week at Wilkes Barre, where he again found the underclay under every coal seam, and collected more specimens. He also made a section drawing of the strata in this big coal field.

"Coal speculations in this valley might be made to a very great profit," Logan noted in his journal. ". . . The farmers do not yet know the nature of the coal ground, and have not much idea of the constancy of coal seams. . . . They will sell their lands at little more than the value of the surface. Anyone making himself a master of this coal field, which is pretty extensive, and keeping his eye on the points from which an exit might be made, could scarcely fail to make money if he had capital to invest."

Logan was not especially interested in making money, but he was deeply impressed with the industrial advantages of the Pennsylvania coal fields and with their future. With amazingly accurate foresight he wrote: "Such a sight as the Lehigh mines present, is to a collier overwhelming. Imagine a seam of coal fifty feet thick, with its covering taken off for a space of five hundred or six hundred yards square and worked like a quarry! . . . When it is recollected that with the coal are associated vast veins and seams of iron ore and huge beds of limestone, it would seem as if Providence intended that Virginia, Pennsylvania, and Ohio should become the workshops of the world. The wealth that these three states will, in the course of a quarter or a half century, arrive at is incalculable."

Logan wanted to round out his trip with a visit to the Pictou coal fields of Canada. Within a few days after his arrival he was able to write to his brother: "I know what the ground contains for about a mile deep in this neighbourhood." What it contained was what Logan confidently expected: underclay filled with *Stigmaria* under each of the coal seams. "My facts I now consider established beyond controversy," Logan jubilantly declared.

And they were. Man at last knew about his coal. A problem that had concerned Aristotle and doubtless many of his predecessors as well as countless successors had at last been solved.

As Logan arrived in Windsor, Nova Scotia, on this trip he noticed some building stone that happened to be lying on the wharf. It looked as though it had come from a coal bed. Where had it been quarried? In a few minutes more Logan was on his way to visit the place, Horton Bluff, about fifteen miles from the city. As he prowled over the rocks, he suddenly stopped, transfixed by a sight that he had certainly never expected to see. On a slab of sandstone coated with mud were the clearly incised footprints of a reptilian-like creature.

Logan knew well that such animals were not supposed to have been in existence during the coal age; at least, no traces of them had previously been found. But there the footprints were—two plain rows of them. They seemed to have been made by toes armed with blunt claws. In one place there was the mark of a whole foot, as though the animal had exerted unusual pressure in stopping or turning. The forefeet had four claws and the rear pair three or four, and the outer one projected in the manner of a thumb. Logan excitedly chiseled out the whole slab and took it with him.

In a letter to a young scientist he had just met, J. William Dawson—later Sir William Dawson and the principal of McGill University—Logan wrote: "Among the specimens which I carried home from Horton Bluff one is of very high interest. It exhibits the footprints of some reptilian animal. . . . The rocks of Horton Bluff are below the gypsum of that neighbourhood; so that the specimen in question (if Lyell's views are correct) comes from the very bottom of the coal series, or at any rate, very low down in it, and demonstrates the existence of reptiles at an earlier epoch than has hitherto been determined; none having previously been found below the magnesian limestone, or to give it Murchison's new name, the Permian era."

Insects had been discovered in the coal measures, but no reptiles until Logan came upon those sharply cut footprints in the stone of a Nova Scotia bluff. It was a highly significant finding.

For several years Canada had been considering the establishment of a geological survey. Logan let some of his friends know that if the step were taken, it was exactly the kind of position which he would like to have. However, he had returned to England when Parliament finally passed the bill and appropriated fifteen hundred pounds for the survey. The selection of a geologist was referred to the Secretary of State for the Colonies, Lord Stanley. The British official promptly made inquiries of De la Beche, Murchison, Sedgwick, and Buckland, the leaders of English geology. Each in turn warmly recommended Logan.

De la Beche's letter was typical of the four. After praising the accuracy of Logan's map of the Welsh coal fields, he added: "Personally I have examined several portions of the country with Mr. W. E. Logan and can safely affirm that no one can be more careful, able, or desirous of attaining the truth.

"He has made communications to the Geological Society respecting points of high interest connected with the formation of coal and recently has communicated to the same society a memoir on Nova Scotia and Pennsylvania important in various respects. . . . I would further observe that Mr. Logan is highly qualified as a miner and metallurgist to point out the applications of geology to the useful purposes of life, an object of the highest importance in a country like Canada, the mineral wealth of which is now so little known."

Logan's appointment was soon settled.

De la Beche had pointed out that Canada's mineral wealth was unknown; its rocks were unknown, its topography was unknown, its geological history was unknown. From the scientific standpoint, this great country of the north was, as Sir William Dawson later said, a "terra incognita." Moreover, much of it was covered with primeval forest; roads were few and limited, and the country swarmed in many places with mosquitoes and black flies. This was the huge country that Logan set out to study and to map.

SIR WILLIAM LOGAN SKETCHES HIS BELOVED CANADA. HAMILTON'S FARM ON THE RIVER ROUGE, WITH THE LOW ROUNDED LAURENTIDES IN THE DISTANCE.

He began his work in the summer of 1843 in the Gaspé Peninsula. Coal had been reported there, and it was important to know if the reports were true. Logan saw a few scanty little seams, but if he were going to examine the rocks more thoroughly there was only one way to do it, and that was to proceed around the coast by canoe. With an Indian, John Basque, and a young man who "knew how to handle an axe and fit up a *camp*, as they call it," Logan set out.

His journal and the skillful, charming little sketches with which he illustrated it tell the story, the story of what it meant to study the rocks of a wilderness:

July 13, and camping in a lean-to on a rocky beach after a

day of measuring the coast, Logan pacing off the distances along the shore, wading and climbing while Basque followed in the birchbark canoe—"It is very dark and the fire brightens up its face. Our pork for tomorrow boils away right busily. The woods are becoming as silent as the grave and not a breath of wind is stirring. . . ."

July 16, and spending Sunday in Basque's summer wigwam, a fourteen-foot square with ends and sides of unplaned boards and a roof of spruce bark—"Two dogs, two cats, two Indians (Basque and his brother), two squaws, two children, two strangers (Stevens and myself) occupied this apartment last night. With a roaring fire in the stove in the middle of July I crept into my blanket sack, without dispossessing myself of my nether integuments; yet I did not find it uncomfortably warm. . . . Basque's wife cooked for us some of the trout we obtained last night. She also gave us roasted porcupine, and certainly it made an excellent dish. It tasted rather better than sucking pig. . . ."

July 25—"All these fishermen fancy that I must be getting something worth much money, considering the pains I take in the collection of specimens. Nothing less than a silver mine answers their notions. . . ."

July 28—A trader, thinking that they were Indians, hailed them to ask if they had any beaver skins. "I put my hand to my mouth and roared out 'I have no skin but my own and that I am unwilling to part with. . . .' "

August 11—"Tonight we are to go out trout-spearing by torchlight to provide our breakfast for tomorrow morning. John has prepared birchbark flambeaux, which consist of strips of the bark, to the number of a dozen, about two feet long and four inches wide, and tied up by strings of cedar root. . . . I do not know what we should do in the woods without birchbark. . . . It also makes a capital substitute for paper, and to save paper I have been using it for my rough calculations."

August 18—"I am fagged. I have had a blow on the head from a great stone weighing half a hundredweight which fell on me. . . . I have had a tumble too on a slippery stone, and I put my foot between two stones and pinched my instep. . . . I am all bruises and my limbs are as stiff as sticks."

September 26—"The coast is so abominably ragged that it is with the greatest difficulty that I can measure it. . . ."

At the end of October, Logan was ready to return to Montreal. While he was waiting for a boat at Pictou, he had to stay in his hotel room; his clothes were so ragged that he looked more like a shipwrecked seaman than the director of a geological survey. No coal had been found, but at least the fact of its absence had been established.

Parliament soon had to be persuaded to provide more funds for the survey. Unlike his colleague James Hall in New York, Logan did not attempt to browbeat the lawmakers; he relied upon a canny sort of persuasion. His first act was to obtain a house where he could display his collection of rocks. "We must put our economic specimens conspicuously forward," Logan wrote to his assistant, "and it appears to me that in the exhibition of these, large masses will make a greater impression on the mind than small specimens. . . . When the unlearned examine minerals . . . they are much addicted to judging the value of the deposit by the bulk of the specimen shown. . . . I should like you to send to Montreal . . . a thundering piece of gypsum. Let it be as white as possible. . . ."

The money was forthcoming, and Logan was off for the Gaspé again, this time cutting into the wild interior, climbing some of the highest peaks, exploring, and mapping the rivers and the rocks.

In the summer of 1845, Logan went west, traveling two hundred and fifty miles up the Ottawa River to Lake Temiscaming. He was up at four or five o'clock every morning to arouse the Indians, "not one of whom would ever stir unless he had my special command," and worked as long as the light lasted. Logan himself made every sight in leveling, every bearing—sometimes twenty to a station—every micrometer angle, every reduction of the distance to chains and links, and every line of protraction. Often the last protractions were not finished by the campfire until two or three hours after midnight. Only then would he crawl wearily into his blanket.

"You may think therefore that I have been a little busy," Logan wrote to his assistant, who was engaged in another project.

In the midst of this pressing work, Logan's attention was drawn irresistibly to the strange, hard, crystalline rocks that lay under the formations from which he collected fossils. There were huge beds of these shiny limestone rocks, which sometimes ran in streaks and bands through equally hard and compact gneiss.

Before Logan could get very deep in the study of this interesting and undoubtedly ancient rock, the government asked him to make a study of the ores around Lake Superior and Lake Huron and to arrange an exhibition of Canadian economic minerals for the London "Exhibition of the Industry of All Nations" of 1851. The highly successful display that he put on was visited several times by Queen Victoria and Prince Albert.

While Logan was in London some curious fossil tracks were discovered in the Canadian sandstone known by the name of Potsdam. In some of the tracks, rows of little dot-like impressions were arranged on either side of a long straight central scratch; in others there was a deep central scratch with smaller scratch lines on either side. Logan showed plaster casts of them to the English authorities on fossils. He himself was inclined to think that they had been made by some kind of tortoise, but eventually it was decided that they were the tracks of "some species of Crustacean, but of a family wholly distinct from anything represented by the Crustacean forms of later geological periods or of the present day." When similar tracks were later found in the same Potsdam sandstone in New York, the finding was confirmed and its significance in showing the shallow-water deposition of the beds was brought out.

Only after this could Logan once more get back to the puz-

zling crystallized rocks. They lay all along the north bank of the
St. Lawrence from the Island of Montreal to Cape Tourmente,
and extended northward to the "metamorphic hills."

In England, Murchison, Lyell's friend and traveling compan-
ion, and Adam Sedgwick had begun the difficult work of grouping the fossil-bearing rocks according to the order of their origin.
But very little attention had been given to the rocks that lay
below; generally they were simply called "primary," the name
Werner had given them. Presumably the rocks that had existed
before there were any living things advanced enough to leave
their remains or marks were part of the original crust of the earth,
and such rocks were all of a kind. But as Logan traced the crystalline limestone and banded gneiss, both of which had been
formed before there was any known life on the earth, he saw
that some of these rocks were older than others. And even they
had been formed from still older rocks. They could not, then,
have been part of the original crust of the earth.

But once again Logan was interrupted. Canada called upon
him to arrange and take charge of a Canadian geological exhibit
at the Paris Exposition of 1855. Again Logan worked day and
night getting the display ready, and again it was a brilliant success. At the close of the exposition, Napoleon III, who then bore
the proud title of Emperor of the French, made him a Chevalier
of Honor. Even higher honors awaited Logan in England. On
January 29, 1856, he was knighted by the Queen, and soon afterward he received the Wollaston Medal of the Geological Society.

Sir William was the first Canadian scientist to receive such
honors, and Canada insisted upon celebrating. On his return he
went straight from the boat to a reception by the Governor General, and that was only the beginning. The Canadian Institute
ordered his portrait painted, and unveiled it at a gala dinner;
the Natural History Society of Montreal arranged a special ceremony at which he was presented with a massive silver fountain
decorated with designs representing the vegetation of the Carboniferous period.

The man who could stand an eighteen-hour day in the wilderness felt himself overwhelmed by the social round. Logan was deeply appreciative of the honors, but his health began to suffer under the strain, and he felt that he had to get back to the quiet of the woods. It was with great relief that he returned in the spring of 1858 to tracing the sinuosities of the crystalline limestone and gneiss. As he paced over the country, counting each step, and paddled over the gleaming, little chain lakes, Logan began to realize the enormous extent of these rocks. There seemed to be little doubt that they occupied the greater part of Canada and that they probably "possessed a very great thickness." They unquestionably were extremely old. And beautiful too. In the white background of some of them sparkled pink garnets; some were a pistachio green striped with a red feldspar; "rocks of striking beauty," Logan thought and said. He named these rocks Laurentian, after the St. Lawrence River.

And then came a surprising find. A geological explorer, John McMullen, discovered what seemed to be fossils in one type of these very old rocks. Wavery rib-like lines extended out from what seemed to be a spine. Could this be an organic remain? Logan and Dawson, then principal of McGill University, made the most careful field and microscopic studies. Their rigorous examination convinced them that this was indeed the fossilized body of a living thing, perhaps of the one-celled animal called a foraminifer. The little fossil was portentously named *Eozoon canadense*—dawn life of Canada. Other specimens also came to light, and they were exhibited in London and at a meeting of the American Association for the Advancement of Science. *Eozoon* became a celebrated scientific issue. As many ridiculed the claim as supported it. Although the question was never finally settled, strong authority ultimately held that *Eozoon* probably was the slightly metamorphosed remains of an early colony of algæ, but not of a one-celled animal.

Whether or not life had left its earliest traces in the Laurentian rocks, their importance was supreme. In the famous *Geol-*

ogy of Canada, which Logan issued in 1865 as part of the survey's work, the shield rocks covering nearly two million square miles were roughly mapped and described. They stretched from the St. Lawrence and the Great Lakes to the Arctic, and from Greenland almost to Alaska. Southern outliers reached into Minnesota, Wisconsin, and Michigan.

THE CANADIAN SHIELD—ANCIENT HEART OF THE CONTINENT.

All of this was a lifetime of work for one man. It was left to Dawson and a long succession of scientists to try to trace out the complex, almost unimaginably long history of the Canadian shield. The story still is far from complete, but it is almost overwhelming even in its briefest outline, for it tells the whole, or very nearly the whole, story of the earth.

Even toward the beginning, perhaps about three billion years ago when the earth was young, the nucleus of the shield stood above the seas that were beginning to fill the low places around it. Tremendous rains that beat down on this great chunk of rock

washed much of its substance into two shallow sea basins, one
lying near the present Lake Superior and the other along what
is now the eastern seaboard. All the while volcanoes poured
their lava and ashes over this bleak, rocky world, and floods of
molten rock, called magma, broke through from below.

Slowly the seas retreated and the heavy load of sediments
which lay on the edges of the shield warped upward into high
mountains. In the crushing and the pressure, the old sediments
and lavas of the shield were crystallized. The steam and the heat
of the metamorphic process transformed them into gneiss, char-
acterized by the dotted parallel lines and bands that sometimes
ran for great distances. Their color and texture might vary,
but there was "a never failing constancy in respect to their paral-
lelism." They would forever record the pressures in their crum-
pling. These were the crystalline, banded, corrugated rocks that
Logan grouped into his Laurentian system. They were not really
the "original crust," for part of them were originally sedimentary
—they had been derived from other rocks—but they were part
of the "basement complex" of the earth.

No sooner were the mountains raised on the edges of the
shield nucleus than the rains began to break them down. Bit by
bit, boulder by boulder, the peaks were reduced to low hills and
the mountain torrents to winding rivers. Another part of the
shield became a low, level plain, not unlike what it is in modern
times. Some of the land around its edges subsided and the seas
made marginal inroads.

Then there was another period of upheaval. Huge domes of
molten rock, intruding from below, buckled the shield's edges
into mountains that may have had the grandeur of the Rockies.
And once more in the endless wearing of time they too were
eroded until only their roots were left, and the shield's plain was
extended once again. It was over this land of low hills, lakes,
and bays that the ice first crept down from the north. Boulders
dropped by that ice indicate that the glaciation was continent-
wide, that it engulfed the whole shield and much more. And

this was only the first of three major invasions of ice which would smooth, scratch, and polish the shield.

Through it all, through eruptions, the upheaval of mountains, and erosion, through the scouring of fire, ice, and water, the Canadian shield in large part remained intact. Some of its crystalline, contorted rocks always kept their heads above the encroaching seas and they were never overlaid with the very deep sediments that have buried the "basement-complex" rocks of the rest of the continent. Thus it is that in the Canadian shield, and in the similar shields of other continents, the past lies so graphically before the eyes of the present.

The shield stood forth with great clarity on the inclusive map of Canada which Logan was preparing to accompany his *Geology*. To have it printed properly in colors that would immediately mark each of the major formations even for the layman, Logan went to London in 1865. He spent days working with London's most expert lithographer, personally applying the colors. He had to use a magnifying glass to follow the limits engraved for each one of them, and on dark, foggy days it was, as he wrote a friend, "really distressing work." His eyes suffered from it.

While Logan labored over the map in London, momentous events were moving forward in America. On April 26 a rumor swept through England that Lincoln had been assassinated. "The loss of Lincoln would be a most serious affair for the world at the present moment," Logan wrote to his brother that night. The next day brought confirmation of the report. But the news from Canada was of a happier nature. The provinces were moving toward confederation, a step Sir William had long favored. He had dreamed of a geological survey that would extend from coast to coast, and federation might provide the opportunity.

When the great moment came, however, Logan sadly realized that he no longer had the strength to cope with such an enormous task. He had returned to Montreal, but was having difficulty with his health, and he had been strongly affected by the deaths of his three brothers, none of whom, like himself, had ever married. Also, his estate had greatly increased in value and was demanding more of his time.

In January 1869, at the age of seventy, Sir William submitted his resignation as director of his country's geological survey. Without exception the officials of the new confederation, the press, and the scientific societies broke into a chorus of regret and of appreciation for his distinguished twenty-six years of service. But Logan, of course, could not wholly part from the survey; he continued to perform many small services for it.

Sir William had always had a quiet though keen sense of humor, and he did not lose it. He stopped one day at the office of a friend to obtain an address. A new clerk who did not know him supplied it, but, taking note of the shaggy white beard, the long hair, the battered old hat, the crumpled suit, and the muddy knee boots, thought he was some backwoodsman just come into the city. To prevent his becoming lost in attempting to find the address, the clerk volunteered to take him there. Sir William, well aware of the situation and enjoying it to the full, happily consented. As they started out, the clerk was amazed first by the old man's vigorous stride. His bewilderment increased as a number of people along the street greeted him warmly and respectfully. His conversation also was puzzling. When the clerk made some remark about having relatives in Wales, Sir William asked where they lived. "Ah, that is on the lime," he said, as soon as he heard the name of the place. He added: "My sister lives at Tenby, which is on the slate."

The moment the "backwoodsman" had been safely delivered to his destination, the clerk hurried to ask who the old man was. It was then that he received the information: "Sir William Logan." Everybody knew about Sir William.

The story is also told of a shopkeeper who felt so sorry for the ragged old man who came in from the country with worn-out boots that he sold him a new pair for about half the regular price. Soon afterward a man hurried into the shop, asking for a pair of the "five-dollar boots." When the owner denied having anything of the kind, he insisted: "I want the same kind you just sold to Sir William Logan."

The five-dollar boots undoubtedly carried Logan on some of the expeditions that he continued to make, including one to the Pictou coal fields, where he had started his Canadian work so many years before. Late in the summer of 1874 he sailed for England to visit his sister in Wales. There he became seriously ill. His health again improved, however, and he busily occupied himself in plans for a nine-hundred-and-fifty-foot boring that he wanted to have made in some of the Canadian formations. Someone had challenged certain of his earlier findings, and he wanted to settle the point in the only way possible: by drilling to determine the actual order of the rocks.

Before the project could be carried out, his illness again took a turn for the worse. His relatives and friends became so deeply concerned that they insisted upon calling in a famous London physician, the man who had been consulted in the last illness of the Duke of Wellington. The doctor made the trip to Wales and, after a careful examination, said that the local physician who had been treating Sir William was doing everything possible. His bill came to £190. Soon afterward Sir William asked the local physician, who had been seeing him twice daily and treating him "with the utmost tenderness," to submit his bill. It was £57. Sir William decided that things needed evening up. When he paid the account he accompanied it by a gift of an additional £100.

Death came on June 22, 1875. But the new dimension that Sir William Logan had given to time would live long after him. By studying the ancient "basement" rocks it had become possible to look back and learn something of what had happened on the earth long before fossil life appeared. The vista was lengthening.

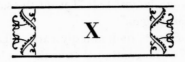

HALL

MOUNTAINS DOWN

Rꜱ꜉꜉ʟᴇ ᴍᴀʀᴋꜱ, symmetrical, patterned, and lovely to behold, marked the smooth surface of the sandstone. Across its face also ran the delicate, wavery trails left by crustaceans of millions of years before. Both these etchings in the sands of the past testified with unmistakable force to the shallow-water origin of the sandstone; it had been formed in a shallow, and not in a deep, ancient sea.

The Canadian Geological Survey had first noted these markings of the shallows on the Potsdam sandstones. With an elated sense of discovery James Hall came upon them in New York too. He was elated because the engraved Potsdam sandstones were old rocks; they were some of the first in that immense sequence of sedimentary rocks that forms the Appalachian Mountains and, stretching westward, underlies the heart of a continent.

It had been assumed up to that time—1850—that the prehistoric seas in which these miles-thick beds of rocks were laid down had been immeasurably deep. But the ripple marks and the tracks of the crustaceans on some of the deepest rocks spoke of shallow seas. Hall's fertile mind began to see another explanation of the way in which these mountains of sediment might have been accumulated. Before he had finished he would give the world a new and surprising account of how many of its mountains came to be.

If the mountains were not piled up by Noah's Flood, how could such masses of water-laid stone have been formed? Hall was well qualified to work with this question, certainly one of the most baffling and interesting of all those which men asked about the earth. As chief geologist and an organizer of the New York State Geological Survey, he probably knew as much about the rocks of New York and the central part of the country as anyone living.

He had made an early start. James Hall was born at Hingham, Massachusetts, on the south shore of Boston Bay, in September 1811. He was hardly beyond the toddling stage when he began to collect shells along the shore. This early interest in nature was stimulated by Increase N. Smith, his teacher at the local grammar school. An able amateur zoologist, Smith taught his keenly interested young pupil how to dissect some of the marine creatures that they collected together.

At nineteen Hall had no doubt that he wanted to be a scientist. Not long before, "Patroon" Stephen van Rensselaer had founded a new kind of school at Troy, New York. Here science was taught by work in the field and the laboratory. Van Rensselaer held that the "aspiring energies of youth" had too long been "chained down to a kind of literary bondage."

It was exactly the kind of school which Hall wanted, and he walked the two hundred and twenty miles from Hingham to Troy to enroll. The senior professor was Amos Eaton, pioneer geologist, and all students were required as part of their course to make at least two fossil- and mineral-collecting trips. For Hall, this was all that was needed. A young man of decision, he determined to become a geologist.

Upon his graduation in 1832 he enthusiastically set out on a fossil-collecting expedition to the Helderberg Mountains, about twenty-five miles south of Troy. The trip was highly successful in its yield of fossils, but on his return Hall abruptly realized that he had no more money and no prospects of a job; he frantically began to pack. He was in the midst of his disturbed preparations for a rapid departure when Eaton came in and relieved the crisis by offering the worried young bachelor of natural science a job as librarian and assistant to the professor of chemistry. Hall's incidental duties included whitewashing the "old bank building" on the campus and tidying up the "sheep pen," as Van Rensselaer called the girls' study room. Hall took all of this in his stride. By 1835 he was a full professor.

The next year, with the establishment of the state's geological survey, Hall was employed as an assistant to Ebenezer Emmons for a study of the iron ores in the Adirondack counties. Always determined and headstrong, he was soon in conflict with his chief, a problem that was solved by creating a new survey district in western New York and putting Hall in charge.

The district was a level, "uninteresting" wilderness of some ten thousand square miles. But if the intent was to box the presumptuous young man into a corner, it miscarried, for the "uninteresting" formations turned out to be filled with a rich array of fossils. Fossils projected from ledges along the creek banks; they seemed almost as numerous as pebbles in the stream beds. The Indians of the region even used fossil cup corals for pipe bowls and strung crinoid stems into necklaces. Hall happily collected fossils by the thousands. But he did not stop with collecting; Hall was a keen observer and a student of meanings. He noticed that certain once numerous species that disappeared in later strata did not vanish suddenly, but gradually became rarer. Rarity preceded extinction; extinction took time.

"At the time our strata began to be studied," he said, "the doctrine of total destructions and renovations of life was generally admitted; the termination of every geological period was supposed to be marked by the annihilation of every living thing and the commencement of the next one by a new and entirely different creation. Further observation has tended to the abandonment of this doctrine; and so far as our knowledge goes, there seems to have been a gradual change from the first period of living things to the present time."

Hall was able to establish a whole series of fossils belonging to periods that had been designated in England as the Devonian and Silurian eras, when life first appeared on the land and fish dominated the seas. A more practical conclusion, in the eyes of state legislators, who complained that this was so much classifying of "dead rabbits," was that there was no coal in New York. Hall's 683-page report was a notable one.

The survey ended with the publication of Hall's and the other reports, and with a legislative investigation. The investigators found that eight species of fossils had been illustrated by one hundred and seventeen figures, and that one, *Spirifera radiolarius*, had been "figured" twenty-seven times. They were quite sharp about it. The state of New York also had been left with a huge collection of fossils. To get out from under this embarrassment of riches, the legislature voted to set up a state "cabinet" or museum with a paleontologist in charge. Hall and Emmons both wanted the job. Only by some fast maneuvering did Hall beat out his former superior. "He had a good salary besides his agricultural work, and I had nothing," said Hall in justification. At thirty-two Hall held the job that he wanted above all others. Although the legislature expected him to complete the work of studying and arranging the fossils in one year, Hall had another idea entirely. "I propose," he wrote to a friend, "to cover the fossils of all the rocks below the coal over the whole United States. I know it will be the work of a lifetime."

No statement was ever more true. The thirteenth and last quarto volume of Hall's *Palaeontology* was published exactly sixty-two years later. Through all the intervening years and volume by volume Hall had to browbeat the money out of the reluctant and often rebellious legislature.

Time and again the legislature would cut off funds. Hall would carry on with his own slender resources and take work in other states until he could force it to support the work once more. He believed in the direct attack. Stamping into a committee hearing, Hall would pound on the table and shout: "New York today stands pre-eminent in geology, but the scepter may depart. . . . It will be thrown away from mere ignorance and ill nature." Moved, or perhaps intimidated, the committee would approve more funds.

While the state gave only grudging recognition to the work being done in its behalf, geologists all around the world honored it. After seeing Volume II, Agassiz wrote: "It must be indispensable to our geologists as long as our Silurian rocks exist." When the great figures of European geology came to the United States, Hall was one of the first men they wanted to see. Sir Charles Lyell made an early visit to Albany and spent many days with Hall, examining the fossils and formations of New York. Agassiz, in his turn, had scarcely stepped from the boat when he asked: "Which is the way to Albany?" The visitors all became friends of Hall's, although, as was the case in anything involving the New York geologist, the course of the friendship seldom was smooth.

One day Hall happened to be in the office of the superintendent of public instruction. Hanging on the wall was a geological map that the superintendent innocently explained he had ordered for the use of the schools. The geological beds pictured on it curved like the blade of a scimitar, and running through them were the gracefully branching arms of an igneous intrusion that the author of the chart, James T. Forster, called serpentine. Around the edges were drawings of fossils that purported to belong to the various strata pictured. Hall took one look, and with a mighty effort controlled his outrage until he could borrow a copy from the superintendent. With it safely in his hands, he exploded.

He sent a copy to Agassiz, who reacted with the same shocked indignation. The Swiss naturalist, then at Harvard, felt it the duty of scientific men to prevent the public's "being humbugged by pseudo knowledge."

Calling in the newspapers, the two denounced the map as "monstrous," "a crude production full of false and antiquated views," "a disgrace to American geologists," and "as ridiculous as though a historian had pictured Napoleon and Alexander meeting in combat in China." The story was a sensation.

Forster, a schoolteacher, brought suit, charging the two scientists with libeling a copyrighted document that had been accepted for use in the schools. He asked forty thousand dollars in damages from Hall and twenty thousand from Agassiz.

The map bore a little note at the bottom, "Corrected by Prof. Emmons," and it was this endorsement by an expert which had in large part persuaded the superintendent to approve the map. Emmons, of course, was Hall's old opponent, and the chance to strike a blow at his rival may have been a factor in Hall's fury, though even normally his fury was easily aroused. Emmons was bitterly resentful of the attack; while Hall and Agassiz were preparing their defense for the trial, he helped Forster prepare a new and less erroneous edition of the map. It was quickly printed in Albany and shipped to New York by the Hudson River night boat.

Hall heard about the shipment; he hastily took the boat himself. The next morning when it docked in New York the new maps were missing. A frantic search of the boat failed to produce them. The suspicion at once spread that Hall had managed to find them and had tossed them overboard during the night. But nothing could be proved.

Many years later John M. Clarke, who had worked with Hall for twelve years and was writing a full-length biography of him, was talking to another former associate of Hall's about the case of the missing maps, and the belief that Hall had chucked them overboard. " 'Do you think he really did that?' said I wonderingly to Prof. Cook. 'Do you think that he would not,' was the answer."

The case against Agassiz came to trial in March 1851. Eight scientists and a mapmaker testified against the map and against the "Taconic" system of rocks which it was supposed to illustrate. In the end, though, the issue narrowed down to the credibility of Emmons. Was he a man of "approved knowledge, learning, judgment, and skill in the art and science of geology," or was he a fraud and an ignoramus? The twelve jurors held that Agassiz was not guilty of libel, and the case against Hall was never called.

Through all of his troubles with the New York legislature and the law, Hall's scientific reputation continued to grow. He was called in to assist with or direct geological surveys in Iowa, Ohio, Canada, and other places—this was the beginning of the great era of the geological survey. Since there were many salary-less gaps in Hall's employment with New York and since his earnings never were adequate for his work, he was free to accept other jobs. The work was giving him a matchless knowledge of the geology of the country.

As he traced the strata from New York into Ohio, Hall was impressed by a striking change. The huge beds of shale—a rock formed from muds—and sandy matter that prevailed in New York diminished when he moved into Ohio and there was a large increase in rocks composed of carbonate of lime. Hall understood the meaning of the change. "In New York," he said, "we are evidently upon the margin of the primeval ocean, as indicated by the character of the deposits as well as organic remains; the southwest unfolds to us that portion where greater depth and more quiet conditions prevailed."

Hall was filling in his picture of the ancient ocean that had once occupied the center of the continent, and this knowledge prepared him to explain the ripple marks and crustacean tracks that he found in the deep Potsdam sandstones. They had been formed on the shallow edges of the sea, on its early shores and just offshore. But where were the other borders? Were they as shallow? Was the whole inland sea quite shallow?

Making his way along river beds or wherever the sandstone was exposed, and tracking through many a wilderness, Hall followed the sandstone west through Canada, along Lake Huron, to the Mississippi and the St. Croix River in Wisconsin. In a two-hundred-mile stretch along the Mississippi were uncountable millions of the same shallow-water crustaceans, trilobites, and *Lingula* that had left their shells and tracks in the Potsdam sandstone in New York.

At the St. Croix River falls, more than half the material in the rocks consisted of the hard-shelled little *Lingula*. They had drifted together "in precisely the same manner as we find shells on a modern beach," Hall reported. Thus, the shallow-water sandstone extended over one thousand miles from east to west and from three hundred to five hundred miles from north to south.

"Over this wide area," Hall summed up, "extending one thousand miles from the known eastern limits of the sandstone we find the most unequivocal evidence of a shallow sea. It is interesting that it presents such a uniform and even monotonous character."

The inland sea as a whole, however, was no more uniform in its depth and conditions than is any modern sea. Along its borders where the waves and the rains and the rivers dropped the debris of the land, it was, as the sandstone testified, shallow and muddy. Farther out it was deeper. As Hall had already glimpsed in Ohio, the kind of bottom and the depth also determined the kind of life that existed in any one section. Out beyond the sands and the muds and the coarse stuff of the beaches, coral flourished—vast reefs of it. In these tranquil waters, almost free of mud, lived the fan-shaped brachipods with their delicately grooved shells, the coiled cephalopods, and the slim, symmetrical, cone-shaped gastropods.

"Along the shore of this ocean," said Hall, "from the northeast to the southwest, from Newfoundland to the southern extremity of the Laurentian Mountains and thence from Canada to Alabama, were spread these immense sediments along the line of the present mountain ranges, while on the north and northwest sides lay the quiet ocean teeming with its inhabitants and scarcely disturbed by the gentle currents which transported the fine and almost impalpable mud, which in its extreme extension may have reached a thousand miles from the centre of the greatest accumulation."

And through countless ages the sediments continued to pile up. Hall also traced the "Niagara" formations. They too had been laid down in shallow seas, for their surfaces were marked by the trails and tracks of shallow-water organisms. The Niagara strata ran west for five hundred miles from the Hudson River along the islands of Lake Huron and into Wisconsin at Green Bay.

Hall in addition made a careful study of the coal measures that lay atop the other primeval sea formations. In Pennsylvania they were eight thousand feet thick; in Nova Scotia, fourteen thousand. Again there was the same pattern. The coarser sediments lay along the line of the present Appalachian chain, with a gradual thinning out to the westward.

The coal beds consisted almost entirely of land-derived materials, and plants of land origin marked the successive layers. There seemed to be no question that the area occupied by the coal measures was the land on which the plants had grown, and that they had been destroyed by successive inundations or submergences. The sea was losing ground; it made only feeble and transitory returns, though when this occurred the flora were covered by coarser materials.

In addition to the Potsdam sandstone, the Niagara formations, and the coal measures—to which Hall gave the closest study— many other strata were laid down in the ancient inland sea. But always the same law had held true: in all the great periods of sedimentary deposition the greatest loads of material had been spread over the shallows in the east. Only a relatively thin film of finely divided stuff had reached the deeper waters in the midwest.

The almost unimaginable consequences of this age-long deposition were clearly visible: the Appalachian Mountains and the plains of the midwest. During the vast ages of deposition more than forty thousand feet of sediments were accumulated along the present line of the Appalachians. In the waters of the midwest, which received only a little of the substance worn from the land, the deposits totaled only about four thousand feet in thickness. Thus, more than ten times as much land material had been piled up on the shores of the primeval seas as in their center.

In time the sediments had become the mountains of the east and the plains of the midwest. The form of both, their substance, their contours, their elevation, had been set by the lay of the ancient sediments.

Hall could see where these remarkable findings were taking him, but the immense problems that were raised required long and careful thought. How could forty thousand feet of sediments, more than seven and a half miles of them, have accumulated in shallow waters? How had mountains been created out of the thick floor of a sea? Why were the mountains bent into great folds? Why were their strata often fractured and broken?

Hall kept these tantalizing problems turning in his head while he continued during most of the fifties with his paleontology and with other projects. Occasionally he would talk about them to the members of his staff and to visitors seated in the low, scoop-shaped chair that stood beside his desk. While the visitor sank almost to the floor and almost out of sight, Hall towered above him, erect and straight-backed, on the piano stool he used for a desk chair.

The geologist also worked steadily on the material bearing upon the big theoretical question of mountain formation. He was generally up at the break of day; with a cup of tea at his elbow, he would put some of this work out of the way before his staff arrived for the day. Many a night also went into this work. Hall often did not go home, but spent the night in a sparsely furnished room adjoining his office; it held only an iron cot, a washstand, a looking-glass, a small table set with a spirit lamp and teakettle, and a shotgun. But if he could not sleep he would wander out into the office or museum. The staff could trace his nocturnal route by the drops of candle grease on tables and fossils.

In 1856, Hall was elected president of the American Association for the Advancement of Science at a meeting on his home ground, in Old Geological Hall at Albany. As he took office he reminded the scientists gathered there that the A.A.A.S. had grown out of several informal bull sessions that he and half a dozen other geologists had held in that same hall eighteen years before. They had seen the need of an organization where all the geologists could meet, and some of their group had taken the initiative in forming the Association of American Geologists in 1840. In 1847 the organization had expanded into the A.A.A.S.

In 1857, at the Montreal meeting where he gave his presidential address, Hall was at last ready. He chose as his subject "The Geological History of the North American Continent." The assembled scientists were startled by the conclusions he had reached: The Appalachians had been formed, not by upheaval of the earth's crust, but by the accumulation of vast sediments along the shallow shores of the primeval American sea. As more and more sand, gravel, and other heavy debris of the land was piled on the coastal sea floor, it gradually sank under the tremendous weight. In this way the fantastic forty thousand feet of sediments had accumulated in a long trough.

Obviously, Hall added in defense of his hypothesis, North America was never covered with an ocean forty thousand feet deep. "On the contrary," he said, "the ripple marks and marine plants prove that the sea was at all times of a shallow or moderate depth. The accumulation could only have been made by gradual subsidence."

Hall was prepared to follow his argument through. As the earth's crust sagged under the weight of the sediments—it of course sagged most where they were thickest and heaviest—the strata at the bottom and at either side were rent, fractured, wrinkled, and folded.

"I maintain," he declared, "that it is impossible to have any subsidence along a certain line of the earth's crust from the accumulation of sediments, without producing the phenomena which are observed in the Appalachian and other mountain ranges." The Appalachians were rent, fractured, wrinkled, and folded exactly as they should have been according to Hall's theory!

Informally, after his address, Hall invited skeptics to test this principle by a very simple little experiment. Take a package of flat sheets of paper, he directed, hold the edges firmly and depress the center. Those who tried it soon discovered that as the center of the pack sagged, the upper sheets buckled and wrinkled. "Since beds of stone cannot slide over each other the way sheets of paper do, the lower side must become broken too," Hall pointed out.

The Appalachians provided another confirmation of Hall's theory. The beds bent upward into U-shaped folds, he explained, would be most subject to erosion; they soon would be worn down into valleys. On the other hand, downward-curved or arched folds would be better protected and would turn into prominent mountain crests. Thus, peaks became valleys, and valleys peaks. Hall emphasized that many such cases were found in the Appalachians.

One disturbed critic of Hall's ideas would later call this a theory of mountain-making with the mountains left out. If Hall was right, how had the mountains achieved their height?

In his address Hall anticipated the point. He conceded that the folding would not add to altitude. He argued that although there had been no local upthrusting of strata, there had been a general continental rise. In this way the whole thick book of sediments was raised. As the winds, rains, and other elements cut into this high plateau the ranges, the peaks, the valleys, and the ravines were carved from the great uplifted mass of stone.

No mountains were formed in the Mississippi valley—none

could have been formed, Hall said—because the sediments were not thick enough. The scant four thousand feet of stone was not sufficient to make highlands; the plains were inevitable.

And, summing up, Hall drove home his point: "I hold that no mountains . . . can occur without the long continued accumulation of sediments."

Hall had fortified his thesis with all the data he had gathered in his country-wide study of the formation of the country's eastern and central rocky cover. Nevertheless, his audience was shocked, and the shock did not wear off as discussion and later study further clarified Hall's ideas.

Soon after the Montreal meeting, Henry Jackson, head of the Smithsonian Institution in Washington and a friend of Hall's, wrote to him that his theories were of "such a remarkable character that had they not come from you, I would suppose there would be nothing to them. . . . I beg that you will be cautious."

In replying, Hall freely admitted that his ideas had seemed "so strange to some" as to "hazard, or rather as the expression is, to 'compromise'" his scientific reputation. He did not yield in the least, however; he considered that he had already shown the caution that Jackson urged.

"I have exercised the most scrupulous care that all I have advanced should bear the test of the most careful examination," he said, "and I would as soon commit a moral falsehood as a scientific one." He insisted that he had merely come to a simple and natural conclusion from the observed facts, and added: "I am surprised that the same idea should not have occurred to every observer."

To those who harped on the criticism that he had fallen back upon a general elevation of land to explain his mountains, Hall justly replied that he had not intended to offer a new theory of elevation or to go beyond what had already been proposed on that score by others. What he did intend to say was that mountain formation was due to sedimentary accumulation and subsequent continental elevation.

"If I can sustain the great principle which I advocate, viz—that the mountains are not produced by upheaval but by accumulation and continental elevation, I shall feel that I have done something to advance the science of geology in true principles," he wrote.

Hall's address was not printed at the time it was given. It did not appear in type until two years later, in 1859, as a preface to Volume III of the *Palaeontology*. Hall had then carried his thinking a little further: he was willing to apply his theory to the other great mountains of the world and to add another surprising link to it.

The Rockies were higher than the Appalachians, Hall maintained in the preface, because additional sediments had been piled up on top of the older ones. In the west the seas had held sway for longer. Above the same kind of coal measures which marked the top of the water-born beds of the Appalachians, enough additional sand, gravel, mud, and shells had been deposited to form the tremendous ranges and peaks of the Rockies.

Along an ancient shore approximating what is now southern Europe, Hall believed that deposits had accumulated for the millions and millions of years stretching from the Paleozoic, the second-oldest period in earth's history, to the Mesozoic, or middle period. "No wonder there are high summits in the Alps," he exclaimed. "The accumulation must have been enormous."

And the deposition had continued still longer off a primeval Asiatic shore; the deposits had become still thicker as younger accumulations were heaped on the older. "If you add the accumulations during the Cretaceous and Tertiary [the younger part of the Mesozoic] you get the Himalayas," Hall succinctly and dramatically added. "I believe that all mountains of great height will be found to embrace the newer geological formations in their mass."

This perhaps was the first time anyone had suggested that newer mountains were higher than the older and that "a part of this was due to the rising mass being loaded with a greater accumulation of the later formations."

During the next three and a half decades—the sixties, the seventies, the eighties, and on into the nineties—Hall was principally occupied with the completion of the *Palaeontology* and with the legislative battles this continued to entail. His luxuriant side whiskers and beard turned to white, and a leg injury forced him to use a cane. But Hall's face still was notably smooth and determined, and the cane was used as effectively to shake under the noses of the pinchpenny and recalcitrant legislators as to aid him in walking.

His continuing work with paleontology only confirmed his theory of how mountains came to be. The well-known geologist Clarence King asked him in 1881 if he had made any change in his views.

"I do not know that my views have undergone any material change," Hall replied. "I cannot believe that mountains can exist without, in the first place, *accumulation* of sediments—which must be along coastlines. . . . Then we know that these accumulations did not take place in a deep sea, for in the semi-metamorphic rocks we have ripplemarks, fucoids, and mud cracks at various depths through 20,000 feet of thickness. I believe therefore that these great accumulations produced a depression of the crust. . . . Mountains are not elevated as mountains, but as part of the continental movement.

"I was led to this conclusion by a study of the New England ranges—the Adirondack (Laurentian) and the Appalachian as far south as Virginia and by a comparison with the thinning expansion of the same formation in the west. . . . I can only say that I have seen nothing to change in any material degree my general views of mountain building. Were I to review and rewrite my views I might present some points more clearly, but the hoped for time has not come to me, and I must trust to you and to others to interpret with what limits you will the expression of views based perhaps on too limited an observation and acquired amid the more serious labor of tracing out and identifying by their fossil contents the widespread Paleozoic formations of the United States on the east of the Mississippi River."

Hall was speaking here in his most formal and measured manner. More characteristically, he told another friend: "You may uplift, upheave, convulse and cataclysm to all eternity but you cannot make mountains without the thickness of strata."

And Hall was right. It was not many years before geologists everywhere were acknowledging it. As early as 1907 the French geologist Haug in his *Traité de Géologie* said: "To James Hall we owe another determination which has become the basis of modern orogenic theory. The author has shown that the position of the folded regions of the earth coincides with the zones of greatest sedimentation. Today we accept this law: Mountain chains are formed on geosynclines." In 1913 James Geikie in his *Mountains, Their Origin, Growth, and Decay* added: "James Hall appears to have been the first to formulate the opinion that a deep trough or basin of depression has in all cases preceded the process of mountain making."

At last, after centuries of puzzling over the water-made rocks and the fossils of the world's mountains, men could begin to understand how such rocks had been formed and where they had come from. An important part of the answer to one of the most interesting questions about the earth had been provided by the belligerent but clear-sighted New York geologist.

Hall lived for four years after the completion of the monumental *Palaeontology.* He had come close to the goal he had set sixty-two years before: he had covered most of the fossils in the "rocks below the coal." In the thirteen volumes of the *Palaeontology* and in two other books Hall had published 4,539 pages and 1,081 full-page plates of fossils. It was a record in American geological writing.

In 1898, at the age of eighty-seven, Hall died. He had not been ill; he just "ceased living." To the last, James Hall was not downed.

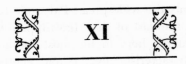

POWELL

GRAND CANYON

I N MAY 1869 four stout little rowboats were tied up on the edge of the unknown. They were about to carry the "Major"—Major John Wesley Powell—and a party of nine men down the tumultuous Green and Colorado rivers, through the unexplored, the abysmal, the ominous canyons of those rivers.

The Major had been amply warned against such a foolhardy expedition. The west abounded in tales of hunters and prospectors who had entered the gorge in boats, only to be swept to their death in fearful whirlpools or in underground passages where the river "plunged into the bowels of the earth." It was widely believed that the river was lost under the rocks for several hundred miles. Others told the Major about falls so tremendous that their roar could be clearly heard on distant mountaintops. And once in the canyon, they said, anyone who survived the river could never make his way out again. Parties lost on the brink of the canyon and dying of thirst had tried in vain to get down to the mocking roar of the water. There was no way in and no way out.

One old Indian, Pa-ri-ats, lifted his arms vertically above his head, looked between them toward the sky, and told Powell about one member of his tribe who had tried to cross the river: "The rocks h-e-a-p, h-e-a-p high; the water go h-oo-woogh, h-oo-woogh; water pony buck; water catch 'em; no see 'em Injun any more, no see 'em squaw any more; no see 'em papoose any more."

Nor were more "scientific" warnings lacking. The best maps

available left a great blank space, three hundred to five hundred miles long and one hundred to two hundred miles wide, between the known upper reaches of the Green and the Colorado and the lower stretch where the combined rivers ran into the Gulf of California. Thus, a large part of what is now southern Utah and western Colorado was marked "unexplored" in 1869, a warning in itself that this was forbidding country not easily conquered.

Professor Brewster of Yale, who was in Colorado at the time, pointed out to Powell that the river had an average fall of ten to fifteen feet per mile, and that it would "almost certainly have great falls." He thought the project "a mad scheme."

Powell's answer was: "Have you ever seen the river? It is the muddiest you ever saw." Powell later added: "Rapids I expected, of course, but not falls. I was convinced that the cañon was old enough and the muddy water swift enough and gritty enough to have worn down falls to mere rapids. . . ."

Powell understood that a large, muddy river would in time have fashioned a graded course for itself even though it ran through the bottom of a chasm. The Major was in large part a self-taught scientist, lacking in scientific background. He was, however, a remarkably keen observer, and he reasoned from what he saw. He saw that when the summer sun melted the deep snows that covered the mountains in winter, millions of cascades came tumbling down the precipitous slopes. "Ten million cascade brooks unite to form ten thousand torrent creeks," he said, "ten thousand torrent creeks unite to form a hundred rivers beset with cataracts; a hundred roaring rivers unite to form the Colorado, which rolls in a mad, turbid stream, into the Gulf of California."

Powell also saw that if this flood had poured down onto an already flooded plain, there would have been only a bigger and wider inundation; no gorges would have been cut. But when it came down into a nearly dry country, its tremendous cutting power was not spread thin; its streams cut deeper and still deeper, eliminating all fall-creating obstacles, until the banks became towering cliffs of solid rock.

It was partly because he so well understood the action of rivers and their shaping of a country that Powell dared to defy what was supposedly the best information and embark on an expedition that still held the gravest risk. He expected to learn still more about how the earth had taken on its present form; that concerned him as much as filling in the blanks on the maps. Powell also suspected that the canyon walls might afford a cross-section view of a large part of the earth's history. In his official request for Federal aid he wrote: "It is believed that the Grand Cañon of Colorado will give the best geological section on the continent." Actually, even he could not know how superb a cross-section it would be and how completely it would expose the events and changes of hundreds of millions of years.

In a practical way, Powell was well equipped to work with such problems. He had been born on March 24, 1834, at Palmyra, New York. His father and mother, Joseph and Mary, had come from England in 1830, dedicated to Methodism and to the mission of carrying it to the frontiers of the new land. Palmyra was one of the earlier stops on a route that would carry them across the country, through Ohio and Illinois and on to Wisconsin.

John Wesley, called Wes, spent much of his childhood in Jackson, Ohio, a small town in the southern part of the state, where southerners and northerners had uneasily mingled. As the son of a man who was preaching abolition on the circuit of his churches, Wes was beaten and stoned at school by older pro-slavery boys. His parents feared for his safety. When "Big George" Crookham, a successful farmer with an interest in science and education, offered to teach him, his parents gratefully accepted.

Crookham had set up a combination science museum, school, and library in a cabin on his farm. He and Wes would read aloud and then talk about what they had read—in this way

Powell knew Hume's *History of England* and Gibbon before he was ten. But it was the rest of the program which was to influence his life most profoundly. The two would go on long walks, sometimes hunting for fossils, sometimes digging into Indian mounds, sometimes visiting quarries, sometimes studying animals and plants.

This unusual but excellent education was interrupted when the Rev. Mr. Powell decided to move to Wisconsin. Some former Indian lands in Walworth County were being opened to settlement. For young Wes, the new farm often meant fifteen hours a day of the hardest kind of labor, clearing the land and planting the fields. As he worked, however, he went on with the collecting Crookham had taught him. While he drove produce to town he would pore over any scientific books that he could get. His whole interest was in science, and he wanted badly to go to college. His father would have helped him if he had been willing to prepare for the ministry, but Wes would not commit himself. He preferred to make his own way.

He did it principally by teaching. Over the next nine years Wes taught school, while trying to get the science he wanted at various Illinois and Ohio colleges. He also went on long collecting trips. In 1856 he took a skiff down the Mississippi from St. Paul to New Orleans. The next summer he floated down the Ohio from Pittsburgh to the Mississippi. Another trip took him down the Illinois.

The year stretching between the springs of 1860 and 1861 changed this fluctuating, preparatory round. In 1860, not long before he cast his vote for Abraham Lincoln for president, he was appointed principal of the public schools of Hennepin County, Illinois. He had been teaching there for the two preceding years. Recognition also was coming to him in science. He was lecturing on geology and geography on a small-town lyceum circuit, and his collection of mollusks had taken first prize at the fair of the Illinois State Agricultural Society. When the State Natural History Society obtained a charter in the spring of 1861, Powell, as a rising young scientist-teacher, was elected its secretary. In the pleasure of all of this, Powell went to Detroit to ask his cousin Emma Dean to marry him.

And then, suddenly, came the Civil War. On May 8, 1861, immediately after a call for men was issued in Illinois, Powell enlisted as a private in the Twentieth Illinois Infantry. An orderly noted in the record book: "Age 27, height 5' 6-½" tall, light complected, gray eyes, auburn hair, occupation—teacher." Powell wrote a friend that he wanted to do his part "in the extinction of slavery." By June he was a second lieutenant and by November a captain and a member of Brigadier General U. S. Grant's staff at Cape Girardeau, Missouri. As a personal favor, Grant gave him a few days' leave to go to Detroit to marry Emma Dean. Wes had promised Emma that she might travel with him, and they did not let a war interfere with that plan. She returned to Missouri with him. Powell was placed in charge of Battery F, Second Illinois Light Artillery, and by the next spring, when they were ordered down the river to Savannah, Tennessee, his men were excellently trained. On April 6 the Confederates attacked at Shiloh.

As some of the Union forces fell back, Battery F firmly held its strategic spot. Confederate Minié balls stripped the branches from the trees around them. Casualties among the surrounding infantry were frightful. Powell fought on gallantly until, at a moment when his right arm was raised in the signal "Fire," he was struck in the wrist by a Minié ball that glanced off toward his elbow and buried itself in the flesh. It was a bad wound. One of the generals put Powell on his own horse and sent him to the rear for medical attention. When he finally was taken back to Savannah, Emma was waiting for him. Despite her nursing, the wound became worse, and amputation was ordered.

All through his long and painful convalescence Powell did not waver in his determination to go back to the army. After six months he personally wrote to General Grant, saying that he could return if his wife came with him. The General replied by enclosing a "perpetual pass" permitting Mrs. Emma Dean Powell to enter and leave all military lines without further authority. Powell went through some of the bitterest fighting of the war, although even in the trenches at Vicksburg he did not forget his interest in science. He collected fossils exposed by the trenches and sent them off for safekeeping just before the battle opened.

By 1865 Powell was in command of the artillery of the Seventeenth Army Corps. He was then a major. Refusing higher rank, he resigned on January 2. He had undergone a second operation on the extremely painful stump of his right arm, and he came out of the army almost a skeleton, weighing only a hundred and ten pounds.

That fall the Major was made professor of geology and natural science at Illinois Wesleyan University at Bloomington. Instead of adopting the textbook-recitation method then generally used for the teaching of science (except at Harvard, where Agassiz was revolutionizing the teaching of zoology), Powell took his classes on field trips and had them do laboratory work. In his laboratory his pupils would put a piece of galena on a charcoal block and extract a little pellet of lead. They gathered herbariums and examined the stomachs of crows. Students crowded into these unusual classes.

Soon after he went to Bloomington, the Major organized a local chapter of the State Natural History Society. Its collections —principally the fossils Powell had gathered during the Civil War—were kept at near-by Illinois State Normal University at Normal. A museum was needed so that they could be arranged and properly displayed. The Major did not have too much difficulty persuading the state legislature to appropriate a thousand dollars a year for the maintenance of the Society's collections and fifteen hundred a year as salary for a curator. The local board thereupon insisted that Powell accept the curatorship as an extension of his professorial duties. At the time this happy decision was reached he suggested to the board that the collections might be notably enriched by sending an expedition of students and naturalists to the Rocky Mountains or the Dakota Bad Lands. This was a dream of Powell's. His enthusiasm always could move others, and the board not only approved, but urged him to undertake the expedition.

Some five hundred dollars was set aside for expenses. This, of course, was not nearly enough. In April 1867 Powell went to Washington to secure further support. He called first on his old friend and commander, General Grant, then Secretary of the Army. Grant could not get him funds, but he approved his request for army rations for a party of twelve. The Major next obtained a pledge of free fares and freight from four railroads. Illinois Industrial University, later the University of Illinois, and the Chicago Academy of Sciences contributed six hundred dollars with the assurance that the expedition would supply them with duplicate series of specimens. The Smithsonian Institution furnished the last necessity, scientific instruments. Powell knew how to accomplish the things that he believed important, and thus it was that the Rocky Mountain Scientific Exploring Expedition came into being.

None of its twelve members had ever before been in the mountains. The zoologist was a Methodist preacher; the entomologist, Powell's brother-in-law, the superintendent of schools at Bloomington. Mrs. Powell and Powell's sister acted as ornithologists. Most of the others were students. On June 1, 1867, they left Council Bluffs, Iowa, with two heavily loaded wagons and a dozen riding-animals. During the summer they suffered all the inevitable trials of the greenhorn, but they did manage to climb Pike's Peak and to make huge collections. Much that they brought in was new and unknown, largely because the region itself had been so little studied that almost any collection was fresh and valuable. Powell's pleased museums and supporters were glad to finance a second summer of work in 1868.

That summer they made the difficult ascent of Long's Peak. As they made their way down, exuberant over having reached the summit, Powell made a little speech. He expressed the hope that their success would be an augury of greater achievements "in other ways." He had the other ways in mind. During the first summer in the mountains Powell had met a mountaineer, Jack Sumner, who had talked to him about the possibility of exploring the Colorado and Green rivers by boat. The same idea had already occurred to Powell, for he had sensed the great scientific interest of the canyons. In asking Congress for assistance for the second summer's work he had said that exploration of the rivers would be one of their goals. It was largely for this reason that he had again been authorized to draw rations from army posts.

While he drove his party to make every possible scientific measurement and to collect every promising specimen, Powell made as many studies as he could of the river canyons. What he saw further convinced him that they could be run by boat, if the boats were properly built. By the end of the summer his plans for exploring the gorges were nearly complete. Winter camp was set up near the Green River. Powell, however, had to make another trip east to line up support. Again the most he could get from the Federal government was a pledge of rations. Fortunately, he was permitted to divert his salary as curator to the trip, and his Illinois institutional friends contributed again.

Powell went to see a boatbuilder in Chicago. He ordered three boats, twenty-one feet long, to be built of well-seasoned white oak. To strengthen them for the riotous rivers that lay ahead, he specified that they must have double ribs, double stem and stern posts, and watertight bulkheads at either end. A fourth boat of white pine was built only seventeen feet long to gain maneuverability. Powell planned to ride ahead in it to reconnoiter the way. The boats looked very much like an ordinary fisherman's rowboat, but they could carry forty-five hundred pounds each and they had long stern sweeps for steering. They were placed on a flatcar and shipped west.

The country's first transcontinental railroad was just being

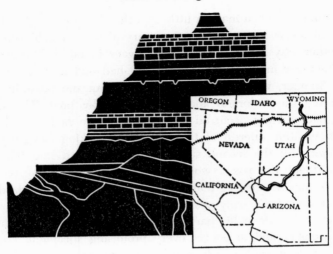

POWELL'S ROUTE. THE SECTION THAT THE MAJOR EXPLORED BY BOAT
FROM GREEN RIVER, WYOMING, THROUGH THE GRAND CANYON. (AT
THE LEFT) A GENERALIZED CROSS-SECTION OF THE GRAND CANYON.
AT THE BOTTOM IS THE DARK, ANCIENT SCHIST, AND ABOVE, THE
DEEP STRATA OF SEDIMENTARY ROCKS.

completed. On May 11, 1869, the day after the eastern and
western spurs were joined in a ceremony a few hundred
miles farther west, the boats were unloaded from the cars at
the place where the new railroad crossed the Green River in
southern Wyoming. Powell, Sumner, and the other eight men who
would start down the river were camped under the recently
built railroad bridge.

Powell had estimated that they would be gone for ten
months. The boats therefore were loaded with a large quantity
of food, ammunition, and tools, and, for their scientific work, a
number of barometers, two sextants, four chronometers, thermometers, and compasses. Part of each supply was stowed in
each boat, so that if one capsized, the loss would not be ir-
reparable.

At noon on May 24 most of the people of Green River,

which then had a population of about one hundred, gathered on the bank to see the expedition off. The men boarded their boats. The flag was raised, the Major waved his hat and, to the cheers of the interested but highly skeptical onlookers, the boats moved down the swift, shallow current of the Green. Soon all four, the Major's *Emma Dean,* the *Maid of the Cañon,* the *Kitty Clyde's Sister,* and the *No-Name,* disappeared around a bend and into the "Great Unknown."

On May 29 Powell and George Bradley, a young man whom the army had released for the expedition, climbed a thousand-foot height to survey the country ahead. Just beyond loomed the Uinta Mountains. Riding easily along the swift-flowing river as they came into the mountains, the Major could think about them and the problems they raised.

"You must not think of a mountain range as a line of peaks standing on a plain, but as a broad plateau of many miles wide, from which mountains have been carved by the waters," he said. "You must conceive too, that this plateau is cut by gulches and cañons in many directions and that beautiful valleys are scattered about at different altitudes. The first series of cañons we are about to explore constitute a river channel through such a range of mountains. The cañon is cut nearly half way through the range. . . ."

From his preliminary reconnaissance Powell knew that the river would turn and twist its way through the mountains, but he did not know what they would find in the "mysterious" Flaming Gorge, the first canyon to which they came. Anxiously, on the thirtieth, they started into it. At first the going was easy, and they soon emerged into a little park. Then the river took a swing to the left and a steeper canyon gaped before them.

"I stand on the deck of my boat and seek a way through the wave-beaten rocks," said Powell. "All untried as we are in such water, the moments are filled with intense anxiety. Soon our boats reach the swift current; a stroke or two, now on this side, now on that, and we thread the narrow passage with exhilarating velocity, mounting the high waves whose foaming crests dash over us, and plunging into the troughs until we reach the quiet water below; and then comes a feeling of great relief."

Soon they came to rapids that seemed too dangerous to run. Here the expedition made the first use of a technique they would employ innumerable times. The boats were "lined down" the rock-strewn, rushing rapids. Lines were attached fore and aft, and from a beach or other foothold on the side of the river the crew let the boat out slowly until it reached the worst part of the rapid. Then they let go. Over the boat would go. The crew below, handling the other rope, would pull it in. Without such a control the boats would never have been recovered.

In retrospect this early "lining" would seem like play. Very near the start Powell had diagnosed the cause of the rapids. Whenever a side stream with steeper gradient entered the Colorado it piled up a dam of boulders in the bed of the river. As the river rushed over them, rolling them on, breaking them with its mighty power yet always being confronted with a new load as each spring's flood tore down the side stream, the furious rapids were born. Another problem that puzzled many laymen was solved.

On June 8 they entered another deep canyon, which they named Lodore, where the waters seemed to rush down endlessly. Here they began to learn fully and grievously about river waves.

"The waters plunge down ten or twenty feet to the foot of a fall; [1] spring up again in a great wave; then down and up, in a series of billows that gradually disappear in the quiet waters below, but these waves are always there, and you can stand up above and count them," Powell recorded. "A boat riding such waves leaps and plunges along with great velocity.

"Now the difficulty in riding over these falls, when the rocks are out of the way, is in the first wave at the foot. This will

---

[1] Powell habitually used the word "fall" to refer to steep rapids.

sometimes gather for a moment, heaping up higher and higher, until it breaks back. If the boat strikes it the instant after it breaks, she cuts through and the mad breaker dashes its spray over the boat and would wash us overboard did we not cling tight. If the boat, in going over the falls, chances to get caught in some side current, and is turned from its course so as to strike the wave 'broadside on' at the same instant, the boat is capsized. Still we must cling to her, for with the water tight compartments acting as buoys, she cannot sink; and so we go, dragged through the waves until still waters are reached. We then right the boat, and climb aboard. We have several such experiences today." [2]

A little farther along the Major saw a dangerous rapid coming abruptly below a bay of smooth water. He pulled into the shore and signaled the other boats to follow. The next did, but a few minutes later he glanced up to see the *No-Name*, with Oramel G. Howland, a former Vermont printer, his brother, and Frank Goodman, plunging ahead.

The *No-Name* went through the first rapid, but ahead lay another in a channel filled with rocks that broke the waves into whirlpools and beat them into foam. Powell, running along the bank, saw the boat strike a rock and rebound with a shock that broke open its compartments. The men lost their oars, and the *No-Name* went broadside into another rock with such force that she was broken in two. Still running, Powell could see the head of one man bobbing around in a whirlpool; another was clinging to a rock; the third was washed ashore on a small island. All three were rescued, though with difficulty. Safe on solid ground once more, they shook hands all around with as much feeling, Powell said, as though they had been on a voyage around the world and had been wrecked on some distant coast.

But with the *No-Name* had gone a substantial part of their rations, and, they discovered with absolute dismay, all their barometers. Someone had failed to distribute them among the

[2] They wore only their underwear in running rapids.

boats. Without barometers, the measurements essential to their scientific work could not be made. That night Powell debated whether he should go overland to Salt Lake City and attempt to get more from New York. They had noticed the afternoon before that part of the wreckage had washed up on a rock. Powell had barred going after it, for it was in a very dangerous place. But the next day they decided that the attempt had to be made. Taking all possible precautions, they reached it, and it proved to be the part of the wreckage that held the barometers. Powell breathed a profound sigh of relief. The men cheered for another reason: in the same compartment was a three-gallon keg of whisky which they had secretly stowed aboard. Powell by that time did not want to object: "I think it will do them good as they are drenched each day."

The canyon walls reached higher, the water grew rougher, and more trouble came to them at Lodore. One evening, when Powell had climbed the banks to make barometric measurements, the cook made their fire too close to some dry willows. In a flash the little island on which they were camping was aflame. The men raced for the boats. In the scramble the cook grabbed up their mess kit, but just as he reached the water he stumbled and dropped the whole outfit into the water. It was gone in an instant. The next day, farther down the river, they recovered a few tin cups, a basin, and the camp kettle. That was all they had left and yet, Powell noted, "we do just as well as ever." The twenty miles of the Canyon of Lodore seemed to have subjected them to all the trials of the river. It was in fact only a foretaste.

The canyons grew deeper, the rapids swifter. Frequently the three boats had to be "lined down" in a chain-like arrangement, and sometimes even this was impossible. Then they had to portage, boats and all, around the rapids.

They were dumped into the water so often that it became almost the normal state of affairs. Their flour and bacon, which of course became soaked, had to be dried out regularly. They would run the flour through a piece of mosquito netting, always losing many lumpy pounds. The bacon had spoiled under the constant wetting, but only occasionally were they lucky enough to catch some fish or shoot a mountain sheep to supplement this lean, tiresome diet.

And there were any number of narrow escapes. Climbing a canyon wall to measure the thickness of some of the strata, the Major suddenly found himself "rimmed"; he could go neither forward nor backward. Holding on with his one arm, he shouted for help. Bradley, who was with him, had no way to reach him. The Major's arm was trembling with the strain. In this crisis Bradley stripped off his long drawers and lowered them over the ledge. Waiting for one steadying second, the Major let go and grabbed them. Bradley pulled him to safety.

Sometimes the wind blew up the canyons with hurricane force, whirling sand and dust with such power that the men had to cover themselves with their blankets. During the day the sun beating down through the narrow slot of the canyons created an almost unbearable heat. At other times the gloom of the canyon depths, the feeling of being buried in the depths of the earth, was hard to bear. Men could lose their ordinary scale of values when they were so completely dwarfed by nature.

On the other hand, there were moments and passages of great beauty. As they came around one sharp turn of the wall the canyon ahead seemed to sparkle with a million brilliant gems. As they came closer they saw that springs breaking from the rock high overhead had created a spray that the sun turned into a scintillating veil. The rocks just below were covered with moses, ferns, and flowering plants. They called this canyon "Vasey's Paradise" in honor of the botanist who had been with them the preceding summer. The walls of the canyon, twenty-five hundred feet high, were of marble, polished to a fine satiny sheen. They were soon to see why. It began to rain. Within a few minutes, water washing down from the adjacent red sandstone country poured over the rim of the canyon; sheets of

bright red mud cascaded down the walls. The marble, it was
evident, had been polished by sand.

On August 13 they were ready to enter the forbidding waters
of the Grand Canyon itself. Only a month's rations remained,
and they were acutely aware that they were beleaguered three
quarters of a mile down in the earth. They were conscious both
of isolation and of burial. Against those inescapable lofty walls
almost closing over their heads, the river itself shrank into insig-
nificance; man felt very small. There was another ominuous
sign. In the past, whenever the river had cut through a dark,
hard, shiny schist that lay below the enormous layers of sedimentary rocks, the river was "bad," filled with treacherous rapids and
huge rocks. Here the river once more ran through the schist.

The schist soon towered a thousand feet above them and the
walls of the canyon rose more than a mile straight overhead.
And the foaming, rushing waters filled the gorge completely.
There was not even a foothold on the straight walls which they
could use for "lining down" the boats; there was no way to
portage over the ferocious, boiling rapids. Here was the ultimate
choice: they had either to run the rapids or to abandon the river.
They pushed off. In a few moments they were swamped, and
they churned and tossed about entirely out of control. But somehow they came through.

Ahead, there were only more of the fearful rapids. By lining
and portaging they pulled through again, though in a state of
near-exhaustion. The only place to stop for the night was a narrow ledge forty feet above the water but not a decibel removed
from its ceaseless, oppressive, deafening roar. Wrapped in their
ponchos—for a heavy rain had begun to fall—they miserably sat
out the night.

Occasionally, even in the Grand Canyon, the river would re-
lent. For a few hours they would sweep along smoothly and
swiftly. On these occasions Powell could study the record of the
earth stacked above him with the clarity of a primer. He no
longer dared to stop for detailed scientific measurements, for

they were in a race with hunger—their rations were now reduced to unleavened bread made from moldering flour, a few dried apples, and coffee. But an almost incredible show was spread before Powell's eyes. "The secrets of nature were openly proclaimed," he said.

Powell could see that after the "basement" rocks were formed there had been volcanic eruptions and intrusions; the dikes, or lava-filled fissures, ran through the rocks in many places. In these upheavals the early rocks had been metamorphosed into the hard, crystalline schist that was making Powell's passage a torture. But above the hated black schist came huge layers of sedimentary rocks. The seas had moved in. Powell estimated that ten thousand feet of shale, sandstone, and limestone had been deposited, though during the subsequent dry period much of it had been eroded away.

The dry period had not left much of a record. It might have lasted for millions of years, but only a thin band of rocks testified to its existence.

Then the sea had come back, once more flooding over the land. Powell saw evidence that during the untold ages in which it had once more held sway, another ten thousand feet of sediments had been deposited. The dry era that had followed had again eaten into the layered rocks, though a majestic thickness of them remained. As he floated along, Powell calculated that there had been "three great periods of oceanic sedimentation, three great periods of atmospheric erosion, and three great periods of eruptive activity."

The last eruptive period had spread great protective sheets of basalt over the softer, more yielding sedimentary rocks. This period had continued into recent times, sometimes pouring cascades of lava down into the canyon. One of the last of these was about to spell further trouble for the expedition.

On August 25, Powell, riding ahead as always in the *Emma Dean*, came upon "monuments of lava" standing in the river. Most of them were low rocks, but some were shafts more than a hundred feet high. In another three or four miles they increased in number, and then he suddenly signaled for a stop; a cataract lay ahead. Here was the kind of sharp, big fall which Powell had predicted would not be found in the river. It only proved, however, how accurate his reasoning had been. Here was a fall created, not by the normal action of the river, but by a lava invasion so recent that the river had not had time to wear it away. Enough lava had poured down the walls to fill the bottom of the chasm to a depth of from twelve hundred to fifteen hundred feet over a distance of from three to four miles.

The Colorado had been dammed, and had backed up into a long lake. But not for long as geologic time goes. With its grit and its power the river had at once started to cut a new channel. By the time the expedition arrived, most of the lava had been cleared away, though basalt with a fine columnar structure still lined the sides of the canyon. And at the point where the lava had cascaded down and where it was therefore thickest, a great fall had formed. They portaged around it. As they went farther down the river they could see how the lava had run out into side canyons.

"What a conflict of water and fire there must have been," said Powell. "Just imagine a river of molten rock, running down into a river of melted snow."

Below the lava they sped along, once making a remarkable thirty-five miles in one day. To add to their better fortune they found some squash growing in a little Indian garden up a side gorge. They made away with ten or twelve, excusing themselves, Powell said, because of their great need. The stolen squash was made into a sauce. "Never was fruit so sweet," Powell gratefully recorded.

"A few days like this and we shall be out of prison," Powell added in the euphoria of the moment.

But the river turned south, a dread sign. That meant, as they knew from bitter experience, that it would cut once more through the hard black schist. Here the walls of the gorge towered higher and blacker than ever before. Lateral streams had piled enormous rocks all across the channel. The water foamed and roared and rushed with a hideousness surpassing anything they had previously seen. Powell climbed the schist pinnacles to see if a portage could be found. There was none. And the rapids were much too long for "lining down" the boats. Once again they either had to run the awful course or abandon the expedition. And to venture into those surging, fiercely boiling rapids looked like certain destruction. It was the blackest and most despairing moment of all.

The elder Howland asked to speak to the Major, and the two walked up a little creek a short distance above their camp. Howland protested against going on. If that were the decision, he said, he, his brother, and Bill Dunn would quit the expedition; they would attempt to make their way up the walls and across the desert to the nearest settlement.

Powell spent the night pacing a few yards of sand beach. Should they go on? Should he further risk the lives of all of them? More of the schist lay ahead; the gorge was deeper, their food was nearly gone, and he did not know what they would meet, though he believed that they were approaching the end of the Grand Canyon and their voyage.

"To leave the expedition unfinished, to say that there is a part of the cañon which I cannot explore, is more than I am willing to acknowledge," he decided. "I am determined to go on."

At daylight the Howlands and Dunn still felt that the only course was to abandon the river. Gravely the others voted to stay with Powell. It was a grim decision for both groups. Life and death might well hang upon it. They believed that it did.

After a solemn breakfast the three who were leaving were given two rifles and a shotgun and asked to take a fair share of the rations. The latter they refused. The cook, nevertheless, left a pan of bread on a rock for them. Powell wrote a letter to his wife and gave it to the elder Howland. Sumner handed him his watch, with the request that he send it to his sister if he should not be heard of again. One set of the duplicate records they had kept was entrusted to Howland. Once more Howland begged Powell and the others not to enter the canyon they were facing: it would be mad, they would never get through, for the river was heading south and into more of the schist. All the factors were reviewed again, but both sides stood firm.

The *Emma Dean* was left behind, and Powell went aboard the *Maid of the Cañon*. While the three dissenters watched from an overhanging rock, the *Maid* shot out into the river, grazed one great rock, and plunged into a rapid.

"The open compartment is filled when we strike the first wave below," said Powell, "but we cut through it, and then the men pull with all their power toward the left wall and swing clear of the dangerous rocks below. We are scarcely a minute in running it, and find that although it looked bad from above we have passed many places that were worse."

The other boat followed without greater difficulty. At the first possible point below they all landed and fired their guns, hoping to indicate to the others that they had come through safely. They waited several hours on the chance that the Howlands and Dunn might hear, take the smaller boat, and follow them. Then there was nothing to do except to go on.

In another bad section they were almost lost, but once again they survived. About noon on August 29, with a sense of deep unbelief, they abruptly emerged from the Grand Canyon of the Colorado. All at once they were in a valley where the sky was wide and open. Almost as if they were seeing them for the first time, they marveled at the green of the grass and at the birds flying about in the trees. The ordinary was no longer ordinary. The next day they suddenly saw three men seining in the river. "They seem far less surprised to see us than we do to see them," Powell recorded. "They evidently know who we are."

The loss of the expedition and the death of its members had been reported several times and the news had been carried by newspapers in all parts of the United States. However, some of the reports had been denied. On the chance that the party might have survived, or that some remains of the expedition might come floating down the river, Brigham Young, the head of the Mormon Church, had sent a man to watch the river. He was one of the group they met. In a few minutes the half-starved men were feasting on bread and cheese. Soon afterward a Mormon bishop arrived, bringing melons and other luxuries they had almost despaired of ever tasting again.

At this point, with his mission accomplished, Powell left the river; the Colorado was no longer an unknown.

A few days later, as Powell began the trip back to Illinois, sad word came about the fate of the Howlands and Dunn. A telegram came through: "Powell's three men killed by three She-bits. Indian report that they were found in an exhausted state, fed by the She-bits, put on trail leading to Washington, after which they saw a squaw gathering seed and shot her. Whereupon the She-bits followed up and killed all three. . . ."

Powell immediately pronounced the story that the men had attacked the squaw a libel. "It is not in the men's faithful and genial nature to do such a thing," he declared without hesitation. Later Powell traced down the true story. The three men from the expedition had been mistaken for three marauders who had killed the squaw. Their account of coming down the river was not believed, and they were shot down with arrows while they lay asleep.

Despite this tragic development, Powell was a national hero. His courage and daring in conquering the rampageous river stirred Congress and the people, as did his story of a high plateau that had been carved into mountains and gorges by the endless work of rains and rivers. During the next five years Federal support made it possible for Powell to make three additional expeditions to the west. In 1871 he made a second trip down the Colorado, this time with food and supplies stored at points along the way. Powell's one long report, *Exploration of the*

Colorado River of the West and Its Tributaries, was a composite
account of both trips.

In 1874 and 1875, with the title "Director of the Second Division of the United States Geological Survey of the Territories,"
he explored the plateau country and the Uinta Mountains. His
earlier broad understanding of the area's formation and of the
earth's evolution was filled in and confirmed. It was all, Powell
saw, a matter of the earth's changing surface.

The whole vast plateau area had been uplifted, although
slowly and gradually. "The upheaval was not marked by a great
convulsion," said Powell, "for the lifting of the rocks [in the
Uintas] was so slow that the rains removed the sandstones almost
as fast as they came up." Again, he emphasized, "the mountains
were not thrust up as peaks, but a great block was slowly uplifted and from this the mountains were carved."

Despite the work of Hutton, Playfair, and Lyell, there were
many who still regarded the "deformation" of the earth's crust
as one of violence. They could conceive of mountains and their
wild, tumbled formations only as the product of upheaval and a
vast crunching process. W. M. Davis, who wrote Powell's biographical memoir for the National Academy of Science, explained: "He had great influence in convincing his contemporaries that uplift as well as erosion and deposition is a slow
process. . . . The doctrine of geological peace on earth gained a
vast backward extension into periods of the past that had long
been conceived as ages of violence."

Powell thus helped to alleviate some of the horror the world
had felt when it was forced to realize that the earth had gone
through huge eruptions, sea invasions, and ice ages. Imperceptible change was not so much to be feared, though it might be
more difficult to imagine.

From his trips down the Colorado and other rivers, Powell
also understood, as few others could, the carving power of rivers.
Others before him had seen that water wears down mountains
and that rivers cut their valleys. But in some cases, he said, the

rivers were running before the mountains were uplifted. This, he thought, was true of the Colorado. For such rivers Powell invented the accurate descriptive term "antecedent rivers."

And the carving by rivers went on at varying rates. When the mountains were young and steep and torrents tore down their slopes, the process was fast. Powell would never forget the size of the boulders the side streams had rolled down into the Colorado. On the other hand, when the process was nearing its end and the land lay in a smooth plain, the process would be slow. No one before him had made this point quite so specifically and vividly as Powell.

"The degradation of the last few inches of a broad area of land above the level of the sea would require a longer time than all the thousands of feet which might have been above it," he wrote. ". . . But here the disintegration by solution and the transportation of the material by the agent of fluidity come in to assist the slow processes of mechanical degradation. . . . Ultimately the whole land surface is reduced to a lowland but little above sea level."

Powell was saying that changes were rapid in youth and slow in the old age of the land. But they were certain. "Mountains cannot long remain mountains," he declared at a geological meeting, "they are ephemeral topographic forms. Geologically all existing mountains are recent; the ancient mountains are gone."

Davis, who was listening to the speech, always remembered how the Major had emphasized his point with a vigorous wave of his empty sleeve: "If the Adirondack Mountains had been uplifted in Cambrian times [as was then generally believed] they would have been worn down *over and over again!*"

In 1879 Powell's survey and the two other Federal geological surveys were united into the United States Geological Survey. Clarence King, whose survey had provided the first systematic account of the western geological formations, was made the first director. Upon his resignation two years later the post was pressed upon Powell. Powell proved as vital a bureau head as he had been an army major or an expedition leader. He also had that *sine qua non*, the ability to work effectively with Congress.

In 1880 the survey had an annual appropriation of $100,000. Ten years later, under Powell, it was receiving $719,000. The staff, a happy, distinguished one that was immensely loyal to the Major, had grown accordingly. Powell would walk through the halls humming cheerfully as he dropped around to talk to staff members. Memos were not for him. Nor were grudges. He met Colonel C. E. Hooker, a Confederate officer who had lost a left arm in the fighting at Shiloh, and they quickly became friends. Thereafter when either purchased a new pair of gloves, he sent the unneeded one to his wartime enemy and peacetime friend.

When Powell first began to work in the west, almost the entire area from the edge of the plains to the mountains was designated on maps as "Great American Desert." That infuriated Powell. By the time he had become head of the Geological Survey, however, a change was occurring. The Homestead Act of 1862 had opened up the area, and a few years of above-average rainfall prompted promoters to spread the word that the climate was changing. They argued that cultivation of the soil and the building of railroad and telegraph lines were producing the climatic alteration. "Rain follows the plow" was the alluring, deceptive slogan. Many credulous people were buying land and moving in. Powell could see disaster in the making.

As director of the Survey, he urged Congress to create a commission to study the physical, climatic, and economic resources of the dry areas of the west. When the request was granted he and his staff of experts put two years into the most thorough study of a region that had yet been made. Their *Report on the Arid Regions of the United States* was issued in

1879. Nearly three quarters of a century later Bernard De Voto called it "one of the most remarkable books ever written by an American," and "a book which opened a new era in Western and national thinking."

Powell, with the certainty of his facts and conviction, told the country, and particularly the land-proud and the land-crazed, that non-irrigated lands in the vast area stretching from the one-hundredth meridian [3] to the mountains would have to be used according to the availability of water. Land receiving an average of less than twenty inches of rainfall should be withdrawn from agricultural use, he said. Land where the rains averaged between twenty and twenty-eight inches should be regarded as in danger of drought and cultivated with special precautions. Powell thus was warning that a large part of the land in an area comprising almost forty per cent of the United States was unsuitable for traditional farming.

Powell went further. He proposed that pasturage homesteads in the semi-arid regions should have 2,560 acres, and farms in irrigated tracts, 80 acres. This was regarded as an outrageous rejection of the 160-acre homestead on which "America had been built."

Powell also said that irrigation was a large undertaking that would require government assistance and supervision. The right to use water, he declared, "should inhere in the land to be irrigated."

The report could not have been more farsighted or more explosive. Promoters, cattlemen, railroad lobbyists, local flag-wavers, and settlers either descended upon Washington or raised such a roar at home that it could be heard unmistakably in the capital. Where principle and matters of such grave importance to the country were at stake, Powell would not yield. Congress retaliated by cutting the survey's appropriation from

[3] The one-hundredth meridian runs about through the center of Texas, Kansas, Nebraska, and the Dakotas.

$719,000 to $631,000. In 1892 they slashed it to $430,000. This was the old technique of destroying a bureau to get rid of its head.

Powell could not resist; on May 4, 1894, he submitted his resignation. His arm was again troubling him badly, and in his letter to the President he said: "I am impelled to this course by reason of wounds that require surgical attention."

After undergoing another operation on his arm, the Major moved into a quiet haven as director of the Bureau of American Ethnology, a division of the Survey. Powell had early become interested in Indians and had learned some of their languages. He constantly had moved unmolested through Indian territory that was considered dangerous. As head of the bureau, he published *A Study of Indian Linguistic Families* and other works. Once more he gave distinguished service to the government.

In 1902, while the Powells were spending the summer in Maine, the Major suffered an attack that he himself easily diagnosed as angina. He had no doubt about its gravity.

On June 17, however, Powell was immensely cheered by news from Washington: President Theodore Roosevelt had just signed a bill establishing the Federal Reclamation Bureau, a step for which Powell had fought for twenty-five years. Some of the other measures that he knew to be essential to the conservation of the west and the welfare of the nation also were gaining over selfish opposition. A few years later Roosevelt would withdraw 1,200,000 acres for conservation, thus acting upon another cherished principle of Powell's.

But Powell had gone before that. He died on September 17, 1902.

Men knew more about how the mountains, the plateaus, and the canyons of the west had come to be because the Major had daringly traveled down a tumultuous river and explored an unknown country. How greatly the world was indebted to Powell became clearer as time went on. Half a century after his death two major biographies of him were published: *Powell of the*

Canadian Shield country. Ancient rocks worn low by the passage of millions of years are streaked with "glint" lakes.

A great "fault" slashes the country near Great Slave Lake in northwest Canada. Here at some unknown time in the past the earth was cracked by an earthquake.

PLATE IX

The Grand Canyon. Half a billion years or more of earth history are laid bare. Panorama from Point Sublime as it was drawn by William Henry Holmes on one of the expeditions of Captain Clarence Dutton.

PLATE X

graph made by J. K. Hillers in 1871 two members of the second Powell expedition look down into the Grand Canyon.

Three little rowboats drawn up on the edge of what was a great unknown only two years before, the canyons of the Green and Colorado rivers. The boats are similar to those used in the first exploration of the canyons in 1869. Photograph by Hillers at the expedition's starting point on the Green River.

PLATE XI

Sir William Logan, Canadian geologist who discovered the great age of the rocks of the Canadian Shield.

Thomas Chrowder Chamberlin. A new theory of the earth grew out of his studies of the ice ages and of climatic changes.

Major John Wesley Powell. The leader of the first expedition to explore the Colorado River by boat talks to a Paiute Indian during a visit to the Kaibab Plateau in 1873.

PLATE XII

Ribbons of ice. Gleaming, sinuous glaciers flow down from the mountains of Canada's Baffin Island to unite in a greater glacier that thrusts far down the valley.

PLATE XIII

Remains of a glacier in a now green land. This "esker" in Sheboygan County, Wisconsin, is a gravel deposit formed in the bed of a glacial stream that ran through an ice-walled channel.

Island mountains in a dry land. Mountains, often steep and bare, resemble islands in this desert sea of sand.

PLATE XIV

World in the making? From such "knots" as this great one in the nebula near the star Eta Carinae, the earth and the other planets may have formed. Photograph taken at the Boyden Station of Harvard College Observatory, Bloemfontein, South Africa.

PLATE XV

The Devil's Tower in Wyoming

PLATE XVI

Colorado, by William Culp Darrah, and *Beyond the Hundredth Meridian,* by Wallace Stegner.

"Seventy-five years ago," said Bernard De Voto in his introduction to Stegner's book, "he pierced through the misconceptions to the realities. . . . He was a great man and a prophet. Long ago he accomplished great things and now we are beginning to understand him."

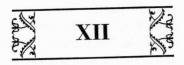

XII

DUTTON
MOUNTAINS UP

STANDING UPON A SOUTHERN SALIENT of Utah's Markagunt Plateau, Lieutenant Clarence Edward Dutton looked out upon a "magnificent spectacle." The altitude was nearly eleven thousand feet above the sea and he could see southward over the plateau and Grand Canyon country of the west for nearly a hundred miles. In the extreme distance was the calm desert platform, its surface mottled with indistinct lights and shades. Against the southeastern horizon projected the pale-blue escarpment of the Kaibab Plateau, which stretched away to the south until the curvature of the earth carried it out of sight. To the southwest rose the dark mass of Mount Trumbull and the volcanic cones of the Uinkaret.

The Lieutenant missed no measure of the unusual beauty of that vast panorama, but as he studied the amazing plateau country, perplexing questions arose in his mind.

As a geologist working with Major Powell and the United States Geological Survey, he knew well that the plateau on which he stood had not always had its lofty elevation. On the contrary, it had several times been at sea level and below, for most of that enormous mass of stone had been formed at the bottom of a shallow sea. That was unmistakable. The sedimentary rock and the fossils it contained, even the ripple marks with which it was often scored, proved the point beyond debate.

In the course of time that once flat, even sea bottom, that smooth pavement of the sea, had been upraised. It had cracked in the process into a few big segments, but most of the segments had been lifted so evenly that the horizontal beds of stone scarcely had been disturbed. It was almost as though a stack of books had been raised without disturbing the order of the stack. And if erosion had not worn away several miles from the top of the rising land, the plateau country would have been two or even three times higher than it was.

What had caused that immense elevation? What had raised a hundred thousand square miles of the earth's surface two miles and more above the sea? Could the erosion of the top of the plateau, the removal of its upper layers, have been a factor in the uplift? With his eyes fixed on the mountains, Dutton was, in essence, asking: What had produced them? How had they come to be?

By the late 1870's and the 1880's, when Dutton was carrying on his studies of the west, much had been learned about mountains. The old misconceptions had of course long since been discarded, and among these were the picturesque fables that mountains were blisters puffed up by winds trying to escape from their underground prisons, or the backwash of the Flood, or the upthrusts of some past cataclysm.

A hundred years of geology—if the modern geology of mountains could be dated from the time of Guettard and his discovery of the true nature of the mountains of Auvergne—had shown what mountains were, and the source of their vast substance. But *how* deep troughs of sediments had been uplifted into mountains standing thousands of feet above the sea still was almost as much of an unknown as it had been in the days of the Greeks. Hall had attributed the elevation of mountains to a general continental rise, but he had not explained the process.

Clarence Dutton did not set out to work on this baffling and great problem. A sense of wonder led him into it.

He was born at Wallingford, Connecticut, on May 15, 1841. After attending school at Ellington, he went to Yale, a handsome, poised, many-sided young man. Dutton was not only an athlete of note, but an omnivorous reader and the winner of the Yale

Literary Prize. The expectation was that he would enter the ministry. He was graduated in 1860, just in time to be swept into the Civil War. Enlisting with the Twenty-first Connecticut Volunteers, he was soon made a lieutenant.

He was in the thick of the fighting at Fredericksburg, Suffolk, and Petersburg, and came out of the war with the rank of captain. By that time he had decided to remain in the army. He took a competitive examination in which his flair for mathematics showed up well, and he received a permanent commission as a lieutenant in the Ordnance Corps. His first assignment was to the Watervliet Arsenal at West Troy, New York. In the letdown that followed the war, the post did not offer much to occupy a vigorous young officer.

Lieutenant Dutton took to studying the Bessemer Steel Works. His first scientific paper dealt with the chemistry of the steel-making process and with the hotly debated differences between steel and iron. But at Troy the scientifically inclined young officer was soon caught up in the excitement that Hall had stirred up in near-by Albany. Hall's contention that mountains were laid down in subsiding offshore trenches was being discussed continuously. Dutton began some geological studies of his own. In 1871, when he was transferred to Washington, his interest in geology was on the rise, and he soon met Powell, then the director of the second division of the Geological Survey. In 1875 Powell asked Dutton to lead a field party to the west. The Lieutenant did his work so well that the next year Powell lobbied a special act through Congress to release Dutton from the army for special duty with the Powell survey. He remained with that survey and with the unified United States Geological Survey, which succeeded it, for the next sixteen years.

Dutton was soon Powell's right-hand man, and Powell sent him into the country that he himself loved best, the canyon and plateau territory of the Colorado. Dutton had an innate feeling for grandeur and he came under the spell of the country too. Two facts immediately struck him: the tremendous elevation the region had undergone, and the tremendous erosion to which it had been subjected. Both were inescapable facts, it seemed to him.

Upon the dark, crystalline schist that had always foretold a rock-filled stretch of canyon for the Powell expedition, there occasionally rested some strata laid down in the succeeding Paleozoic age. In other places, however, there was no sign of early Paleozic rocks, and the great stack of later Carboniferous rocks which formed the upper walls of the canyons rested directly and "unconformably" on the ancient schist.

"Probably there is no instance to be found in the world where an unconformity is revealed upon such a magnificent scale as that displayed at the head of the Grand Cañon," said Dutton. "It is all the more suggestive because it is a region large enough for an empire."

Millions of years had passed between the time the schist was formed and the time the rocks of the upper canyon walls were deposited on top of it. During that great interval, the old rock had been deeply ravaged by an erosion that left no record except a negative one, the absence of the Paleozoic rocks that might otherwise have capped the schist. Only when the region was again submerged was the piling up of the rock again resumed. And so it came about in the canyon that chapter four or five succeeded chapter one; the later chapters followed "unconformably."

And the cycle had been repeated: uplift, erosion, deposition subsidence, uplift, until the final desiccation "began the great erosion which has never ceased to operate down to the present time."

In the "final desiccation" Dutton could see how thousands of feet of surface had been stripped away. In the process, streams and weathering deepened and widened the canyons, and cut the rock faces into bizarre fantasies. As he marveled at the towers, the domes, the ledged cliffs and piles in their vermilions, reds, greens, chocolates, blacks, and whites, Dutton

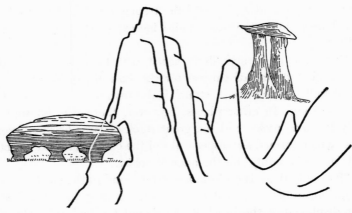

ROCK FANTASIES. THE WORK OF EROSION IN THE HIGH PLATEAU AREA OF THE WEST.

thought of the carved temples and pagodas of the Orient. He gave many of them names suggestive of the mystical East— Vishnu's Temple, Shiva's Temple, Hindoo Amphitheater. Many of the names familiar to visitors to the Grand Canyon were Dutton's imaginative and appropriate inventions.

But the Lieutenant was always aware of the geological forces that had produced the natural drama. Time and again he came back to the fact that the sculpturing could not have occurred had the region not been upraised to such great heights. A low plain would not have been similarly carved. What underlying forces had acted to make the plateau country and the mountains of the west the spectacle they were?

In 1871, soon after he had returned from his first summer in the west, Dutton spoke before the American Philosophical Society at Philadelphia on "the unexplained problem of elevations and subsidences." He did not even prepare a paper—his words were only reported indirectly by the secretary.

It seemed clear, the Lieutenant told the Society, that deep down in the earth, sedimentary and igneous rocks were metamorphosed by the action of pressure, heat, and water into dense, hard, crystalline schists, marbles, and granites. He suggested that such changes might well alter the specific gravity and volume of the metamorphosed rocks.[1] If the volume increased there might be an expansion upward; if it decreased, a subsidence. Assume, he said, that there was a five-per-cent increase in the specific gravity of a thousand-foot bed of rock. That would account for a change of level of fifty feet. In a series of rocks as thick as the Pennsylvania Carboniferous an equal amount of change, Dutton calculated, would produce an alteration of level equal to the average elevation of the American continent above the ocean—about twenty-five hundred feet.

Dutton argued that the same principle might affect the overflow of volcanoes. If a mass several miles below the surface became softer and lighter, and a vent or fissure could be found, it "would inevitably follow the laws of equilibrium of fluids and would not only rise but overflow."

Furthermore, Dutton pointed out, in the case of such a softening and lightening, the heavier overlying rocks would sink into the semi-fluid mass and exert an additional upward pressure. It was significant that all lavas which had been studied were of low specific gravity. "Lt. Dutton said that otherwise the overflow of an Etna would be impossible," reported the secretary.

Some of Dutton's suppositions were not to stand, but he was thinking his way through one of the most complex of problems. During the next fifteen years in the west he discussed it frequently with Powell and others.

In the meantime he completed his two monumental studies *The Tertiary History of the Grand Cañon District* and *The Geology of the High Plateaus of Utah.* With meticulous care for detail Dutton traced the history of both regions and described them with great fullness and clarity. And he did it with undisguised feeling and appreciation. "I have in many

[1] The specific gravity of a substance equals the mass of any volume of the substance divided by the mass of an equal volume of water.

places departed from the severe ascetic style which has become conventional in scientific monographs," he said in his preface to the Grand Canyon book. He believed that the area's "sublimity" had been underrated.

If so, Dutton tried not to make the same error. His glowing words, clothing a scrupulously accurate geological analysis, went far toward portraying the ultimately unportrayable majesty of the Grand Canyon and its country. Dutton also worked closely with William Henry Holmes, whose beautifully lucid and accurate drawings helped to make the canyon book a classic.

But the part of Dutton's mind that asked "how" was never stilled. Several times he wrote down his speculations and the conclusions to which he was more and more returning. However, he probably threw them away; in any event, he did not publish them. He seemingly had scarcely thought of making a formal presentation of what he knew was in large part a radical idea. It was almost by accident that he finally made public the theory that was to make geological history.

The Philosophical Society of Washington had scheduled one of its regular meetings for April 27, 1889. A half-hour was vacant on the program, and it was suggested that Dutton use it. He was listed to speak on "Some of the Greater Problems of Physical Geology." He had three in mind: What is the cause of volcanic action? What is the cause of the elevation and subsidence of restricted areas of the earth's crust? What is the cause of the folding, distortions, and fractures of the strata? All three were, in one sense, facets of the same problem.

The long-standing theory that the mountains had been elevated by the wrinkling of the crust of a cooling earth was still a popular one. It was hard to down, for the assumption on which it was based—that the earth had originated hot and had since been cooling—had not yet been rejected. But for several other impressive reasons Dutton disagreed.

He saw two major objections to assuming that the crust of the earth had shriveled like the skin of a drying apple. In the first place, he argued, there would not have been enough contraction to account for the great mountain ranges of the earth—Dutton did not believe that the earth had cooled very much. In the second place, he pointed out, a contracting crust would wrinkle in any and all directions, rather than in the long narrow folds characteristic of all the major mountain ranges.

In proposing another view, Dutton started with the basic shape of the earth. Scientists were then virtually certain that it was an oblate spheroid, a globe slightly flattened at the ends.

In the fourth century B.C., Aristotle had correctly deduced that the earth was round and not flat. As evidence, there were the round shadow that the earth cast on the moon during an eclipse and the different position of the stars on the horizon if a traveler moved from north to south or south to north. The circumnavigators of the globe later substantiated this deduction. But even they could never give the layman the vivid sense of the essential roundness of his planet which was to come much later when rockets would soar high enough to photograph the earth in its full convexity.

Newton in the *Principia* was the first to demonstrate that the "round" earth was not a perfect sphere. Assuming that the earth was originally a molten mass, he conjectured that its rotation and the gravitation of its particles toward its center would cause the earth to assume the shape of an oblate spheroid. But Newton was never able to prove his point. In 1743, Clairaut, by his equations on the equilibrium of fluids, established the earth's spheroid shape so decisively that he "practically closed the subject," except for later small refinements on which scientists still are working.[2]

Physicists had pointed out that the forces which molded the earth were so irresistible that the earth would have taken on its spheroid shape even if it had been made of solid steel. Since this was undeniably true, why, Dutton asked, did the forces

[2] Sir Harold Spencer Jones in *The Earth as a Planet*. Chicago: University of Chicago Press; 1954.

stop short of making the earth a perfectly smooth body? Why did the continents and islands protrude? Why were there basins occupied by the oceans?

If the earth had been entirely made up of homogeneous matter, Dutton reasoned, it would have been a perfect, smooth spheroid—probably one covered by a universal ocean. But if it were made up of heterogeneous materials, if some parts were denser or lighter than others, there would be, he emphasized, a tendency to bulge where the lighter matter had accumulated and a tendency to sag where the denser matter existed.

"For this condition of equilibrium of a figure, to which gravitation tends to reduce a planetary body . . . I propose the name of isostasy," said Dutton.

The word fell strangely on the ears of the members of the Philosophical Society. It was a new one which Dutton was coining from the Greek to mean "equal standing" or "equal pressure." From that moment on it was to become an important part of scientific language, for it would at last explain a part of the process that accounted for the elevation of the mountains of the earth and that helped to maintain those raised platforms of land—the continents—on which man could live.

Some years before, the English geologist Herschel and the English mathematician Babbage had suggested an equilibrium in the earth, but Dutton was the first to develop the theory specifically and to name it.

The earth, Dutton told the Philosophical Society, provides many examples of exactly the kind of bulges and sags that his theory predicated. "Where great bodies of strata are deposited they progressively settle down or sink, seemingly of their gross mechanical weight, just as a railway embankment across a bog sinks into it," explained the Lieutenant.

They all knew well that in the Appalachians between fifteen thousand and thirty thousand feet of sediments had been deposited in a shallow sea whose depths probably never exceeded a few hundred feet. In the west it was the same. In the plateau country, covering nearly a hundred thousand square miles, from eight thousand to ten thousand feet of sediments had been laid down in the Mesozoic and Cenozoic (middle and recent) ages alone, and there also was abundant proof that the waters had been extremely shallow. Dutton described the "beautiful fossil wood" that he had found in many of the rocks, the beds of coal and oil shale which were proof in themselves that the waters in some periods had been little more than bogs. The ripple marks and cross-bedding on the onetime sands, and the numerous remains of marine mollusks that could have lived only in shallow waters gave added testimony.

"Here the evidence seems conclusive that the whole subsidence went on at about the same rate as the surface was built up by deposition," said Dutton. "In short it may be laid down as a general rule that where great bodies of sediment have been deposited over extensive areas the deposition has been accompanied by a subsidence of the whole mass."

That constituted Dutton's first class of facts. It was essentially Hall's point. But Dutton had a second, equally significant. "Whenever broad mountain platforms occur or have been subjected to a great erosion the loss of altitude by degradation is made good by a rise of the platform," he declared.

In the west that he knew so thoroughly, many mountain ranges were situated on broad, lofty platforms from twenty to sixty miles wide and from fifty to two hundred miles in length. Some of the platforms contained several ranges of mountains.

"All of them have been enormously eroded," Dutton continued, "and if the matter removed from them could be replaced it would suffice to build them to heights of from eight to ten miles; yet it is incredible that these mountains were ever much loftier than now and they may never have been so lofty.

"The flanks of these platforms with the upturned edges of strata reposing against them, or with gigantic faults measuring their immense uplifts, plainly declare to us that they have been pushed upward as fast as they were degraded . . . by erosion."

"It seems little doubtful," said Dutton, "that these subsidences and these progressive upward movements of degraded mountain platforms are in the main the results of gravity restoring the isostasy which has been disturbed by denudation on the one hand and by sedimentation on the other."

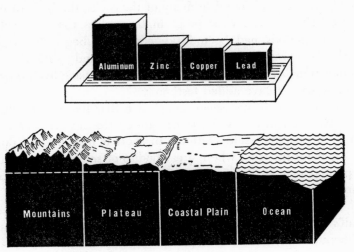

MOUNTAINS AND SEAS IN COUNTERBALANCE. AS MOUNTAINS ARE STRIPPED OF THEIR SUBSTANCE BY EROSION AND ARE LIGHTENED, THEIR AREA TENDS TO RISE; AS THEIR SUBSTANCE IS LOADED ONTO THE SHELVES OF THE SEA, THE SHELVES TEND TO SINK—A STATE OF ADJUSTMENT WHICH DUTTON CALLED ISOSTASY. BLOCKS OF METAL FLOATING IN A PAN OF MERCURY DEMONSTRATE THE PRINCIPLE.

Here was a striking and enlightening explanation of why some mountainous areas rose and continued to loom high even though they lost enough of their mass to be reduced to plains. As Dutton stated it, it was a new and illuminating idea.

What made it more impressive was that it was open to experimental substantiation. There was evidence in addition to that offered by what Dutton called the "experiments of Nature"— the face of the earth itself. Dutton himself had little or no opportunity to test his theory by other experimental means. Nevertheless, some of the supporting evidence was available to him, and he cited it in his speech to the Society.

Gravity tests in many parts of the world had shown that the continents were composed of lighter rocks and the ocean basins of denser ones. This had been noted early in some gravity determinations in the Himalayas. It was later found to be true in all other mountain ranges.

In other gravity experiments along both the Pacific and the Atlantic coasts it was found that a plumb line was invariably deflected toward the ocean and the sediments. This was in complete accord with Dutton's theory. The sediments along the shores constituted an excess of mass that made itself felt on the plummet. Later studies at gravity stations confirmed this finding.

Important scientific consequences flowed from the ideas that Dutton was developing. If he was right, the erosion of the land and the deposition of sediments along the shores constituted a continuous disturbance of isostasy, for the land was being impoverished and unloaded and the littoral was being loaded down. But the forces of gravity would tend to elevate the eroded land and to depress the littoral "to their respective isostatic levels." It would be an even, imperceptible process.

But, Dutton warned, an adjustment would depend upon the intensity of the loading and unloading, and upon the rigidity of the earth. Dutton saw clearly what other scientists later emphasized: any re-balancing would come only when the actual load was heavy enough or the crust weak enough to slump under it. If the crust was so strong that it did not sag regardless of the load of sediments, there would be no compensatory rise in the land.

There seemed to be little question that in many cases the load was great enough to make the crust "give." In some places the sediments reached a depth of twenty miles. Their weight was vast indeed. If they did weigh the crust down, Dutton pointed out, the problem would become "essentially that of a flowing solid." The depressed layers of the earth would move in the direction of least resistance, just as if a hand had pressed down on a bed of mud. If the load had been taken from coastal mountains and deposited on the littoral, the push would be inward, toward the lightened land; that would be the direction of least resistance.

"That gives us a force of the precise kind that is wanted to explain the origin of systematic plications [foldings] in mountains," said Dutton.

Dutton was picturing a viscous or plastic undercrust, one that could yield and move. This did violence to the popular idea or a rock-ribbed earth. In an attempt to make the layman see how rocks might flow in response to pressure, he cited the Greenland ice cap. The mass of the ice, he pointed out, was no greater than the mass of the sediments, and the specific gravity of ice was about one third that of the rock masses. Nevertheless, the ice moved; layers slipped over each other in a way that Dutton argued was not greatly different from the kind of movement which occurred in the earth in response to pressure.

Would the theory of isostasy stand up in application to the actual facts of the earth's surface? Dutton noted that folding and breaking of strata almost everywhere occurred only in sedimentary rocks of great thickness. Such contortions seldom were seen in thin strata—strata incapable of exerting enough weight to upset the earth's surface balance.

Dutton's theory required the shoving up of mountains along shore lines. That was exactly where many major mountains were found. Furthermore, the mountains were ranged in long, narrow belts, which was exactly the way they would have occurred in response to the sideward pressures described in Dutton's theory. The Lieutenant repeated that this would not have been the pattern if the crust had been generally contracting. He also argued that if mountains had been thrust up by the contraction of the crust, the action would have been one continuing through all time, instead of being concentrated, as he was convinced it was, in periods when erosion and sedimentation had unbalanced the earth's crust.

But these were infinitely complex problems, as Dutton well understood. The theory of isostasy rested on the assumption that there were weak places, or at least yielding ones, in the crust. It also dealt only with adjustments that followed the disturbance of the gravity balance in particular areas. Isostasy offered no explanation of the big permanent changes in level, such as the North American continent's gain in elevation. On the contrary, isostasy, by ironing out imbalances, would tend to preserve prevailing continental levels.

"We must look to some other cause which can gradually and permanently change the profiles of land and sea bottom," Dutton warned. "I hold this cause to be an independent one. I also hold the two processes to be distinct and to have no necessary relation. . . . Whatever the cause of great regional uplifts, it in no manner affects the law of isostasy. The real nature of that uplifting force is a mystery."

Dutton was a theorist wise enough to understand the limitations of the highly important new law that he was formulating. It came into play only when there was a disturbance of crustal balance, and thus it did not solve the whole problem of the elevation of continents and mountains. Nevertheless, where there was such crustal disturbance, where the land was lightened by erosion, it tended to rise. Where it was weighted down by the accumulation of sediments, it tended to sink. Furthermore, pressures from the sinking sediments acted against adjoining lightened lands to push them upward, and so coastal mountains achieved their heights. As the law of isostasy has it—and it is now widely accepted as law—mountains are raised in unstable areas by the earth's maintaining of its crustal balance. They are the products of an earthly balancing act.[3]

The Captain—Dutton had been promoted—was a modest man. He put his theory into writing and readied it for publication only after many of those who heard his talk insisted upon

---

[3] Many years later additional studies of mountains were to suggest how the deep troughs of sediments, the sinking, pressure-exerting troughs, were in their turn to be shoved upward and made into mountains. For an account of these studies, which involve the theory of isostasy, see Chapter XVI.

this action. And then he tacked on a little note explaining all the circumstances: "This paper was written hastily to occupy a vacant half hour of a meeting of the Philosophical Society and without thought of publication. . . . It contains a rough outline of some thoughts which have worked in my mind for the last fifteen years and which from time to time I have discussed at length in unpublished manuscripts and in familiar conversation with my esteemed colleagues."

Dutton had supplied a key that others were quick to use. The number of stations making gravity studies multiplied, and there were many new studies of the process of loading and un-loading and balancing which Dutton had named isostasy. A whole literature grew up on the subject.

"Dutton's view, derived only from very scanty geodetic data, stamps him with the mark of greatness," said William Bowie, chief of the Division of Geodesy of the United States Coast and Geodetic Survey. "The general accumulation of geodetic and geophysical data later and the investigations based on them substantiate to a remarkable degree what Dutton set forth in the Washington Philosophical Society paper, which has made him one of the outstanding men among the students of the earth."

During his service with the Survey, Dutton also made studies of volcanoes in Hawaii and of the Charleston earthquake. He had an important part, too, in the famous study of the semi-arid regions of the west which so aroused the ire of special interests. In 1890, even before Powell's resignation as head of the Survey, Dutton returned to the army.

He was made a major and placed in charge of the San Antonio Arsenal, where he remained until his retirement in 1901. During the last years of his life Dutton lived at Englewood, New Jersey, and there he died on January 4, 1912.

Mountain ranges accumulated by the sinking of offshore shallows! Mountain ranges raised to great heights and kept high as the earth adjusted to its losses and gains! A part of the old mystery of how mountains arose to dominate the earth had been cleared away by Hall and Dutton, but only a part. Their surprising and unsuspected discoveries affected only certain types of the world's mountains. The grand plan had not been explained, the "why" still eluded men. But difficult and important foothills had been scaled.

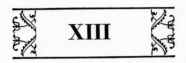

XIII

CHAMBERLIN
ICE, SUN, AND BEGINNINGS

THE KETTLE HOLES had always been there, they said in south-eastern Wisconsin. Sometimes the odd depressions that were found in that part of the country were as shallow as saucers and sometimes they were as deep as sixty feet. As far as the people in the neighborhood were concerned, that was all there was to it.

This local acceptance of kettle holes as unquestionable features of the earth brought a smile from the young geologist who had just been assigned to the area by the new Wisconsin Geological Survey. Almost at first sight Thomas Chrowder Chamberlin was sure there was a logical explanation.

It was not long before he was quite certain that the kettles, as well as the area's rounded and scratched knolls and hummocks, were the work of glaciers that had crept down from the north.

But in 1873 the fledgling geologist had no idea that the additional questions he would ask about the Wisconsin kettle country would lead him into a study of past climates, and from that into a daring challenge of all that the scientific world then believed about the origin of the earth. He could not know that his questions would result in a new hypothesis of how the earth and its solar system came to be—a hypothesis that would have a profound effect on the world's thought.

Chamberlin was born, as it later amused him to say, on the "Shelbyville moraine," a ridge of glacial debris that ran down into Illinois, crossing the Chamberlin farm at Mattoon. The date was September 25, 1843.

When Thomas was only three, his father loaded his family into a "prairie schooner" and moved to Wisconsin, where he took up a farm near Beloit. Their first home there was a log cabin, but it was soon replaced by a larger house. As Tom and his four brothers helped to quarry the limestone that was used in its construction, they came upon many "stone snails and snakes," and made a nice little collection of the fossils.

Tom's interest in fossils, and in the country and its life, was deep by the time he reached Beloit College, but he enrolled in the course in geology primarily to convince himself that the geologists were wrong in maintaining that the world had not been created in 4004 B.C. as his religious training had taught him. Instead it was the geologists who convinced Thomas Chamberlin. When he went to ask about his grade in geology, the professor greeted him with a smiling question: "Well, Chamberlin, would you like to know who stood next?"

Chamberlin had always thought that he would teach. In fact, at the age of eight he had told his brothers "I'm going to school until I can teach the best school in the state." His father, overhearing this defiant statement and the barrage of yells that it drew, told him: "Stick to it, son." While he was still in college, Chamberlin took an examination for a teacher's certificate. One question was: "If the third of six is three, what would the fourth of twenty be?" Chamberlin settled that one quickly: "The fourth of twenty is five under any and all circumstances and is not affected by any erroneous supposition that may be made in respect to a third of six." He never liked "crazy assumptions."

Either because of this answer or in spite of it, Chamberlin obtained his certificate and was appointed principal of the Delavan, Wisconsin, high school. It was at once evident that he would be an unusual teacher. Chamberlin not only arranged special lectures to give his students some idea of geology, astronomy, and the natural sciences, but on a fine spring day dismissed the school with: "Let's go out and see if we can find things in nature worth knowing and thinking about."

After two years Chamberlin was invited to accept the "set-tee" of natural science at Wisconsin State Normal School at Whitewater. He remained there until 1873, when he was appointed both professor of geology at Beloit College and an assistant geologist for the state survey, then just being organized. Chamberlin's assignment to the southeast part of the state was thought to be a relatively unfavorable one; that part of the state was not rich in metals.

As he studied this glacier-marked land, Chamberlin traced and mapped the kettle moraines. They were, he saw, "almost a miniature representation of the terminal moraines of the Alpine glaciers." But glacial materials and glacial signs spread down into Illinois, Iowa, and Kansas, well beyond the "kettle" moraines. The moraines, then, did not mark the limits of glaciation in the United States; they must have been formed after the retreat of the ice had begun. In fact, the ice must have advanced and retreated more than once!

Chamberlin could make out the story. When the ice retreated, the broken and ground stone that it carried with it was deposited at the foot of its melting mass. Great sheets of the rubbly material were spread across the country. But as the glaciers advanced again, this loose stuff was plowed up into immense ridges. When the new tongues of ice pushed into the old moraines, they filled them with great chunks of ice which slowly melted when the glacier once again pulled back. The melting of the imbedded ice chunks left holes in the old moraines; these were the kettle holes.

Chamberlin obviously took pleasure in deducing and mapping these movements of the ice. But some larger questions also were intriguing him; he was putting together a greater story that was partly factual and partly hypothetical. "If care is taken to distinguish between these positions," he told the state Geological Society, "no harm can arise from their association."

And then with the further preface, "I lay myself open to

the charge of undue temerity," he told the Society that the moraines "constitute a definite historical datum line in the midst of the glacial epoch. They are a historical rampart outlining the great dynamic agency of the period at an important stage of its activity." Chamberlin was telling his probably surprised colleagues that the kettle holes and ridges of southeast Wisconsin might identify and date one of the important periods in the history of the world. It was indeed a long and imaginative jump, but it was a very sound one.

Major Powell, who had just become head of the United States Geological Survey, was so impressed by this study that he appointed Chamberlin the director of the Survey's glacial division. His instructions were to study terminal moraines. With this freedom, Chamberlin traced the revealing ridges and festoons of the moraines from Montana to the Atlantic coast. The great glacial movements that had scooped out the Great Lakes and smoothed the surface of a large part of the northern United States were mapped through meticulous study of the indisputable markings they had left.

Chamberlin incidentally solved another troublesome geological problem. A dispute had raged about the nature of loess, the gritty loose dust that is spread so widely across the country, and piled into deep unstratified deposits. Baron von Richthofen, a German geologist, had reaffirmed the claim that it was of "water origin."

Chamberlin had been seeing a lot of loess as he pursued his glacial studies, and he suspected that it had a more complex history. Characteristically, he thoroughly investigated the possibility that it had been spread by floods and streams alone, before presenting his own very different evidence. Chamberlin found that loess started as the fine grindings of the glaciers. The powdered rock was washed out by the glacial streams and spread over their flood plains. When it dried, he had often seen it swept up in big dust whirlwinds and carried away. With the documentation that Chamberlin supplied then and later, the problem virtually was settled. Loess ceased to be a mystery; it stood revealed as a wind-borne, glacial product.

The studies that Chamberlin was contributing to the Survey's annual reports were attracting attention. In Wisconsin his record as an exceptionally able professor at Beloit also was remembered. When the University of Wisconsin began a search for a new president in 1886 they soon decided that they wanted Chamberlin. He was reluctant to leave his glacial work, but when they allowed him a year in which to complete his studies, he accepted the appointment. He went to Madison in the fall of 1887.

Chamberlin was six feet, one and a half inches tall, with the heavy, rugged frame of an athlete and outdoorsman. The suggestion of power was combined with dignity of both appearance and manner. With his ability to work closely and co-operatively with others and to see clearly both objectives and means, he was remarkably well equipped to be a university president—or a scientist.

At the time of Chamberlin's arrival, Wisconsin was at a dividing-point. It had been a college. Would it become a university in fact as well as in name? Chamberlin did not hesitate. But the first step this scientist-turned-president took was to strengthen the humanities. He then went on to develop specialized schools in engineering, agriculture, and the sciences, and instituted a program of graduate studies. He also reorganized the curriculum to provide general education in the first two years and some specialization on "major" subjects during the last two. New buildings were constructed, and the faculty was enlarged and strengthened. These two steps in particular required large additional appropriations from the legislature. Chamberlin won them with little difficulty.

At the end of his first five years Chamberlin had given the university the form it would hold and develop for the next half-century or more. But the president had never ceased to miss science. Furthermore, his insistence on giving the same thorough consideration to the problem of any one student that he gave to a question raised by a trustee burdened him unduly.

The University of Chicago was about to open its doors, and its president, William Rainey Harper, was assembling a distinguished faculty. Learning that Chamberlin was anxious to get back to science, he offered him a post as head of the department of geology. Chamberlin accepted. The Wisconsin faculty, students, and legislature combined to try to persuade him to remain, but Chamberlin knew what he wanted to do. He went to Chicago in the fall of 1892. Within three months he had founded the *Journal of Geology,* and at the new university's second convocation he expounded the philosophy of science which was to influence not only his own department and the university, but science as a whole.

"Conjectures, assertions, opinions, current impressions, preconceived notions, accepted doctrines, all alike are pushed aside to give free scope to untrammeled induction from carefully sifted evidence," he said. "The supreme endeavor is to present a disposition of fairness and openness to all evidence and all inductions. . . . When demonstrative realities are brought forth they are unbiased to the exclusion of all else. They displace all preconceptions, all deductions from general postulates, all favorite theories."

Chamberlin quickly resumed his studies of glaciers, and in the summer of 1894 he joined the Peary Auxiliary Expedition to Greenland. In the first part of their mission, their ship, the *Falcon,* crashed through the ice floes to land new supplies for Peary —he was remaining in the north to make a second attempt to cross the north Greenland ice cap. This done, they left for a three-week exploration of the coast of Ellesmere Land, giving Chamberlin a coveted chance to study glaciers in their own habitat.

South of seventy-seven or seventy-eight degrees of latitude, Chamberlin noted, the glaciers came down to the sea in a tapering tongue. North of that latitude they terminated in abrupt walls, from fifty to one hundred and fifty feet high. Chamberlin could not be sure why this strange change occurred. He thought that it probably was an effect of the angle of the sun's rays, directed against the ice from all points during the continuous daylight of summer. But Chamberlin was grateful for the steep vertical faces of the glaciers; they showed him in clear cross-section the distinct stratification of the ice. At the top lay a zone of pure white ice. The middle section was laminated: layer after layer was marked out by rocky debris ranging in size from great boulders down to fine silt. Another area of pure ice stretched along the bottom. Some of the layers even jutted out sharply over others.

It seemed to Chamberlin that the various layers moved differentially. If this were true, he reasoned, there should be grooves and flutings where one layer scraped over another. He climbed up and around the glaciers to find out, and there the grooves and flutings were. He also found intrusions of earthy matter along the planes of slippage. Chamberlin could conclude not only that the layers moved at different rates, but that internal shearing played an important part in the movements of glaciers. The cruise of the *Falcon* had been richly productive in the direct observation of glaciers.

But it was another observation, an almost incredible one, that impinged with the most insistent force on the scientific and yet imaginative mind of Chamberlin. He had been to some extent prepared for it, and yet to see it with his own eyes was a stirring experience. Beneath these moving tongues of ice—almost under the edge of the Greenland ice cap—figs and magnolias once had grown. Chamberlin saw some of the fossilized remains that provided unmistakable evidence. This land of ice had at an earlier epoch been a balmy land, warm, moist, and sub-tropical. Where snow dazzled the eyes, there had been the lush green of the sub-tropics and their brilliant flowers and fruits. It was almost more of a transition than the mind could accept, and yet the remains were there to prove the fantastic change.

From the first days in Wisconsin when he had seen how the glaciers advanced and retreated, Chamberlin had pondered about the changes in climate which must have brought on this alternate thawing and freezing. In Greenland he realized with new acuteness how important and determinative these oscillations of climate must have been. What had produced them? Why had the world gone through great cycles, not only of warmth and cold, but of wetness and dryness? When he returned to Chicago these were the problems which occupied the thoughtful geologist.

Almost immediately Chamberlin ran into an impasse. These great cycles, these alternations of climate whose effects had been recorded so unmistakably on the face of the earth, did not accord with the prevailing theory of the earth's life.

At the time it was almost universally believed that the earth was steadily cooling off from an original fiery state. For almost a hundred years, since the great French astronomer-mathematician Laplace had modestly suggested in a brief note in his *Exposition du système du monde* that the earth had originated in a vast cloud of blazing gas thrown off by the sun—his nebular hypothesis—this had been the assumption underlying all thought about the earth.

If this was the beginning, the gaseous cloud must then have liquefied into a molten sphere, a sphere wrapped in a hot vaporous atmosphere. As it cooled and a crust formed, the atmosphere turned into a universal ocean, it was held. And as the cooling continued, the contracting crust was believed to have wrinkled into higher plateaus and ridges that became the mountains, and into low places that formed the sea basins. Since that time, the argument went on, the cooling had continued and inevitably would continue. So, it was thought, the earth had come to be and so would it end.

"The loss of heat lay at the bottom of the grand events of the earth's history," said Chamberlin, "and in forming forecasts the loss of heat was made the chief cause of the earth's prospective doom as a habitable planet."

According to the nebular hypothesis, the earth's history was a "stupendous declension." We were moving from a fiery beginning to a frigid end, and from a universal ocean to final desiccation. The presence of glaciers in modern times, and of such wide deserts as the Sahara, were taken as signs that the vital heat and moisture were running low. Glacier and desert foreshadowed the ultimate doom, the last winter.

Once the premise of a hot gaseous beginning was granted— and if there was no other source of the earth's heat—this was a wholly logical deduction. But Chamberlin had gathered a mass of evidence indicating that there had not been a steady decline in temperature, an uninterrupted cooling off. On the contrary, his glacial studies showed repeated fluctuations from cool to warm, and warm to cool. Three major invasions of the ice had defined three cycles in relatively recent times, and proof had been found of glaciation at much earlier periods when the earth, according to the nebular hypothesis, should have been very hot. And then there were the figs and magnolias in Greenland and the striation of former glaciers which Agassiz had found in the jungles of the Amazon. These periods had come at the wrong time; they were out of order if the earth was progressively cooling.

Chamberlin also had compiled data on large salt deposits in New York and India. They could have been formed only in deserts. And yet during the era when they were laid down, the earth, according to the nebular hypothesis, was swathed in a super-saturated atmosphere. It seemed to Chamberlin that the geological evidence cast the gravest doubt on the nebular hypothesis, if it did not contradict it and render it an impossibility. Quietly he began to re-examine the physical and astronomical evidence on which the Laplacian hypothesis was based.

Not long afterward—in 1897—Lord Kelvin, the dominant figure in world physics, arose to address a gathering of scientists at the Victoria Institute in London. His subject was "The Age of the Earth as an Abode Fitted for Life," and his purpose undoubtedly was to rebuke the geologists. From the time of Lyell and Darwin, the geologists had been claiming more and more time for the evolution of the earth and of life. Some of them were even talking about hundreds of millions of years. Lord Kelvin did not conceal the fact that he thought it high time to bring some exactitude into the question.

Assuming that the earth was initially a molten globe with a uniform temperature of 4,500 degrees Centigrade, and calculating the amount of heat that would be lost at the earth's established rate of heat loss, he declared: "We have now good reason for judging that [the consolidation of the earth] occurred not less than twenty nor more than forty million years ago, and probably nearer to twenty than to forty." Kelvin's figures, in an age before the discovery of radioactivity and its heating of the earth, were as unassailable as his authority. But he had squeezed geologists and evolutionists into an impossible position. They could not account for the formation of rocks and the evolution of life in the narrow time span to which Kelvin was confining them.

While the scientific world squirmed in this strait jacket, an unexpected challenge came from America. A David arose in Chicago. Boldly and directly Chamberlin attacked the assumptions on which Kelvin had based his case. "Lord Kelvin's address," said Chamberlin, hitting hard, "is permeated with an air of retrospective triumph and a tone of prophetic assurance."

Kelvin had studded his speech with references to the "certain truth"; he had glibly talked about "half an hour after solidification," and about the "crust of primeval granite." He gave the impression, Chamberlin charged, that the history of the earth is "already passing into a precise science through the good offices of physical deduction."

"Is this really true?" asked the Chicago geologist. "It rests on assumptions which Lord Kelvin regards as 'very sure.' I beg leave to challenge the assumption of a white-hot liquid earth."

As a geologist, Chamberlin argued first that the postulate of the hot liquid earth does not rest on any conclusive geological evidence. The rocks of the earth do not have the uniformity that would be expected if they had formed out of one thoroughly mixed, molten mass. On the contrary, Chamberlin pointed out, the rocks of the "basement complex"—the rocks showing in the continental cores and at the bottom of the Grand Canyon—have a diversity of chemical, mineralogical, and structural character which makes it most unlikely that they came from a uniform brew. He pointed out, too, that the great batholiths or domes that now appear at the surface of the continental shields give every sign of having been intruded into a basement complex that was already solid when they entered it. "It would be a bold petrologist who would insist that it has been demonstrated that the basement complex is simply the molten envelope of the primitive earth solidified in situ," declared Chamberlin.

But Chamberlin's main challenge was made on the basis of "physical laws and physical antecedents." He had been joined at the University of Chicago by Forest R. Moulton, a brilliant astronomer who had the mathematical training that Chamberlin lacked. Together they worked out the physical data that enabled Chamberlin to attack Kelvin's assumptions in Kelvin's own bastion of physics.

The British physicist had rested his hypothesis of a primitive molten earth primarily on deductions drawn from the high internal temperature of the earth and from the nebular hypothesis. Kelvin had said: ". . . We may follow in imagination the whole process of shrinking from gaseous nebula to liquid lava and metals, and the solidification of liquid from the central regions outward."

Chamberlin hit this with a devastating question: "As an abstract proposition in physics, would Lord Kelvin feel free to assert that the water now on the surface of the earth would be retained . . . if the earth were heated so that its rock substance was volatilized?"

Kelvin assumed that the earth had only its original heat to lose. Again Chamberlin questioned, and with a foresight that now seems uncanny: "Is our present knowledge of the earth . . . sufficiently exhaustive to warrant the assertion that no unrecognized sources of heat reside there? What the internal constitution of the atom may be is yet an open question. It is not improbable that they are complex organizations and the seats of enormous energies. Certainly no careful chemist would affirm either that the atoms are really elementary or that there may not be locked up in them energies of the first order of magnitude. No cautious chemist would probably venture to assert that the component atomecules, to use a convenient phrase, may not have energies of rotation, evolution, and position, and be otherwise comparable in kind and proportion to those of a planetary system.[1] Nor would he probably feel prepared to affirm or deny that extraordinary conditions which reside in the center of the sun may not set free a portion of this energy."

Chamberlin and Moulton went on to examine the nebular hypothesis proper. Laplace had envisioned an enormous sun, some five and a half billion miles in diameter, that was beginning to cool. As it contracted, its speed of rotation increased, and great rings of gas were hurled off, just as a muddy wheel that is picking up speed will throw off chunks of the mud. The first ring lost became Neptune. At a diameter of a billion miles, and still greater speed, Jupiter was thrown off, and so it continued, Laplace assumed, until the earth and all the other planets had been cast away, and the sun had reached its present diameter —864,000 miles—and a velocity of two hundred and seventy miles per second. But when Chamberlin estimated the sun's present velocity, he found it to be only one and a third miles per second, and thus only a fraction of what it should have been

---

[1] For Chamberlin's term "atomecules," substitute today's word "electrons."

according to the nebular hypothesis. This was an enormous discrepancy.

Moulton then applied a reverse test. He imagined that all the planets were restored to the sun. That would have put it back to a five-and-a-half-billion-mile diameter and to its inflated state prior to the detachment of Neptune. But calculations indicated that the sun would not then have had the momentum to hurl off Neptune or any other rings of matter. There would have been no planetary births.

Chamberlin and Moulton could only conclude that the nebular hypothesis was untenable, as were the Kelvin estimates based upon it.

But Chamberlin was not one to stop with "destructive criticism." If the nebular hypothesis was "untenable," how was the origin of the earth to be explained? He and Moulton had already been working toward a new hypothesis, but they were proceeding cautiously and carefully.

Chamberlin believed in what he called the "method of multiple working hypotheses." It was designed to offset a scientist's all too human predilections. When Chamberlin approached a problem, he first brought up every "rational explanation" for the phenomena in hand—in this case, all the other likely explanations of how the earth might have come to be. This, he liked to say with the quiet humor that was a part of him, "divides the affections" and tends to prevent any one theory's becoming a "controlling idea." "The investigator," he explained, "thus becomes the parent of a family of hypotheses and by his parental relations to all is morally forbidden to fasten his affections unduly on any one."

It was in this way that he and Moulton approached the problem of the earth's origins. Perhaps, as had been proposed, the earth had been formed by the clashing together of two nebulæ. Every mathematical test was applied. They found that "the laws of dynamics cut a deadly swath" through this and all other proposals of a gaseous nature.

Perhaps the earth had been produced by the coming together of a meteoric swarm. Analysis indicated that a planet put
together in this way would not have had the required momentum to carry it through space.

Perhaps some of the solid "knots" that photographs revealed
in the spiral nebulæ could have served as collecting centers. But
would an earth formed in this way have rotated in the direction
followed by the earth and the other planets? This was a problem that posed great difficulties.

Or perhaps, as Buffon had suggested, the planets were the
debris of a collision of the sun and a comet. But examination
showed that the chaotic wreckage that would have resulted
from such a mighty crash would have been in no suitable state
for gathering into a planetary system like our own. A glancing
encounter of comet and sun was equally beset with obstacles.

Even though there were difficult problems, the nebular knots
seemed to offer the most promising prospect for further study.
Then, on May 28, 1900, came a full eclipse of the sun. Chamberlin and Moulton pored over the dramatic photographs that were
made. As the sun's bright disk was blacked out by the deep
shadow of the earth, great explosive clouds of gaseous matter
could be seen flaring out, shooting up, and rolling away from the
sun's surface. The photographs, which the two scientists later
used in their book, illustrated once more, startlingly, the eruptive
nature of the sun. This fact entered critically into the hypothesis—the famous planetesimal hypothesis—that the two scientists
were ready to propose in 1904.

Suppose, they suggested, that the approach of a star had
stirred the explosive, burning sun into a previously unequaled
violence of activity and outburst. In such a terrible eruption, vast
masses of matter and gas might well have been hurled far out
into space. The scientists calculated that if only 1/745 of the sun's
mass were torn out in such fierce, cataclysmic blasts, it would
bulk great enough to form our entire planetary system.

By exceedingly thorough study they demonstrated that the

large knots of matter from the explosion—planetesimals—would slowly "gather in" innumerable smaller bits of matter and dust. And thus, they suggested, the earth and the other planets had come into being.

Chamberlin, unlike many of his predecessors, did not consider dropping the inquiry at this point. He was a student of the earth, not of the heavens alone. His firm aim was to apply what he termed the "ultimate criterion" to his hypothesis. Could its postulates explain, all through the earth's young and adult stages, those conditions that had made possible "the long sequence of life and its wonderful ascent"? Could the hypothesis account for the earth as it now was, and for its major features? What Chamberlin sought was a complete picture. This was the universal problem that he faced in his book *The Origin of the Earth*, published in 1916.

The Chamberlin-Moulton studies indicated that the "juvenile shaping" of the earth began as soon as the knots of ejected matter—the planetesimals—began to plunge into one of the large knots, the "earth knot," and the mass started to draw together in a dense body.

"It does not seem imperative," said Chamberlin, "to assume that the central temperatures were extremely high. . . . It is our view that the earth remained solid, except as specific conditions enforcing liquefaction arose."

As this heterogeneous mixture of solid materials, air, and water pulled itself together—the "lord of the shaping agencies" was gravity—a whole vast complex of readjustments, recombinations, and recrystallizations was brought into action, according to Chamberlin's carefully reasoned hypothesis. In the interior the compression created a melting heat, and the pressures at the same time made for an increase in rigidity. Radioactivity created more heat. Chamberlin described radioactive materials as "minute self-heating centers" that also were heating up "billions of adjacent molecules."

"The earth-body was permeated by stress differences," said

Chamberlin, "and this tended to force to the surface all mobile materials whose specific gravities were insufficient to resist them. This was a mechanism well suited to preserve the solidity of the earth against the increasing heat and the growing liquefaction by forcing the heat product and a vital portion of the heat itself to the surface."

Chamberlin did not pretend to know how the lavas found their way out—their use of fissures was only a part of the answer —but as a generalization, he suggested that "molten rock is, and probably always has been persistently squeezed out of the earth by the stresses and strains that permeate it."

Heat played a critical part in this Chamberlin reconstruction of the earth's early development. One of the first effects of the heating up of the interior was to force out the free air and water that had been entrapped as the earth came together. Chamberlin was convinced that the volatile gases and the more soluble and fusible elements, plus the radioactive materials, must have made up the first lavas that came to the surface. Thus the atmosphere and oceans would have grown, and the radioactive materials would have gathered in the crust, where modern research has shown them to be.

"If this is in the line of truth," Chamberlin could only say in his time, "the interior heat should never have risen to the great heights often assigned to it . . . for heat was progressively consumed and carried away. This theory is incompatible with a completely molten earth."

Chamberlin summed up the "mutations" that he believed occurred in the inner earth as "a single prolonged process by which the more fluent, solvent, and lighter material of the earth was concentrated toward the surface, while the more immobile, refractory, and heavier matter was concentrated toward the center."

And this process, Chamberlin concluded, would have provided at the surface the carbon, hydrogen, oxygen, nitrogen, sulfur, phosphorus, and other elements necessary for the development of life. This, he added, should have occurred early in the earth's "juvenile history." And thus was the stage set for life.

Such a formation, Chamberlin also found, would provide acceptable explanations for the major features of the modern earth: its continents, mountains, and ocean basins. "An earth built up slowly by accession of solid particles would have retained nearly its maximum resources of combination, adjustment, and compression," he argued. "Such an earth would be capable of great compacting and consequent deformation."

An earth so built would have sufficient strength and rigidity to withstand an accumulation of stresses over a long period, but in the end would yield and adjust to them. Chamberlin in this way was maintaining that the continental shelves could bear an enormous weight of sediments before a re-balancing would occur—that is, before there would be a compensating uplift of mountains on the erosion-lightened continents.

The geologist relied on unusually technical language to make his point, but if a few lay terms are inserted, it becomes apparent that he was very close to an explanation that some students of the earth would advance nearly half a century later: "The picture of the continents as essentially terraces wrought upon diastrophic embossments [terraces added to core areas] is no doubt the truest that can be found, and the contest between the diastrophic forces that emboss by protrusion [emboss by raising mountains] and the gradational forces that terrace by planation and shelf-building [that erode and carry the sediments down to the borders of the sea] is the chief physical battle of geologic history."

Few would dispute the profound conclusion to which this led: the movements that have shaped the earth arose from the very nature of the earth's growth.

Nearly a lifetime of work went into the working out and testing of this hypothesis. Few others have carried their thinking about the earth so far forward and so far backward, or have attempted so coherent an interpretation of the earth's history.

Chamberlin worked at this overwhelming task, with only a few interruptions, from the time of his return from the cruise of the *Falcon* to his death.

One of the few interruptions came in 1909. John D. Rockefeller, who had made large contributions to the building of the University of Chicago, asked several members of its faculty, including Chamberlin, to make a study of what could be done to aid the people of China. For five months the group traveled through China, studying resources and needs.

Chamberlin was then sixty-five, but he went on a thirty-nine-day trip up the Yangtze on a native houseboat, and immediately afterward traveled four hundred miles across Szechuan in a sedan chair. It was a strenuous, taxing schedule. Before the trip had ended, Chamberlin was suffering from stomach ulcers, and the cataracts that had begun to obscure his vision grew worse. Nevertheless, he completed the mission and took great pleasure in writing a report that urged a concentration on efforts to improve the health of China. The outcome was the establishment of the Peking Union Medical College.

In 1918, at the age of seventy-five, Chamberlin retired from the university. By applying his own hypothesis principles, he had worked out a regimen that had overcome most of the difficulties arising from his ulcer. His eyesight worsened, however, and he could read only with the aid of a large magnifying glass. Despite this handicap, retirement only gave him the opportunity he wanted to press on with his work. One fifth of all his published papers were brought out in the last ten years of his life.

New findings on the solar system made it desirable for Chamberlin to revise and expand his *Origin of the Earth,* the major book in which he had set forth the planetesimal hypothesis. As he began the revision he found that two volumes rather than one would be necessary for all that he wanted to present. The first he called *Two Solar Families* and the second was to have the title *The Growth of the Earth. Two Solar Families* came from the press on Chamberlin's eighty-fifth birthday, September 25, 1928, and copies were rushed to his home for a quiet celebration that afternoon. He told friends that he would take a month's rest before beginning work on the second book. Before the month had passed, however, he was taken ill. He died quietly at the university hospital on November 15, 1928.

Eight years after Chamberlin's death, H. N. Russell disclosed a serious, perhaps insurmountable, difficulty in the planetesimal hypothesis. For matter to be drawn out of the sun, he demonstrated, the approaching star that Chamberlin postulated would have had to pass extremely close to the sun, if not to touch it. At the speed at which stars and the sun move, however, the probability of such a collision was called "unbelievably small," if not absolutely impossible. So far there has been no answer to this objection.

In 1941 Lyman Spitzer, Jr., in a study of the behavior of high-temperature gases, suggested that any gases which might have exploded from the sun would have been dissipated before planetesimals could form. Again, no one has yet shown that this is not true. The solar planetesimal hypothesis therefore has suffered two apparently fatal blows.

Bailey Willis, in writing an obituary of Chamberlin for the *Bulletin of the Geological Society of America,* expressed the contemporary estimate of Chamberlin: "Aristotle, 322 B.C.; Copernicus, 1543 A.D.; Galileo, 1642; Newton, 1727; Laplace, 1827; Darwin, 1882; Chamberlin, 1928."

Although this company of the immortals may not be permitted to Chamberlin, he had opened new vistas in the study of the earth. He arrived at understandings from which others could strike out in the tireless search for knowledge. The rejection of Chamberlin's thesis that the planetesimal material came from the sun seems to be firm, and perhaps final. But his carefully supported argument that the earth was assembled cool by the gathering in of solid materials, and his picture of how the earth developed, are being strikingly substantiated by modern geophysics and geochemistry. The newest work is showing that

Chamberlin was as generally right about the development of the young earth as he was about the atom. How remarkably foresighted that was has become evident only since World War II.

Chamberlin also proved to the scientific and lay worlds that the origin of the earth would have to be understood before there could be a final or even a satisfactory explanation of the earth as it is. After Chamberlin, the search had to turn once more to the origin of the earth.

Part Four

INTO INVISIBLE FORCES

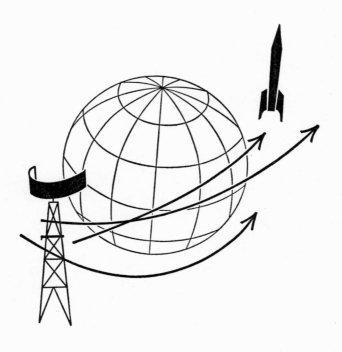

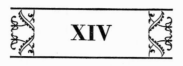

XIV

UREY

THE ORIGIN OF THE EARTH

How had the earth come to be?

Harold Clayton Urey, who had won a Nobel prize for his discovery of heavy hydrogen, unexpectedly found himself asking this ancient, this recurring question. As a chemist working on many other matters, he at first had no intention of delving into this profound and scientifically defiant problem.

In 1949, however, he was asked to give a summer course in "The Chemistry of Nature." Urey is the Martin A. Ryerson Distinguished-Service Professor of Chemistry at the University of Chicago. Half casually he turned to Louis B. Slichter's paper on the heat balance of the earth with the thought of making a few routine notes.[1] At once his casualness vanished. Here again and in persuasive form was the suggestion that the temperature of the earth might be rising rather than falling. This supported Chamberlin's argument that the earth was not on its way from a state of fiery incandescence to a cold old age. Could the reverse be true? Could the earth have started out as a cold accumulation of gas and matter? Could it now be warming up?

Urey at once understood that you would get a very different separation of the elements if the earth was formed cool rather than as a super-hot blazing mass. One assortment of elements, rocks, and metals would be formed if the temperatures were low; and quite a different set if they were high. Here, then, was an opening. By studying the chemistry of the materials of the pres-

[1] L. B. Slichter: *Cooling of the Earth.* Geological Society of America: Bulletin 52 (1941).

ent earth, he might be able to trace back to what the earth had been at the time they were formed. By starting with the answers in the back of the book, he could perhaps work out the problem. Urey was enthralled by the idea.

Two years later, in the Silliman Memorial Lectures at Yale University and in the preface to the book in which they were published, he explained: "One fascinating subject after another came to my attention and for two years I have thought about questions relating to the origin of the earth for an appreciable portion of my waking hours." [2]

Since the problem he had chanced upon was also one of the most complex and confounding of all of those that men consider, Urey was to be equally occupied with it for a much longer period. At a laboratory New Year's party in 1956 a young scientist offered a toast: "Here's to solving the origin of the solar system." Urey smilingly shook his head. "We won't; anyhow that would spoil all the fun."

Oddly enough, chemistry had been little used in the study of the earth's origins. In the beginning the tantalizing question of how the earth came into existence was the domain of the poet and the theologian. The Muses whispered the story of the earth's beginnings to Hesiod; throughout the Middle Ages religion had the final word. Even after Newton in the latter half of the seventeenth century worked out the fundamental law of gravitation and the dynamics of the solar system, it still was primarily the religious leaders who dominated discussions of the origins of the earth. Their concern was to reconcile the new science to the Biblical account of the creation; William Whiston was typical.

For the next two and a half centuries, little progress was made on this ancient question. Geologists were fully occupied in discovering and interpreting the present earth; their eyes were not on the distant beginnings. Not until the very end of the nineteenth century and the beginning of the twentieth were scien-

[2] H. C. Urey: *The Planets—Their Origin and Development.* New Haven: Yale University Press; 1952.

tists forced to turn once more to the problem of the earth's origins. It was then that Chamberlin found that he could not get to the causes of the great periods of glaciation unless he first considered how the earth had been formed.

The question once again became an urgent one. This time, in large part, the astronomers took over. With the help of great new telescopes and mathematics, a distinguished procession worked tirelessly at the vast question: how had the earth come to be? Among them were Sir George Darwin, Forest Moulton, Sir James Jeans, Sir Harold Jeffreys, H. N. Russell, Gerard P. Kuiper, S. Chandrasekhar, Fred Hoyle, George Gamow, and many others. Later the atomic physicists joined in. Werner Heissenberg and C. F. von Weizsächer developed the theory of turbulent gases; they postulated a disk of gas and dust breaking up into turbulent eddies that were to form the planets.

Few thought of the problem of the earth's origins as a chemical one. There was considerable surprise when Urey, a physical chemist, suggested that it was. "Indeed it astonished me that I or anyone of similar training and experience should be able to say anything on the subject," Urey admitted.

What had happened was that physical chemistry had developed both methods and data that could be applied to the study of the earth's origins. Through a long series of experiments the physical chemists had learned what behavior could be expected from the earth's materials at temperatures ranging from the coldest to the hottest obtainable and at a wide range of pressures. The laws that had emerged could be extended to situations and circumstances that could not be tested directly. This is the process the scientist calls extrapolation. It enabled the physical chemists to say with assurance that if certain temperatures and conditions had prevailed at the time of the earth's origin, certain materials would or would not have been formed.

There was nothing unusual in Harold Urey's plunging into an absorbing but unfamiliar study. He does not hesitate to try new roads.

Urey was born in Walkerton, Indiana, in 1893, and grew up on a farm there. With the encouragement of his mother and stepfather, he finished high school and began to teach in Indiana country schools. When he obtained another school post in Montana, he entered the university there.

Up to the time he went to the University of Montana, Urey had thought little about science. In fact, he was scarcely aware of science as a field to which men devoted their lives, or of the tremendous challenge of scientific problems. He thought that he would study Latin and perhaps become a teacher of the classics. His first encounter with two dedicated scientists and two gifted teachers of science, R. H. Jesse, a chemist, and A. W. Bray, a zoologist, quickly altered that plan. Urey made an abrupt shift, for science appealed to his every interest and his deepest feelings. "Before, I never knew the 'world of wonder' as I like to call it," he said. "And since that time I've been fascinated by every science I've studied."

Chemistry won out, however. After a year of work in a commercial laboratory Urey returned to the University of Montana as an instructor in chemistry. Without any further delay he continued in graduate work, taking a Ph.D. at the University of California in 1923 under the direction of a fine teacher, Gilbert N. Lewis.

The following year the young chemist was awarded a fellowship by the American-Scandinavian Foundation for study abroad. He went to Copenhagen to work with the great Niels Bohr, who had just received the Nobel Prize for his theory of the atom. Also studying at Bohr's Institute were several future Nobel laureates. It was a valuable and memorable year.

Urey returned to spend five years, 1924–9, at Johns Hopkins as an associate in chemistry. In 1929 he went to Columbia University, where he remained until 1945, first as an associate professor of chemistry and then as full professor. It was at Columbia that he began his work with the heavy isotopes—the heavier twins—of some of the important elements.

In the course of this research he discovered the heavy isotope of hydrogen, or deuterium, as it was named. For this epoch-making discovery Urey received the Nobel Prize for chemistry in 1934.

Heavy hydrogen has an atomic weight of 2.015. The weight of ordinary hydrogen is 1.008, and that of Hydrogen-3, or tritum, is 3.012.

Thus, two atoms of deuterium weigh 4.030, while one of ordinary hydrogen plus one of tritum weigh 4.020. (Two and two are more than one and three.)

4.030 and 4.020! In those ten points of difference lie the energy that may determine the course, if not the fate, of this world. It is the release of that energy which has made possible the hydrogen bomb. And if the right combination is ever found, the unleashing of that same energy could turn the plain water of the oceans into a fuel which would have thirty times the energy of an equal volume of gasoline. The world would have an almost inexhaustible source of power, one that could last through all foreseeable time.

The Second World War brought another sharp shift in Urey's work. He became one of the three program chiefs of the Manhattan District project, which did the basic research on the atom bomb. Part of Urey's work dealt with heavy hydrogen and the heavy water that is derived from it.

For his war work, President Truman presented him with the Medal of Merit and the following citation: "As director of the laboratories of Columbia University in which the diffusion method of separating uranium was developed for this staggering new instrument of war, his great scientific experience and ability, his initiative and resourcefulness and his unswerving devotion to duty have contributed immeasurably to the attainment of the objective. Dr. Urey's accomplishments reflect great credit upon himself and upon the military service."

At the end of the war, the University of Chicago established its Institute for Nuclear Studies to carry on the fundamental atomic research that had been in part interrupted by the work on the bomb. Some of the country's top scientists joined the staff, including Urey. At Chicago he shares an office suite with Dr. Willard F. Libby, discoverer of a precise method of dating the past by the use of radioactive Carbon-14. Urey's windows look out on the battlements of the stadium where, in 1942, the world's first atomic chain reaction was established. A plaque marks the spot today.

POINT OF DESTINY. NEAR THE UNIVERSITY OF CHICAGO STADIUM, WHERE THE FIRST ATOMIC CHAIN REACTION WAS ESTABLISHED, STANDS A CAR BEARING LICENSE NUMBER 2014 739—THE ATOMIC WEIGHT OF HEAVY HYDROGEN. IT BELONGS TO HAROLD C. UREY, NOBEL PRIZE WINNER, WHOSE DISCOVERY OF HEAVY HYDROGEN LAUNCHED THE HYDROGEN AGE.

Parked near by on a good many days is a dark blue Studebaker sedan bearing Illinois motor-vehicle license plate number 2014739. That is the atomic weight of heavy hydrogen carried out to a few extra decimal places, a number that may ultimately be as significant as the reaction recorded on the plaque. The car belongs, of course, to Harold Urey.

With his broad approach to science, Urey could not ignore the political consequences of the historic experiments in atomic physics. He was one of the first scientists to urge the democracies to adopt a political organization commensurate with an atomic age. He took an active role in the move to bring the United States and other democracies into an American type of federal union. He also spoke with candor and courage for the freedom of science, even when the tide was running strongly in the other direction. He not only advocated the removal of needless, hampering restrictions on research, but called for more private participation in the development of peacetime uses of atomic power. He argued that this, rather than exclusive government control, would bring the most rapid progress.

As Urey continued his basic research, he happened upon a number of what the layman might call "side leads"—clues indicating that research might yield highly interesting answers to certain problems related to the central one of the origin and development of the earth.

One key question raised by Urey's studies on the earth's early stages was: Could the conditions that would make life possible have prevailed on the kind of early earth which seemed likely to have existed? It was a crucial test. If conditions precluded the life that actually developed, the hypothesis would be questionable.

Stanley L. Miller, a twenty-three-year-old graduate student of Urey's, began to experiment. He passed an electrical discharge, comparable to a lightning flash in nature, through a mixture of gases similar to those which Urey thought might have been part of the earth's primitive atmosphere. After one day the water that also was used in the experiment turned pink. After a week it was red. A very important reaction had taken place: amino acids had been produced in the water. These complex compounds, which are present in all forms of life, had been synthesized by the passage of the electricity through the gases. The portentous conclusion announced in 1953, was that such complex, organic acids might have been formed when the earth was young by naturally occurring physical and chemical processes. The implications were great.

At a meeting in Switzerland after the war, Urey was discussing his work on the differences in isotopes. He pointed out that the concentration of a rare isotope of oxygen, Oxygen-18, is different in fresh and marine water. In the discussion that followed, Professor Paul Niggli remarked that the same difference of concentration should show up in fresh and marine deposits and that this might offer a means of distinguishing between them. Urey said that this was undoubtedly true. On returning home and thinking of Niggli's suggestion, it occurred to him that, since more Oxygen-18 appears in shells when the water is colder, the ratio of Oxygen-18 to ordinary Oxygen-16 might possibly be used as a thermometer of the past. The amount of Oxygen-18 present in deposits could indicate temperatures that had existed hundreds of millions of years before.

Urey had talked himself into a new project. He was "immensely eager to measure temperatures of the past ages of the earth," for there might lie important data on the development of the earth. "Fortunately," he adds, "I was able to find a number of young men who were also intrigued by the possibilities, and together we have worked on these problems since the summer of 1946."

Shells were collected from England, Tennessee, South Carolina, and other places. The most useful were those of belemnites, creatures that had vanished from the earth about sixty million years earlier. Their finely marked fossil shells show each year of growth as clearly as do the rings of a tree. By complicated experiment Urey and his co-workers determined how much Oxygen-18 would occur in the shells at each degree of temperature. By measuring the amount of Oxygen-18 in each ring of growth they could thus tell what the temperature had been in that long-ago year when the belemnite had attained that growth. As Urey had hoped, they had a new and accurate thermometer of the past—it was just as good a thermometer for the present, but in tests of current temperatures it is far easier to use a regular thermometer than to go through the intricate analysis for Oxygen-18.

Cesare Emiliani, a research associate of Urey's, has since employed the method to measure the temperature at which various strata were laid down on the sea bottoms. Thirty-foot cores were cut from the bottoms of the seas; such a core displays the deposits of more than six hundred thousand years. By measuring the fluctuations in the amount of Oxygen-18 in the various layers, Emiliani was able to chart the alternate cycles of warmth and cold through which the world had gone in the last six hundred thousand years.

Were the belemnites wiped out sixty million years ago by a great change in temperature? Could another change in temperature have accounted for the disappearance of the dinosaurs? If the temperature record could be read with enough completeness, would a regular, perhaps a predictable, alternation of heat and cold be found?

These were questions mostly for others to answer. Urey and his associates were providing the means, or a possible means, for answering them.

Urey talks about these matters and about the origin of the earth easily, simply, pleasantly. Although a slide rule lies on his desk at his right hand, he does not give the impression that he is wrenching himself away from the language of mathematics in order to use plain words. In fact, he sometimes thinks out some of the fantastically difficult problems with which he deals in sentences rather than in symbols. The words he uses, though perhaps not the ideas, would be understandable to anyone.

But getting the time to think things out is not easy. Urey once delighted a faculty meeting by proposing half seriously that all telephones be made one-way, for outgoing calls only. This same gift for direct words and thought has settled many a point. Another faculty meeting was considering the university's policy of prohibiting work on non-university commercial research projects. The debate had gone on for some time when Urey brought it to an abrupt and uproarious close by remarking: "Well, there certainly is a lot to be said for a laboratory in which everyone is not working on soap."

Urey's interest in the origin of the earth was aroused at a very favorable moment. The newer concepts of science—the molecular theory of gases, thermodynamics, radioactivity, and the quantum theory—and advances in astronomy and geophysics had disclosed apparently fatal errors in the old belief that the earth had been torn from the sun and that this flaming fragment had whirled off into space, there to liquefy and cool into the planet that we inhabit.[3] In one form or another this had been the basis of nearly all the major scientific theories from 1796, when Laplace proposed the nebular hypothesis, to 1945, when Von Weizsächer suggested a very different one. Even Chamberlin's planetesimals were fragments torn from the sun's mass.

The solar foundation on which science had built for a century and a half was crumbling; a dramatic and long-accepted hypothesis of the earth's origin was breaking down. But if the earth's substance did not derive from a solar outburst, what was its origin?

For some time the powerful telescopes of the astronomers had shown certain black spots in front of the great nebulæ that occur throughout our galaxy, the Milky Way. Investigation indicated that these opaque globules of dust and gas have about the mass of the sun. Perhaps they might turn into stars. Though the detailed mechanism of star formation is not understood, studies indicated that if these vast accumulations should once be somewhat compressed, gravity might well collapse the globules into a tight mass. The pressure and temperature from such a collapse would be enough, calculations suggested, to start the thermonuclear reaction of a star—in other words, to turn it into a blazing sun. To an overwhelming number of scientists this now appears to be the way our sun was born.

"As the astronomers have suggested," said Urey, "it would seem reasonable to believe that if a star such as the sun resulted

[3] See Chapter XVI.

from a process of this kind there might be enough material left over to make a solar system. . . . Theories along this line are more plausible to us today than the hypothesis that the planets were in some way removed from the sun after its formation had been completed. In my opinion the older hypotheses were unsatisfactory because they attempted to account for the origin of the planets without accounting for the origin of the sun. When we try to specify how the sun was formed, we immediately find ways in which the material that now comprises the planets may have remained outside of it."

Out of the leftovers, out of the immense remaining masses of the nebular gas and dust, may have come the earth, the moon, and the other planets: Jupiter, Saturn, Neptune, Uranus, Venus, Pluto, Mars, and Mercury. Thus, perhaps each coagulated or accumulated out of the cosmic dust. There is now little disagreement about this theory; leaders of the astronomical and physical sciences generally believe, and can offer impressive evidence to support their belief, that this was probably how our earth and the other planets came into existence.

There is not much disagreement even though this shakes and virtually discards another theory once favored and widely accepted—the belief that as huge tides rose on a young molten earth, a great wave hurtled off and rounded itself into the moon. The basin of the Pacific Ocean was held to be the place from which the moon's substance was wrenched. This was a theory first proposed about sixty years ago by Sir George Darwin, the famous astronomer who was the son of Charles Darwin.

As early as 1911, Moulton argued powerfully that such an origin of the moon was nearly impossible. Sir Harold Jeffreys reinforced his point in 1931. Since that time additional evidence, some of which will be discussed later, has indicated that they were right. Many astronomers, and Urey agrees, now regard the story that the moon is the child of the earth and the Pacific Ocean its birthplace as little more than folklore: a colorful, imaginative tale that refuses to die.

But with the conclusion that the earth, its moon, the sun, and the planets evolved from a primordial cloud of dust, agreement ends. Beyond this point the uncertainties, the unknowns, the conflicts are limitless.

How did the earth and the other planets accumulate from the beginning nebula?

Did the earth melt at the outset of the accumulative process, or later, or not at all? Was the earth initially hot or cold?

What happened after the earth rounded into form? [4]

How were the rocks, the continents, and the oceans produced on this evolving globe? Did the water of the seas and the atmosphere come from the earth's interior?

These are immeasurably hard problems, and yet without facing them it is not possible to try to answer the next questions, questions of how the major structures of the earth came to be, and of how this sphere developed into the varied, rich, and relatively stable platform on which men live. To explain the appearance of a house and know what can be expected of it, it is essential to understand how it was built.

When Urey turned to the inescapable problem of the earth's origin, he began, incredibly enough, with neon, the gas that has turned America's nighttime streets into a glowing fretwork of reds and blues and greens. Some years before, Henry Norris Russell of Princeton University and Donald H. Menzel, now director of the Harvard Observatory, had pointed out that natural neon was very rare in the atmosphere of the earth but comparatively abundant in the stars. Since neon formed no chemical compounds, they theorized that neon, and probably other volatile elements of the early atmosphere, including water, had escaped from the earth. The present atmosphere and oceans, they suggested, might have been formed later by the movement of water, nitrogen, carbon, and other materials from the interior of the earth to its surface.

---

[4] What went before, and how the nebulæ came into existence, is another profound mystery and point of conflict.

But how had the neon and other volatiles escaped from the earth, and when? Urey critically asked these two questions. Thornton Page, then at Yerkes Observatory, and Hans Suess in Germany had demonstrated that volatiles could not have evaporated from a fully formed earth, for once the earth had assumed its present shape its gravitational field would have been too strong to permit the volatile gases to get away. That put the escape back to an earlier period.

But if the earth had been hot in that early stage, Urey pointed out, not only the neon and surface water would have gone, but all water. "How do you bury water in molten materials?" he asked. Urey was convinced that if the earth had been hot then, in its accumulative stages, it would be dry and oceanless today.

There was one way out of the impasse. At low temperatures water does not enter into volatile combinations—it does not turn into vapor or steam. On the contrary, at low temperatures water forms hydrated silicates, the material of the rocks, and great quantities of it could be "buried" in the earth, just as they are today. Thus, Urey argued, if the young earth had been even cooler than the present earth, it might well have retained interior water that could later have emerged and filled the oceans. In this way, and by the study of what would have happened to other solubles and volatiles, Urey quickly came to the assumption that the earth in its earliest beginnings had been cool.

This, however, raised another question. Could the earth have been formed in such a way that it might have remained cool? Von Weizsäcker had proposed in 1945 that turbulence in the giant clouds of gas and dust might lead to their assembly into planetary bodies. Later, Gerard P. Kuiper, professor of astronomy of the University of Chicago's Yerkes Observatory, suggested that the original dust clouds might first have broken up into a number of turbulent eddies that he called proto-planets. There probably had been one such precursor accumulation for the earth and one for each of the planets, he said.

In any event, it seemed very likely that the dust of the eddies had gradually accumulated into the solid "bodies" which generally are called planetesimals. Urey is of the opinion that they came together through the low-temperature coagulating action of the water and ammonia that were part of the nebular gases. Perhaps they were accumulated in huge snowstorms, extending over regions as wide as those between the planets today. And some of the planetesimals may have become as large as the moon.

At first the temperature of the planetesimals was low, Urey believes. As they knotted more tightly together, however, unstable chemical compounds of carbon, nitrogen, oxygen, and hydrogen would have generated enough heat to melt the silicates formed from the dust—these are the rocky compounds that today make up a large part of the earth's crust—and to reduce the iron oxides to iron. If that were the case, the molten iron would have sunk through the silicates and run together in large planetesimal pools. At this stage, temperatures may have risen to 2,000 degrees Centigrade, and thus the accumulating planetesimals went through a "high-temperature" phase.

But large amounts of volatile hydrogen, helium, methane, water, and nitrogen were escaping from the still widely spreadout eddy. There would have been no thick insulating layer of gas to hold them in, and in the absence of such an envelope atmosphere "radiation from the planetesimals would quickly lower the temperatures to approximately those now existing at the respective distances of the planets from the sun," Urey pointed out.

Near one end of the eddy revolved a thickening swarm of planetesimals. From time to time lesser planetesimals—lesser is a relative term, for some were a hundred miles or more in diameter—would crash into the growing solid mass. They left deep craters where they struck, and these craters may still be seen today. For this bombarded ball, science now believes, became the moon.

But near the center of the vast eddy an even larger swarm of planetesimals swirled around a still greater central knot. And here again the lesser bodies of the swarm were drawn in to crash with mighty impact into the gathering body.[1]

"Earthly explosions during the past decade," said Urey in his book on the planets, published in 1952, "give a very slight impression of the expected effect—the violent explosion, the spread of missiles, the rising plume in the atmosphere, the in-rushing winds. Material would be blown away and fall through the atmosphere at far points."

"And so perhaps," said Urey, "the earth was formed."

Out of an eddying cloud of dust, out of cosmic snowstorms, out of chemical heating processes, and collisions that dwarf the most staggering known to man came the earth and its substance, if this theory is correct. This picture of a cool accumulation, an early heating up, a subsequent cooling, and the final accumulation and warming to present temperatures stands in striking variance to the traditional image—the flaming mass exploding from the sun and turning into a molten and now cooling sphere.

"The chronology of events given is a complicated one," Urey conceded, "but the true one certainly is even more complicated. There is a tendency on the part of all investigators to search for a simple explanation of observed facts and to accept such simple explanations rather than more involved ones. This attitude is correct, of course, when applied to statements of fundamental laws, as experience shows. However, phenomena observed in nature which are the result of the operation of these laws are always very complicated, so much so that the details escape the capacity of the human mind."

But what happened after the last of the planetesimals had crashed into the earth, and the accumulation of the earth was complete? How did the earth get its core, which very strong evidence indicates is a core of molten iron? How did it get its

[1] Craters made by the impact would soon have disappeared on the earth's changing surface. Even mighty mountains are eroded away.

surrounding mantle of rock, and the thin outer crust on which men live? Urey and those who adhere to the low-temperature, planetesimal concept give an answer very different from that of the older group who believed in the sun-derived molten earth, and of others who think that there was an early melting when the planetesimals came together.

Lord Kelvin, who assumed that the earth had been drawn hot from the sun, had pictured the early congealing of huge blocks of solid material on the cooling surface of the molten ball. Sinking "like great battleships," the blocks were at first re-melted by the awful heat of the sub-surface. At length, however, Lord Kelvin argued, enough solid material remained intact to begin the formation of a hard core. Lord Kelvin thus envisioned the earth solidifying from the center outward.

The discovery of radioactivity abruptly put an end to this theory, however logical it had been in its day. The vast stores of heat released by the decay of radioactive materials, it was clear, would have prevented such an inner congealing and cooling of the earth.

Jeans and Jeffreys, assuming that the earth had condensed at incandescent heats from a high-temperature cloud of gas, reasoned that in such a furnace the iron in the earth's materials would have melted out and sunk to the core. In 1944 the German physical chemist A. Eucken suggested that the iron would have condensed first in the interior.

But to Urey such proposals were unsatisfactory because they did not take into full account the way in which metals and minerals would actually behave under heat, pressure, and other very complex conditions.

In its early assembled stage, Urey points out, the earth was largely a mixture, a lumpy mixture, of iron-nickel alloy, iron sulfide, and silicate or rocky materials. It was therefore far from uniform in composition, and far from being a thoroughly mixed mass. Some of the differentiation may have occurred when the planetesimals crashed into the earth, melting the areas in which they struck and turning those areas into pools of molten magma. These pools, Urey suggests, possibly with iron at their bottoms, may eventually have cooled into the primitive continental masses.

Rock-ribbed, firm, and solid though the earth seems to men, it is in well-established fact far more a plastic sphere than an unyielding one. Thus, obeying the laws of gravity, the heavier, denser parts of the earth, such as its iron, would have settled toward the interior. The lighter parts, Urey thinks, may have moved together and formed the primitive continents, the first wide areas to stand above the formless general surface.

But such movements create heat. Urey suspects that enough heat may have been generated to raise the internal temperature of the earth to something like its present value, about 2,000 to 4,000 degrees Centigrade. In the melting that would have resulted, more iron-nickel and more iron sulfides would have melted and sunk down through the rocky slag from which they had separated. And as additional movements created additional heat, the iron would have sunk until it formed the molten core that most scientists now are convinced occupies the center of the earth.

Heat also was being created by radioactivity. Warmed by these "minute self-heating centers," the hard, compact rocks of the mantle may have become sufficiently plastic and viscous to move in response to pressures almost as a soft clay does. The Dutch geophysicist Vening Meinesz has pointed out that these movements, immensely slow though they must have been, may nevertheless have set up convection currents in the earth.

"These convections are continuing at the present time and constitute the principal machines for mountain building and continent maintenance," declared Urey.

And thus, according to Urey's reasoning, was the earth's stage set.

But—and Urey leans thoughtfully back in his chair and loses himself gazing into the distance—"We don't *know*." The scientist explains: "We are in a better position now to work on these problems, but the new studies that have become possible only show us that the whole problem is vastly more complicated than anyone could have imagined."

With what at first seems irrelevance, he adds: "I'm always looking for a star." It is not in fact a departure from his train of thought. If the sun and earth and our whole solar system were formed from one of the unnumbered dust nebulæ of the universe, it is very likely that additional stars and additional earths are coming together now from other nebulæ. There must be other stars in all stages of formation. Urey is looking for a star that may supply some new and revealing clue to how our solar system and earth came to be. He has pored over the records of odd and peculiar stars, searching hopefully for a hint. So far he has not found it.

But in science you do not give up. "You start with one little patch," said Urey, "and then you branch out."

Urey thinks that some lines of Oliver Wendell Holmes's, read in a somewhat different connotation, are applicable to scientific problems in general, and in particular to the special one of how the earth came to be:

Build thee more stately mansions, O my soul,
As the swift seasons roll!
Leave thy low-vaulted past!
Let each new temple, nobler than the last
Shut thee from heaven with a dome more vast,
Till thou at length art free,
Leaving thine outgrown shell by life's unresting sea!

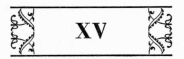

XV

JEFFREYS, BULLARD, AND RUNCORN
THE INTERIOR OF THE EARTH

*"We cannot approach a full understanding
of what we observe at the surface without
considering what is going on at great
depths."* [1]

As we look up and outward we can see far into limitless
space; we look upon the sun 92,900,000 miles away and upon
the even more distant stars. As we gaze downward toward the
earth we live on, our vision generally halts at our feet. We
cannot see even an inch into the earth.

At quarries and other excavations a minute fraction of the
hidden subterranean earth has been laid bare. At the Grand
Canyon and a few other deep gorges nature permits us to see
more than a mile into the depths. The deepest mines, in South
Africa, enable men to go a little farther still into the earth, and
at oil wells men's implements have bored down twenty thousand
feet. But this is about all. By direct vision and with our tools
we can reach less than one per cent of our exceedingly im-
penetrable earth. For all of its nearness and immediacy, the
interior of the earth is perhaps more inaccessible than the nearest
star.

Until the twentieth century devised experimental means for
studying this unseeable and impassable interior of the earth,

[1] Sir Harold Jeffreys in *Earthquakes and Mountains*. London: Methuen
& Co. Ltd.; 1950.

men could only speculate about the dire regions that lay below the shallow surface they knew. They did not doubt that they were dire.

"A place of darkness where vast Earth has end," wrote Hesiod, "a drear and ghastly wilderness, abhorr'd e'en by the gods; a vast vacuity." There dwelt Death and Night and the subterranean gods, and there through shades of blackest night the "Stygian branch of ocean" flowed.

Aristotle in his turn pictured the underworld as a cavernous place where great winds blew so violently in their attempt to break forth that they often shook the earth.

To others it was a region of fire, and of hell and damnation. "A fiery gulf," wrote Milton—

> *A dungeon horrible on all sides round*
> *As one great furnace flamed, yet from those flames*
> *No light, but rather darkness visible*
> *Served only to discover sights of woe,*
> *Regions of sorrow, doleful shades, where peace*
> *And rest can never dwell, hope never comes*
> *That comes to all; but torture without end*
> *Still urges, and a fiery deluge, fed*
> *With ever-burning sulphur unconsumed.*

To John Ray and the theologians, here too were the "fountains of the deep." Through great underground lakes and reservoirs surged the tides that fed and stirred the waters of the surface.

The interior of the earth—seat of darkness and destructive winds, of consuming fire and water! Place of deep chasms, fearful gulfs, and yawning caverns! Through all the ages that men have thought and wondered about the ninety-nine per cent of their planet which they cannot see, it has always been with overtones of awe and dread.

But with the coming of the twentieth century, and particularly in the last decade, science has found the experimental means to begin the probing of this redoubtable nether world.

And as sometimes happens, the new picture of the earth's interior which is taking shape is almost more surprising (though it is less horrendous) than the one long built without facts by fertile imaginations.

Many now are studying the interior of the earth, outlining its structures, measuring its forces, analyzing its materials. Leadership in this search often has come from three English scientists, Sir Harold Jeffreys, Sir Edward Bullard, and S. K. Runcorn.

As director of the International Seismological Summary, to which more than five hundred seismological stations regularly report, Sir Harold Jeffreys is outstandingly the man with his finger on the pulse of the world. By studying the tremors that constantly run through the earth, whether set off by an earthquake, the explosion of an atom bomb, or even by the jarring of heavy traffic, he has been able to tell the world much about the hidden interior of the earth, for the tremors speak revealingly of the nature and the structure of the subterranean regions through which they pass.

If the ground through which they travel is solid, the tremors or waves behave in one way; if it is liquid, in another. If it is made of one kind of material, they move at certain velocities; if of another, at different speeds.

In introducing the chapter on elastic waves in his famous book *The Earth, Its Origin, History, and Physical Constitution,* Jeffreys was moved by their odd behavior to quote from *Through the Looking Glass:*

> *One, two! one, two!*
> *And through and through*
> *The vorpal blade went snicker snack.*

Jeffreys is Plumian Professor of Astronomy at the University of Cambridge and has dealt with the most profound problems of the earth. His studies of the earth waves are only one phase of the scientific activity to which he has given his undivided attention since he became a fellow of St. John's College of Cambridge in 1914 after previous study at Rutherford and Armstrong Colleges at Newcastle and at St. John's. Jeffreys was born on April 22, 1891.

Having chosen a field as vast as the earth, Jeffreys avoided other distractions whenever possible. He is even married to a fellow mathematician, the former Bertha Swirles, and together they published a book, *Methods of Mathematical Physics.*

Much of Jeffreys's own work has been concerned with mathematics, which he believes must hold the key to the modern attempt to understand the earth. "The results aimed at," he explains in the preface to his book on the earth, "are quantitative, and there is no way of obtaining quantitative results without mathematics. . . . If geophysics requires mathematics for its treatment, it is the earth that is responsible, not the geophysicist."

The earth clearly was responsible. It had firmly refused to yield its long-held secrets to any other methods.

But it was 1897 before an instrument was invented that made possible the quantitative, precise study of which Sir Harold was speaking. In that year John Milne invented the seismograph, an instrument that could exactly measure the movements of the earth and record them in a series of ups and downs on a re-

AND TOWERS COME TOPPLING DOWN. A SIXTEENTH-CENTURY PICTURING OF AN EARTHQUAKE, AND A MODERN RECORDING OF ITS EFFECTS —A SEISMOGRAM.

volving drum of paper. Milne had suspended a pendulum in such a way that it did not vibrate immediately when the earth moved, for if the whole instrument had responded there would have been nothing to measure against. A point of stability was the key to the first seismograph and to all that have followed it.

Seismograph stations were soon established in most parts of the world. Man at last had a way of studying the always terrifying and often destructive earthquake, and of probing the vast unknown interior of the earth. But each station could record only a limited aspect of these events.

"Little can be done with the records of a single station in comparison with what can be got from comparison of a large number," Jeffreys explained.

To provide such a comparison the International Seismological Summary was established at Oxford in 1922. It was later transfered to Kew Observatory and Jeffreys became the director. The I.S.S., as it is known to the scientists, now works out the center and time of occurrence of some six hundred earthquakes a year. In some cases it also calculates the depth of occurrence.

From this great, world-wide mass of data and from the studies of individual stations, it soon became clear that the earth is always in motion. A line of heavy trucks rumbling down a highway sends a series of vibrations through the earth, as those who live beside highways know all too well. The rocking of trees and buildings in a high wind also sets off disturbances that produce a second or two of irregularity on the seismograph records. A storm at sea and the pounding of the waves on the coast create a larger disturbance. But all of these are the small quiverings of the earth, the microseisms whose source can easily be seen and understood.

It was the major disturbances of the earth, the earthquakes that made violent peaks and sharp, jagged valleys on the seismograph records, which told most revealingly about the mysterious interior of the earth. The first and most basic information they

registered was that the earth is not fluid in the zone, well below
the surface, where earthquakes occur, but on the contrary is a
solid to about half the depth of its radius. In other words,
approximately the outer half of the earth is a solid mass.

Laboratory work had shown that the kind of earth waves
created by an earthquake could not be set off in a fluid. Only
a fracture in a solid produces such a disturbance. (You cannot
crack the water in the bathtub.) Therefore, in his book *Earthquakes and Mountains,* which was written for the layman, Jeffreys briefly defined an earthquake as a fracture in the earth's
rocks that is produced by internal stress.

Seismograph studies soon brought out two other crucial findings: the fracture may vary widely in size, and the effect that it
produces on the surface depends upon where in the earth it
occurs.

The waves generated, Jeffreys pointed out, travel through
the earth, but are strongest in the neighborhood of the fracture.
In the most extreme cases they produce a motion in the ground
of sufficient intensity to crack the crust all the way to the surface and to destroy any cities or works of man that lie in the
way. In the San Francisco earthquake of 1906 the ground along
one side of a great fissure was permanently displaced for more
than twenty feet, and this "fault" continued for several hundred
miles.

"We may safely say," declared Jeffreys, "that every fracture
visible at the surface has at some time or other been the seat
of an earthquake." And, Jeffreys added, the majority of the
fractures have been the seats of many earthquakes.

A small break in the earth's crust may produce a tremor to
which the seismologists assign the minimum earthquake magnitude of 1.5. From this point the disturbance may range upward
to the most severe shock of which there is record, the disastrous
earthquake off the coast of Ecuador on January 31, 1906. It
attained a magnitude of 8.6. The San Francisco earthquake of
the same year was almost as severe, with a magnitude of 8.25.

The Bikini atom-bomb burst had the smaller though still respectable magnitude of 5.5.

With the data of the seismographs, Jeffreys and other scientists in the field have been able to fix an earthquake's point of occurrence. About seventy per cent of the quakes, they have established, occur within thirty-seven miles of the earth's surface. Only about thirty per cent have deeper focal points. The latter, called deep-focus earthquakes, happen only in a belt surrounding the Pacific and in a few places on the Alpine-Himalaya chain of mountains.

In a quake, the seismologists reasoned, what happened at the surface should depend upon how near or how deep the focus, or actual break, might be. If the fracture were near the surface, the effect would be most violent. If the shock were a deep one, the waves would have farther to travel to reach the surface, and the quake might be less severe, though spread over a greater area.

"This is true," declared Jeffreys. The great Tokyo earthquake of 1923 which wrought such devastation in Japan was a shallow shock, not more than thirty-seven miles deep, and it was felt for only about four hundred and fifty miles. Another earthquake studied in the area had a depth of about two hundred and fifty miles. It did far less damage, but its shock was detected more than eight hundred miles away. The deepest known earthquake had a depth of about four hundred miles—it occurred south of the Celebes.

And thus the picture of the earth's interior began to fill in. The stresses that gave rise to earthquakes, even the deepest of them, occurred in the outer part of the earth.

Laboratory work with solids had indicated that when a fracture occurred, two different kinds of waves raced out from the break. And very early the scientists who were studying the earth saw that this was also the case when there was a break in the earth. One wave from an earthquake arrived at the surface sooner than the other, and for this reason was called the "pri-

mary wave." The second to come in was named the "secondary."
It was like Jeffreys's "One, two! one, two!" and through and
through the waves went snicker snack.

Later it was learned that the primary waves were in fact
pressure waves. More accurately, Jeffreys has explained, they
are longitudinal waves. They give a push, or sometimes a pull,
to the materials through which they travel. They are now called
simply "P-waves."

The later-arriving "S-waves" are distortional or transverse
waves. As Jeffreys said, to clarify the matter for the layman,
they may be thought of as "shake" waves. The original designa-
tion of "S" could therefore be appropriately retained.

The seismologists also have identified surface waves, which
somewhat resemble waves in water, except that they are controlled by elasticity rather than gravity.

The two types of "body" waves—P-waves moving in the direction of propagation, and S-waves in a transverse direction—
therefore take different routes through the earth. This accounts
for the difference in their arrival times.

But neither, it was discovered, pursues an even, unblocked
path through the earth, and this fact supplied the next important
clue to the inner earth. Some strange and revealing phenomena
began to appear as the scientists recorded the arrivals of the
P- and S-waves on their seismographs in all parts of the world.

To their surprise, they found that if an earthquake occurred
at the south pole, for example, P-waves running out from it
would emerge at the surface throughout the southern hemisphere and beyond to a point fifteen degrees above the equator,
in the vicinity of Guatemala. All through South America the
shock would be felt. But between Guatemala and Winnipeg,
seismographs would pick up very few of the shock waves. Nearly
the whole of the United States would be undisturbed; the country would be in what Jeffreys and the seismologists call a
"shadow zone." But from fifty-two degrees north to the north

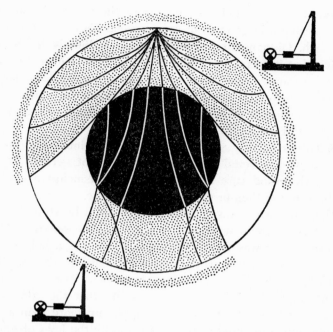

SHADOW OF THE EARTH'S CORE. AS PRESSURE WAVES FROM AN EARTH-
QUAKE STRIKE THE EARTH'S CORE, THEY ARE DEFLECTED, AND THUS
DO NOT REACH CERTAIN "SHADOW ZONES" (HERE INDICATED BY WHITE
AREAS). SO DOES SCIENCE OUTLINE THE SIZE AND SHAPE OF THE CORE.

pole the waves from the south pole would again come in with
full force.[2]

In every quake, it was soon learned, there were such "shadow
zones." The immediate question was: why? In 1906, R. D. Oldham first worked out the answer, and with it he contributed a
major discovery about the interior of the earth.

The P-waves, Oldham demonstrated, were not getting
through to the "shadow zones" because they were being de-

[2] I am indebted to K. E. Bullen, professor of applied mathematics at
the University of Sydney, Australia, for this illustration of the shadow effect.

flected; they were being turned from their normal course by encountering a large mass of some special kind in the center of the earth. Oldham jumped quickly and brilliantly to the conclusion that it was a core! The earth, he held, had a core, and, what was more, a core composed of some material dense enough to bend P-waves. That meant that it had to be much denser than the materials through which they had been passing in the outer part of the earth.

Scientists eagerly went to work on this intriguing finding. Then they discovered that S-waves were not getting through this newly found core at all; at least, no conclusive evidence has been found then or since of their passage.

Here, however, was a problem that could be studied in the laboratory. S-waves were sent through various materials. When the experiment was tried with fluids, there was a halt as complete as that which apparently was occurring in the middle of the earth. And P-waves were slowed and bent. The facts pointed directly and strikingly to the probability that the core was a fluid. Since it was known that iron made up more than a third of the original material of the earth and, by the laws of gravity, would probably have moved to the center, the evidence was strong that the fluid might be molten iron, not unlike that which pours from the furnaces of a steel mill.[3]

The scientists pressed on, aroused by these exciting new possibilities of finding out about the unreached interior of the earth. By studying the exact occurrence of the shadow zones, Beno Gutenberg, then of Germany and now professor of Geophysics at the California Institute of Technology, located the outer boundary of the newly discovered core at 1,800 miles below the earth's surface. That gave the core a radius of 2,160 miles, for the earth's whole radius was 3,960 miles. In this way Gutenberg disclosed that more than half of the earth's body was taken up by this great fluid core. The molten center of the earth was enormous!

[3] See Chapter 18.

But just as science succeeded in outlining the core, there was another surprising development. Miss I. Lehman, of Denmark, who was working with the few stray P-waves that do get through into the "shadow zones," saw that this might be because they found the going faster in the center of the core. Perhaps they were being given an impetus by passing through a non-fluid core within the core. Jeffreys began to check this proposal carefully against his extensive data on the waves of the earth and soon concluded that it was in all probability right. He found that the inner core very likely had a radius of 800 miles. And it might well be, he suggested, that this core was a solid. And thus an inner core was defined and added to the picture of the earth.

But what lay between the fluid core and the surface on which we live? All earlier scientific work had indicated that it was a solid, probably rock, but there knowledge ended.

Jeffreys's records showed that the P- and S-waves did not maintain the same speed throughout the non-core part of the earth. At the surface they were slow. Then as they passed deeper into the earth their speed increased until they struck the core and were slowed again. This pattern was emphasized by the P-waves, which were bent by the core but re-emerged from it. As soon as they passed through it and re-entered the earth beyond, their speed again increased.

At this point in the study it became essential to know the exact speed at which the P- and S-waves traveled. Such determinations were exceedingly difficult to make, for P-waves striking the core or other obstacles sometimes were converted into S-waves, and S-waves into P-waves. Jeffreys suspected that errors had crept into the early travel-time tables. With K. E. Bullen, who was then associated with him, he began to work out new tables. Their method was, essentially, to pull the tables up by their own bootstraps. The epicenter (the point on the surface vertically above the focus of a quake) and time of occurrence of a number of earthquakes were worked out, according to the best travel-time tables then available, from the times at which their P- and S-waves had arrived at a number of seismological stations. The results were then used to improve the tables, which were in turn used to improve the findings of position. Allowance also had to be made for the ellipticity of the earth. Nevertheless, by this bootstrap operation the tables were gradually perfected. In 1940 Jeffreys and Bullen published new tables that still are internationally used.

About the same time, in 1939, Gutenberg and Charles F. Richter, of the California Institute of Technology, independently prepared another set of time tables. The two sets were in amazingly close agreement. They varied by only one or two seconds in the time given for a wave to cover great distances. Students of the earth at last had accurate working tools.

With the new tables, it was soon determined that in rocks near the surface P-waves traveled at a speed of about three kilometers per second. At a depth of twenty to thirty miles, however, they suddenly speeded up to eight and a half kilometers per second, and they traveled at increasing speeds until they reached the core. S-waves followed the same acceleration pattern, though at speeds about two-thirds those of the P-waves.

The dramatic change in speed at the twenty-to-thirty-mile point indicated some decided change in the earth. Here, it seemed, was another dividing-point, a discontinuity, and it was named the Mohorovičić or M discontinuity, for the Croatian seismologist who first discovered it. It marked the boundary of the earth's outer layer, the crust on which we live. The speed of the waves thus revealed the thickness of the crust—twenty to thirty miles—and outlined another zone in the earth.

Between the M and the core lay the 1,780-mile zone through which the waves attained their highest speeds. Although there were strong indications of layers in this great area, too, the behavior of the waves indicated that it was remarkably uniform in composition. It showed no sign of the great variety of rock found at the surface. Here, said Sir Edward Bullard, "the complications of geology seem to be left behind." This uniform, clearly solid, rocky wrapping was called the mantle.

It was in this way that the waves coursing through the earth at last gave men a picture of the inner structure of their earth— the solid inner core, the core of molten iron, the great mantle of rock, and the wafer-thin outer crust. The scientific earth's likeness to a golf ball, with its liquid or plastic center, its thick wrapping of elastic bands, and its thin, tough cover, is so apt that it has appealed to scientists as well as laymen.

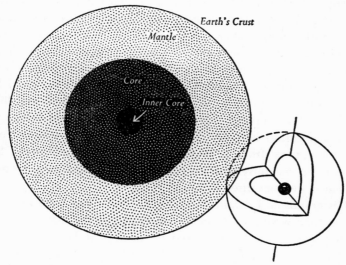

THE EARTH'S INTERIOR, AS SCIENCE NOW DRAWS IT: CRUST, MANTLE OF ROCK, CORE THAT PROBABLY IS MOLTEN IRON, INNER CORE THAT MAY BE SOLID IRON. THE CRUST ON WHICH WE LIVE IS RELATIVELY NO THICKER THAN THE SHELL OF AN EGG.

This inner earth that science is defining has banished the "antres vast," the fiery gulfs, the Stygian rivers of tradition. In another way, though, it might be argued that the core of molten iron, the mantle, and the crust are almost as odd an assemblage as that imagined by the philosophers of the past.

．　．　．

The general identification of the major structures of the earth's interior only opened up still more complicated problems: what do these structures consist of, and what are the forces that make them what they are? The magnitude of the task moved Jeffreys to quote Kai Lung: " 'So far,' admitted Lao Ting, 'it is in the nature of a vision. There are of necessity many trials and few can reach the ultimate end. Yet even the Yangtze-Kiang has a source.' "

One of those actively seeking the source is Jeffreys's younger colleague Sir Edward Crisp Bullard. Bullard is a scientist who may have inherited his interest in the observation of the earth. His maternal grandfather, Sir Frank Crisp, was a London lawyer with a personal and scientific interest in mountains. Since he lived on the flat banks of the Thames at Henley, where there were no mountains to which a man could lift up his eyes, he built a mountain in his own garden. It was a hundred and fifty feet high and complete with waterfall, miniature iron deer, and a telescope in an imitation Swiss chalet. When he was not enjoying the view from or toward his man-made mountain, Sir Frank often was busy with his collection of antique microscopes. He had more than three thousand of them.

His grandson, Edward Crisp Bullard, who was born in 1907, in due time went to Cambridge to read physics. After he had taken his undergraduate degree he continued his work for a Ph.D in the laboratory of Lord Rutherford, and later had the further good fortune of assisting Sir Gerald Lenox-Conyngham in the department of geodesy and geophysics at Cambridge.

In 1933 Bullard set out on the first of several trips to Africa to make gravity studies and measurements in the Great Rift Valley. The paper in which he reported his findings was considered a model of its kind. It probably was influential in his election as a fellow of the Royal Society of London in 1941.

During the war Bullard served with the British navy as an officer in charge of research and development on mine-sweeping and the protection of ships from mines. At the close of the war he returned briefly to Cambridge as a reader in experimental geophysics, but in 1948 accepted an appointment as professor of physics at the University of Toronto. He had been in Canada for only a year and a half when he was called back to England to become director of the National Physical Laboratory.

For his work there and for his contributions to geophysics, Bullard was knighted in 1953. He remained at the laboratory until 1956, when he resigned to return to Cambridge.

As science outlined the layered internal structure of the earth, questions about the properties of each of these divisions arose. What were they like? What kinds of matter constituted the interior of the earth?

It had been clear since the eighteenth century that the earth was a spheroid rotating about its axis, and that it had a mean density of about 5.52 grams per cubic centimeter, or the right firmness to hold it to its spheroidal shape. If the densities of the various zones could be worked out, an invaluable clue to their composition and structure would be obtained. Bullard and Bullen were among a number of scientists who turned to this investigation.

By the most complex of computations they determined that the density of the earth increases from the 2.8 of the so-called basement rocks that underlie the continents to about 12 at the core. The earth thus becomes extremely dense at its center, Bullard points out in discussing these and other studies in the chapter on the interior of the earth which he contributed to *The Earth as a Planet*. Much of this density must be due, he suggests, to compression of the inner materials by the enormous superincumbent load on them. But another factor could be the concentration of denser materials inward.

The work so far has not settled the further question of whether the density and compression increase steadily with depth, or whether they increase in steps corresponding to the major zones of the earth. But in either case it is certain that the earth is solidly packed. No room is left for the caverns of old.

Science still has no direct way of studying the materials of the inner earth—the deepest samples available are still the borings brought up from the oil wells. Beyond this point reliance must be placed on experiment and mathematics.

Most scientists now assume that the elements which are rare at the surface of the earth also are rare in its interior. "There is considerable justification for this view," says Bullard, "since with some intelligible exceptions (such as the rarity of nitrogen and neon) the relative abundance shows the same general trends in the sun, the stars, the meteorites, and cosmic rays as it does on earth. The light elements are the common ones, and the heavy elements are extremely rare." In all probability, therefore, the interior of the earth is made up of the same elements as the surface and the remainder of the solar system.

But the problem is what compounds, what materials have been formed from these elements under the peculiar conditions of the earth's interior. In seeking the answer, the scientists were not without resources. They knew that the density of the mantle varied from 3 to 6 grams per cubic centimeter, and they also knew from the Jeffreys-Bullen tables that P-waves passed through the mantle at speeds ranging from 8 to 14 kilometers per second. Were there any known materials of such densities through which P-waves would travel at such speeds?

The answer was soon forthcoming. "The only compounds of the common elements that will give such a low density and high velocity for P are the silicates," reported Bullard. "These are in any case the natural material to suggest for the mantle, since the material emerging from volcanoes and that found in igneous intrusions consists almost entirely of silicates."

And one rock in particular fitted the specifications almost exactly. It was dunite, a hard, dense rock made up largely of the mineral, olivine. It had the density of the mantle, and the waves traveled through it at mantle speeds. Neither granite nor basalt gave the same results. What was more, dunite was known to occur deep in the earth. Big chunks of it occasionally are hurled up to the surface by volcanoes; otherwise, it is not found on the crust. Density, wave velocity, and the actual evidence of the earth thus indicated that at least the outer part of the mantle might be made of the solid, blackish dunite. And science could report that one of the major materials of the inner earth had been identified with considerable certainty.

The scientists, Bullard among them, applied the same detective techniques to the study of the core, and the testing of the evidence that seemed to indicate a molten-iron composition. The core had been assigned a density of 10 to 12 grams per cubic centimeter.

"The only common substances substantially heavier than a silicate at atmospheric pressure are iron and its oxides," said Bullard. "The molten oxides could not exist in contact with silicates since they are mutually soluble. The natural choice of material for the core therefore is molten iron. Some plausibility is given to this idea by the occurrence of meteorites composed entirely of iron."

If the meteors are the debris of a planet, similar to the earth, which for some reason has broken into pieces, the iron meteors may well be bits from its core. They may be samples showing the earth what its own interior would be like if a piece could somehow be carved out, or if this planet were shattered into bits and its center thus exposed.

Some scientists, however, have objected to the iron theory. W. H. Ramsey has argued that the core may be composed of dunite converted into a liquid metal by the enormous pressures. Bullard agrees that such a change could occur, and concedes that it is possible that the core may consist of an alloy of such a metallic silicate and iron. But there is as yet no final answer. Majority opinion now strongly favors a core of molten iron.

What the still mysterious inner core may be made of is even more uncertain, though it seems to be a solid elliptical body inside the liquid. Several scientists have suggested that it may be composed of iron solidified by the vast pressures of the center

of the earth. Bullard only says that, on the basis of the research
that has been done, "There seems little immediate prospect of
learning more about the inner core."

Nevertheless, the interior of the earth is no longer the complete blank that it was to science only a few years ago. The
sulfur and brimstone of myth are gone, and it now seems fairly
certain that the earth grades downward from heavy, to heavier,
to heaviest; from the sedimentary rocks and granites and basalts
of the crust, to dunite, to molten iron, and perhaps to solid iron.
The earth we live on undoubtedly is solidly based.

No folklore is more deeply ingrained than that of the consuming heat and fires of the inner earth. Poetry and prose
pictured the eternal blazing furnace that was the center of the
earth, and even science well into this century assumed inner
heats surpassing any known to man.

As mines were pushed deeper and deeper into the earth this
belief in an enormously hot interior seemed to gain support.
Temperatures in these entries into the earth increased with
depth. At the Carnarvon bore in South Africa the heat climbed
one degree Centigrade for every 70 feet in the first half-mile—
a cut through sedimentary rocks. In the next half-mile, where
the shaft passed through igneous rock, the temperature increased
by one degree Centigrade for each 137 feet.

In the 9,000-foot-deep oil well at Long Beach, California,
the temperature of boiling water, 100 degrees Centigrade, was
reached at 7,200 feet, and at the well's bottom, 9,000 feet, the
temperature rose to 120 degrees Centigrade. And the evidence
indicated that the temperatures would mount still higher at
greater depths. Molten lavas coming from depths far exceeding
those of the mines and wells, though from levels still shallow
in comparison to the total thickness of the earth, registered
temperatures as high as 1,200 degrees Centigrade.

Since heat in a solid flows from a region of high temperature
to one of lower temperature, the increase in temperatures with
depth implied an upward flow of heat from the center of the

earth. Such was the assumption made by Lord Kelvin and by many others who came after him. Even after the discovery of the heat added by radioactivity, some scientists still gave an important place in the heating of the earth to the outflow of original heat.

New studies by Bullard and other scientists, many of them made in the 1950's, dramatically challenged this older thesis. In the first place, Bullard noted in summarizing this work, the heat coming from the interior is relatively unimportant to surface-living man. "The rate of flow of heat from inside the earth is 25,000 times less than that arriving from the sun when it is overhead," he wrote. "The temperature of the surface therefore is controlled by the sun and not by the internal heat."

Having put the internal heat of the earth in this new minor position, Bullard added: "It seems almost certain that not more than twenty per cent of the observed heat flow can be derived from the original heat locked up in the earth when it was formed."

The English geophysicist pointed out that even if the interior temperatures were as hot as once assumed, and even if they still stood at several thousand degrees, very little of this heat could make its way to the surface through the thick and thickening layers of rock in the mantle.

Most of the internal heating up of the outer zones of the earth comes, it is now clear, from radioactivity. All rocks contain measurable amounts of the radioactive elements, such as uranium, thorium, and potassium. Bullard has calculated that if the rocks of the crust have only half the radioactivity of surface granite, the eighty per cent of the heat flow charged to radioactivity can be accounted for.

How hot, then, is the crust of the earth? Nearly all of the data had been compiled from mine and well measurements, which meant measurements in the crust below the continents. Bullard was anxious to learn in addition what the heat might be under the sea. Such data would be important not only in general studies of the heat of the earth, but because most of the theories proposed to explain the rise of mountains and continents assumed a greater heat flow under continents than under oceans. By driving a tube containing thermometers into the bottom of the ocean Bullard hoped that measurements could be obtained.

In 1949, when he was invited by the University of California to spend some months at the Scripps Institution of Oceanography, he began the development of the necessary apparatus. From a steel cylinder equipped with thermometers, clocks, and many other scientific instruments, he extended a 15.5-foot needle-like nose called a probe. The apparatus was successfully used in the Pacific by R. Revelle and A. E. Maxwell, and in 1952 a second one was built at the National Physical Laboratory. It was placed aboard the R.R.S. *Discovery II* for tests in the Atlantic.

At five different locations the steel wire attached to the instrument was let out and the needle-nosed probe plunged into the sediments on the ocean floor. The probe bent as it penetrated, but the necessary measurements were obtained.

They were unexpected and surprising. They showed that the temperatures under the ocean were almost as high as those under the land. If further studies should confirm these unlooked-for results and prove the existence of high temperatures under the oceans there would be a tendency, Bullard noted in his report to Royal Society, for the slow convection currents in the mantle to rise under the oceans and sink under the continents.[4] This, the reverse of what had been generally assumed, would create new problems in using uprising currents to explain the elevation of the mountains and continents. As happens very frequently in science, new findings had brought new complications. Additional studies will be necessary, but science now has an instrument with which to make part of them.

[4] These are the slow movements in the rocky mantle which Vening-Meinesz has proposed.

If twenty per cent of the heat reaching the crust comes from below and eighty per cent from radioactivity in the crust, Bullard estimates that the temperature at the base of the crust must be 470 degrees hotter than that of the surface. In the past this lower part of man's zone on the earth may have been hotter, for the radioactive material in the crust is constantly decaying and the heat-generation must have been greater in the past than it is today. On this basis, Bullard suggests that the base of the crust may have been molten between three billion and four billion years ago, a figure that accords well with the ages given to the oldest crustal rocks by other methods of calculation.

And how hot is the earth farther down? This, Bullard believes, must remain a matter of speculation. In trying to answer such a question, science is at once driven back to the basic problem of how the earth came to be. The earth's central heat would be one thing if the earth had been initially hot and molten. It would be quite different if the earth had been formed cold and solid, and had subsequenly melted and then cooled, or if the earth had begun cold and then warmed to its present state.

If the cool-origin hypotheses were accepted, Bullard notes that compression might have raised the central temperature to about 550 degrees. In the course of four billion years, he estimates, radioactivity could have added another 1,100 degrees, giving the earth's center at present a possible temperature of about 1,600 degrees.

But this is not a question that can now be settled. Although it is certain that the people of the earth's surface stand in little danger of being roasted by the escape of heat from the center of the earth, there still is no accurate way to estimate positively how hot that center is.

If, however, the temperature at the bottom of the twenty-to-thirty-mile crust is not much more than 450 degrees, a curious problem is created. Many of the lavas that pour out over the earth from erupting volcanoes come from that vicinity. What melts the rock, what raises its temperature to the glowing, red-hot 1,100 or 1,200 degrees at which lava reaches the surface? The problem is made all the more difficult because the mechanism must obviously be one that is local and intermittent in its action. As Bullard observes, volcanoes are "uncommon objects." They occur only in special places on the earth and they remain active for only a fraction of geological time.

Bullard in his studies rules out chemical heat as an adequate source of energy for volcanoes, and his figures also indicate that the necessary heat is not accumulated by any special concentration of radioactive materials. "There is no generally accepted view as to where it does come from," he explains, "but there seems to be good reason to believe that it is derived from the dissipation of mechanical energy associated with earthquakes."

When an earthquake occurs—that is, when some part of the earth's underlying rocks fractures—part of the energy, as Jeffreys has so vividly shown, is radiated out through the earth in waves. The friction created by the cracking and the distortion of the rock turns another part of this energy, and perhaps an equal part, into heat. Although such heat would not spread far, it probably would be sufficient, Bullard argues, to produce melting on a large scale in the zone of deformation.

"This view ascribes earthquakes and volcanic heat to the mechanical energy associated with the distortion of the crust," Bullard sums up. "It explains the general association of volcanoes and earthquakes without requiring particular earthquakes to be associated with particular eruptions."

If this idea is correct, it would be expected that earthquakes would develop first; then, if the deformation continued long enough, volcanoes and earthquakes in the same area; and later on, perhaps, volcanoes alone. By and large, this seems to be the way it has worked out around the earth. Around the Pacific, in Japan, and in the East Indies, where volcanoes are ever alive, earthquakes frequently shake the land. In Italy, Sicily, and the

African Rift Valley, where volcanoes also are still active, earthquakes largely have ceased. The volcanoes in Hawaii and other
mid-Pacific islands are a special case and, it is believed, can be
accounted for by other means.

But science still does not know what produces volcanoes,
those "pure liquid fountains of tempestuous fire." It can only be
said that as the search goes on, it seems to point increasingly
to their linkage with that other most tumultuous of the acts of
nature, the earthquake.

Another curious phenomenon of the interior of the earth has
puzzled men since the time of the Greeks, and probably long
before them. The Greeks tried to explain the strange stone from
the land of the Magnesians which could draw iron filings toward
it. Lucretius in his turn speculated about it. And then it was
learned that a "magnetized" needle tends to point to the north.

In 1600, when William Gilbert, the English physician who
has been called the father of electricity, wrote his *De Magnete,*
he knew that if such a needle is free to move in all directions,

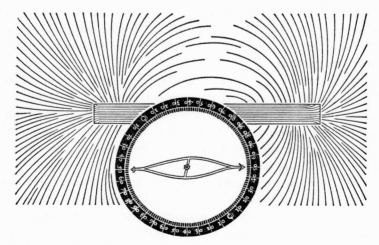

GILBERT'S COMPASS AGAINST A MAGNETIC FIELD.

its north pole will dip in the northern hemisphere and point above the horizon in the southern.

Trying to solve this perplexing problem, Dr. Gilbert made a sphere of loadstone and mapped its lines of magnetic force with such dip needles. As he did so, he saw that the needles behaved almost exactly as they did over the surface of the earth. The doctor thus reached the surprising though sound conclusion that the earth itself is a large magnet, producing its own magnetic field.

But if this were true, how was it magnetized? This question has engaged the best efforts of many scientists in all the years since. Among those who have lately given it particular study are Bullard and Stanley Keith Runcorn.

Runcorn is professor of physics and director of the department of physics at King's College, Newcastle-upon-Tyne, in the University of Durham. Before accepting this appointment in 1956 he was assistant director of research in the department of geodesy and geophysics at Cambridge and a fellow of the university's Gonville and Caius College. He was born in Southport in November 1922 and educated at Cambridge and the University of Manchester. It was while he was at Manchester, as a junior lecturer working for his Ph.D. degree with P. M. S. Blackett, that he became interested in the problems of the earth's magnetism.

Blackett was then investigating the idea that the earth's rotation might have produced its unexplained magnetic field. To test his theory, he developed a highly accurate instrument for measuring magnetization. Making use of the new instrument, Runcorn turned his attention to the behavior of the earth's magnetism during geological time.

With the measurements he has made and the samples he has collected in Colorado and many other places in the world, the English geophysicist has made findings that promise to explain one of the strangest changes the world has ever undergone: the blossoming of a tropical climate in the Arctic, and the freezing of the hot lands of the equator in an Arctic winter.

Embedded in the rocks of the western plateaus and canyons Runcorn discovered untold millions of "fossil magnets"—magnetized grains of iron that had turned toward the magnetic poles when the lava of which they were a part flowed hot from the earth. On that long-ago day they lined up toward the magnetic poles like rows of soldiers on parade. When the lava cooled, they were "frozen" into those positions for all the ages that their containing rock might endure.

Exactly as fossilized shells and bones record the form of living things long since vanished from the earth, so did the fossil magnets picture the magnetic poles and field of their day. With these "natural compass needles" Runcorn could begin to read the magnetic history of millions of years ago.

The English geophysicist pushed on further with his studies, collecting other specimens in some of the very canyons that Powell and Dutton had once explored. He found that sedimentary rocks also preserve the magnetic record. When the magnetized particles were eroded from old volcanic deposits and washed down to the shores of lakes or seas, they tended to line up once more in obedience to the pull of the poles. And when the sediments hardened into stone, the grains were fixed in the pointing postures they had assumed, and will continue to hold until their rocks again crumble into sand or dust.

As startling as this ancient line-up was, what it implied was even more astonishing. The fossil magnets did not point to the present magnetic poles. Some of them, incredibly, pointed in exactly the opposite direction.

"Reading these magnets in rocks at various places around the world, we find evidence of astounding changes in the earth's main axial field," said Runcorn. "During the Tertiary period [between 60 and 100 million years ago] the north and south geomagnetic poles reversed places several times."

Runcorn was saying that the north magnetic pole—it does not exactly correspond to the north geographic pole—had once been at the south pole and that the magnetic south pole had once occupied the position of the north. Furthermore, his studies indicated that this reversal had happened not once, but several times. The earth apparently could magnetize itself in either of two directions.

Some scientists, finding it difficult to accept such a reversal of the magnetic poles, have suggested that the magnet grains may have failed to point truly at the time they were fixed, or that they may have become magnetized in a reverse direction. Runcorn takes note of these objections, but adds: "The more rocks and locations we examine, the more evidence accumulates that the earth did reverse its field several times."

More than a century ago the German mathematical physicist Karl Friedrich Gauss proved that the magnetic field of the earth had to originate inside the earth itself. It was not some effect from without.

"Today," says Runcorn, "there can no longer be much doubt that it is generated by electric currents due to the motion of material in the interior."

Thus, a new problem was posed: what part of the interior could have generated the currents that brought about the reversal of polarity? The scientists quickly ruled out motion in the crust; there are no signs of movement there which could generate electrical currents. Runcorn also eliminated the possibility of the necessary motion in the mantle, for movements in the mantle are extremely slow. The liquid core, however, fitted the requirements almost precisely. Currents in its molten iron (if that is what the fluid should prove to be) could move with sufficient rapidity to generate electricity and magnetize the earth.

If the electric currents in the core should flow from north to south, Runcorn points out, they might set up a magnetic field in the east-west direction; then the fluids of the core moving across this "electric mode field" could generate the currents that produce the earth's north-south magnetic field.

Assuming that the magnetic field arises out of the motions of a liquid core, Runcorn holds that it is not difficult to explain the reversal of the magnetic poles. Some very possible changes in the currents and the movements of the liquid of the core could bring about the shift of the magnetic poles from north to south in a relatively short time.

But the mapping of the fossil magnets is showing that another distinct and even more astonishing change may have come about in the earth. In addition to reversing themselves, the magnetic poles may have moved about as the magnetic axis shifted. To visualize this effect, imagine that your pencil is an axis. Change its tilt and notice how its poles—its point and end—move their position.

As the magnetic axis changed its angle, Runcorn found, the magnetic poles moved slowly and gradually during the six hundred million years of magnetic history which he could read in the rocks. The magnetized grains pointed in different ages to different positions for the magnetic poles. Their pointing enabled Runcorn to trace the north magnetic pole from a position off the California coast about six hundred million years ago to a point in the middle south Pacific some five hundred million years in the past, to one on the Asiatic coast about two hundred million to three hundred million years ago, to another near the geographic north pole today. On the map of the world the route of the "wandering poles" describes a giant and still unclosed loop.

This shift in the magnetic axis and the consequent wandering of the magnetic poles would have occurred, Runcorn postulates, only if there had been a shift in the earth's geophysical axis. Only, that is, if this earth, this roundish planet, had "rolled about."

"We can only suppose," says the English geophysicist, "that the earth's axis of rotation has changed also. In other words, the planet has rolled about, changing the location of its geographic poles, and pulling the magnetic axis with it."

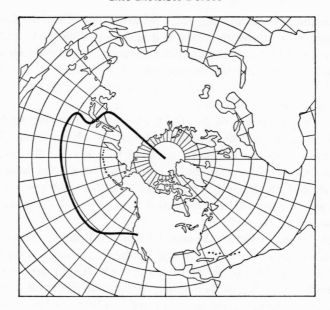

WANDERING POLE. "FOSSIL MAGNETS" INDICATE THE PATH OVER
WHICH THE NORTH MAGNETIC POLE WANDERED DURING THE LAST
600,000,000 years.

Scientists in many related fields are following these findings
with the most acute interest. If Runcorn's magnetic evidence is
right and if the earth has "rolled about," an explanation is provided of the figs and magnolias that Chamberlin found had
once grown under the Greenland ice cap and of the glaciers
whose marks Agassiz discovered along the equator.

If the geographic poles have shifted, the present tropics
once would have been at the north pole and their green lushness
would have been buried under the snow and ice of the Arctic
winter. A great glacier might well have crept down the valley
of the Amazon.

And the north of today would have basked in the equatorial
sun. Then figs and magnolias could have grown in Greenland,

and the trunks and leaves and debris of innumerable trees and plants might have fallen rotting into great swamps, to form the thick coal beds that now underlie the ice of Spitsbergen. It is an almost inconceivable picture.

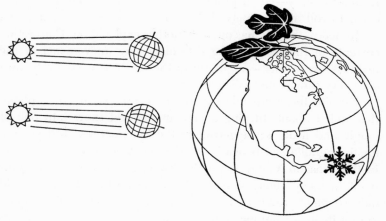

THE EARTH "ROLLS ABOUT." AT ONE PERIOD IN THE PAST, THE NORTH POLE WAS TURNED TO THE SUN. FIGS AND MAGNOLIAS GREW NEAR GREENLAND AND THERE WERE GLACIERS AT THE EQUATOR.

To understand it, the earth must be thought of in the round. For a model, pick up an orange and imagine that a near-by light is the sun. See how with a turn an "equator" in the full warmth of the sun may become a region removed from these intense rays, a region of faint sun and Arctic cold. This seems a possible fate for a sphere rotating in space.

Astronomers have come forward with an explanation of why such a cosmic rolling about may have happened at one distant time in the earth's long past. The rise of mountains or the formation of a continental ice cap, they say, could disturb the earth's rotation on its axis. The added weight in a few places might cause the earth to wobble, much as a chunk of mud on a golf ball can throw it off its even flight. Thomas Gold, astronomer at Great Britain's Royal Greenwich Observatory, points out that if such a "wobble" should develop, the axis would shift until a new balance was attained and the "wobble" eliminated.

Gold has estimated that even modest crustal changes—and he includes the rise of mountains and the formation of ice caps in this category—could produce a wobble that would cause the earth to roll about ninety degrees in less than a million years.

Runcorn, though, has offered another explanation. Convection currents in the mantle—the extremely slow movements in the mantle's dense rock—might cause the earth as a whole to turn over very slowly, he has suggested.

Despite these possible explanations, the picture of a planet that rolled about, turning a land of ice and snow into one of jungle and heat, is staggering to the imagination. And yet the fossil magnolias lie beneath the ice, the etching of the glaciers in the Amazon Valley is unmistakable, and the fossil magnets point to many changes in the magnetic north pole, and could only so point, Runcorn believes, if the earth had rolled about during its long spinning through space.

Yet only a beginning has been made in the study of the vast and inaccessible inner earth. One of Sir Harold Jeffreys's quotations from Ernest Bramah seems particularly appropriate to the present status of the investigation: "'The matter is as long as the Wall and as deep as seven wells,' grumbled Sheng-Yin, 'and the Hoang-Ho in flood is limpid by its side.'"

There is nevertheless the strongest presumption that science has identified for wondering man the major structures of the interior of the earth, its most important materials, and the forces that are moving and shaping not only the underworld but, through it, the surface on which we live. The dire speculations of centuries have at the same time been proved unfounded. The nether world of Hesiod has collapsed. And the seat of Hell is gone at last. But it is still a formidable inner earth that science is revealing, and a strange structure for men to live atop.

WATERS

GREAT AND FIERY OUTPOURINGS

No roads led into the canyon. Far back from the rim, A. C. Waters, professor of geology at Johns Hopkins University, parked his car and set out on foot. A geologist studying the lavas that are spread deep over more than 150,000 square miles in Oregon, Washington, and Idaho does not expect to ride.

The somber Snake River Canyon into which Waters made his way cuts more than a mile into the piled-up lava. Along both sides rise nearly vertical cliffs faced with the black, six-sided columns of basalt. It is one of the most spectacular sights on the continent, outrivaling the more famous Grand Canyon in depth, though not in coloring.

But equally impressive in the eyes of the geologist was the enormous thickness of the lava exposed in the towering canyon walls. Twenty-three separate flows, one above the other, were massed to a depth of more than five thousand feet, and yet the hard, dense rock was as uniform as if the flows had been layers of steel poured from one giant batch.

To Waters this spoke significantly of its origin. By studying and mapping such lava flows and the more violent outpourings of hundreds of huge volcanoes that had once dominated this northwestern section of the United States, the geologist hoped to gain additional understanding of these most spectacular of all the phenomena of nature. What caused the earth to shudder and shake and throw out molten rock and fire? What brought forth the overwhelming incandescent floods? Man had uneasily asked these questions for centuries.

Empedocles had early told the world that the terrifying volcanoes were a breaking forth of the consuming fires of the interior of the earth. Although many others believed in a watery center of the earth, the conviction that the mysterious interior was a place of raging fires remained influential. In the early eighteenth century the Abbé Anton Lazzaro Moro, a serious student of the earth, harked back to it as he studied the reports of how the volcano Monte Nuovo had been born on one fearful night in 1583 near the town of Puzzuoli in the Neapolitan district of Italy. It was said that the quiet countryside had suddenly risen up into a gigantic "bubble" that burst with an earth-shaking explosion. Such quantities of ash and lava erupted from the flaming vent that a cone more than four hundred feet in height was built in a few terrifying days.

"All mountains, islands, and level lands have been raised up out of the bosom of the earth into the position which they now occupy by the action of subterranean fires," declared the Abbé with what was in part astonishing foresight.

Even so careful an observer as Guettard subscribed to the likelihood that volcanoes were created by subterranean fires. He thought, however, that they were produced by the burning of coal and other inflammable materials. Hutton a little later argued that volcanoes were only the vents of the subterranean furnace.

"A volcano is not made on purpose to frighten superstitious people into fits of piety and devotion; nor to overwhelm devoted cities with destruction; a volcano should be considered as a spiracle to the subterranean furnace in order to prevent the unnecessary elevation of the land and the fatal effects of earthquakes," said the Scottish physician. Volcanoes, in his view, were safety valves.

As later scientists wrestled with the problem of how the earth came to be, and many adopted the Laplacian hypothesis of a molten globe consolidated from a fiery gaseous mass, there was a fairly easy explanation of the molten outpourings and of volcanoes. The hot fluid materials of the interior were simply assumed to be breaking their way through the crust.

This facile and understandable answer to the ancient question was badly impaired when seismology demonstrated that both the crust and mantle are solid and rocky. If, in addition, the earth was formed cool, as an increasing number of scientists were convinced, two difficult and new problems were created: how was the rock that streams white-hot from fissures and volcanic cones melted, and how could the great variety of volcanic rocks have been produced? Both were problems that Waters had to face. And the Pacific northwest was an unsurpassed place to confront them.

Few scientists have had so gigantic an accumulation of material to work with. Analyzing it, and using its dramatic surface to deduce what had happened, was to be the work of years. But Waters came to this project with not only a geologist's professional zeal, but the devotion of a native son.

Waters was born in 1905 at Waterville, Washington, in the sight of the Cascade Mountains, the towering range that parallels the Pacific coast through Washington and Oregon and is topped by the magnificent cones of Rainier, Hood, and Shasta.

As a boy he climbed around the slopes and came to know them well. When he went to the University of Washington, however, it was with the intention of becoming a lawyer. Somehow he took more than the law student's usual quota of courses in chemistry, physics, and zoology. He was more than ordinarily interested in such subjects, but there was one thing wrong with all of them: they kept you tied up in the laboratory.

Then Waters enrolled for a course in geology. He realized almost immediately that this was the science for him. Suddenly many of the things he had always known about the mountains—their structure, their rocks, the way they had worn down—took on new meaning. And then there came the further discovery that the great cones and the thick lavas that he had always taken for granted were not the usual run of things in the world, but actually something extraordinary. And added to this, here was a science that made mountain-climbing a part of your business. Law was quickly dropped.

After taking his degree at Washington, Waters went to Yale to do graduate work in geology. He thought at the time that he would eventually go into industry. This was a plan that was soon changed when he undertook some teaching; he liked it so well he wanted to go on with it. Perhaps another influential factor in his decision was that teaching and research would give him a chance to study the remarkable region in which he had been born. His summers could be spent in the mountains.

Waters taught for several years at Stanford University. During the war he worked for the United States Geological Survey on the government's strategic-mineral program. In 1952 he went to Johns Hopkins University at Baltimore as professor of geology.

By this time Waters was well launched into his big project, the over-all study of the northwest volcanic area. The outflow of molten materials had been so immense that it had turned the whole area into a high lava plateau, a plateau that was to be capped still later with soaring, glacier-clad volcanic peaks. Only in India was there another such sheet of lava covering the earth. There, in the Deccan, the welling up of molten rock had produced a continuous basalt plateau extending over nearly five hundred thousand square miles and reaching a depth of about ten thousand feet.

The activity of Vulcan in the Pacific northwest was not far behind, as Waters was soon to see. Over a number of years he worked his way, geologist's hammer in hand, up and down the Washington and Oregon coast. He included in his trek a study of the Olympic-Coast range and of the rich valleys that separated the coastal mountains from the Cascade Mountains a little farther inland.

Around the Olympic Mountains, which tower so majestically over Puget Sound and the Pacific, ran a horseshoe-shaped for-

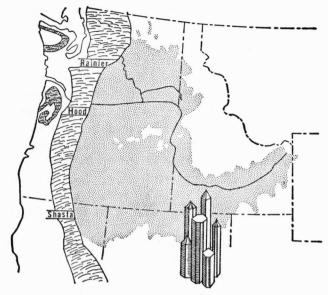

THE GIGANTIC NORTHWESTERN LAVA PLATFORM. ALONG THE COAST, IN ROUGHLY HORSESHOE SHAPE, ARE TWO OF THE DEEPEST LAVA OUTFLOWS; NEXT, THE VIOLENTLY ERUPTED CASCADE MOUNTAINS; AND, TO THE RIGHT, THE VAST OUTPOURINGS OF MOLTEN ROCK WHICH COVERED THE LAND ALONG THE SNAKE AND COLUMBIA RIVERS.

mation of basalt. In places in this area, flow after flow of molten rock had accumulated until it reached the fantastic thickness of fifteen thousand feet, or nearly three miles. Another huge section of the same black flows stretched between Portland and Tillamook. Although not so deep in this part of the Oregon coast, it still attained the imposing thickness of nearly six thousand feet. These had been gargantuan outflows. Waters estimated that forty thousand cubic miles of this rock had been deposited in a sixty-thousand-square-mile strip that now edged the ocean.

Almost at first glance Waters noticed one striking point about this basalt. Enormous masses of it were filled with little almond-shaped cavities that held other materials. He saw, too, that many of the flows were made up of the billowy masses that the geologists descriptively call "pillow lava"—it is not unlike a bed pillow in size and shape. Often the masses were also surrounded by and interlayered with sedimentary rocks.

All of this—the pock-marking, the pillow form, and the "interfingering" with water-formed rocks—pointed to one conclusion: the basalt had been formed in the sea. These were lavas that had pushed through great cracks that must originally have opened offshore. They had spread in wide sheets and tongues over and into sediments washed down from adjoining lands. When all of the fine stuff stirred up by the far-reaching disturbance of the sea bottom settled down into the cracks and crannies in the wavy lava, it carried with it a host of marine shells and fish killed in the upheaval or by the heating of the water.

Judging by the fossils in the interbedded sediments, Waters concluded that the lavas had been irrupted during the Eocene period, roughly thirty million to fifty million years ago. The vulcanism had been intermittent, however. Often thick sands and other sediments had sifted down and buried the onetime fiery extrusion before another flood of lava came. The sites of underwater accumulation also had shifted from place to place. Waters could trace all of this history in the coastal rocks, for ultimately this lava-intruded sea bottom was uplifted to form the Coast Ranges bordering the Pacific.

About one hundred and fifty miles inland from the present edge of the ocean rise the Cascade Mountains. Here, in contrast to the relatively quiet fissure outflows and sedimentary deposit that had built the coastal mountains and valleys, Waters found an ancient scene of overwhelming violence. The core of this lofty range of mountains had been erupted in some of the mightiest explosions the earth can produce, explosions that still minimize any set off by man.

Again the record was clearly inscribed in the rocks. The rock called andesite was its evidence. More than seventy-five per cent of the range core was made up of this gray, speckled stone.

Andesite takes its name from the Andes, where it also was produced in a long series of cataclysmic outbursts.

Huge steam explosions, partly under the sea and partly above it, had blasted this stone forth with a fury that must have shaken this part of the world. "Probably much of this material was erupted in explosions of the ultra-Vulcanian or Peléean type," said Waters. The geologist referred to the terrible explosion of Mount Pelée in Martinique—we shall speak of it later—and to such similar outbursts as the destruction of the island of Krakatoa in 1883. The ill-fated island in the Sunda Strait between Java and Sumatra was wiped from the surface of the sea in an explosion that sent a tidal wave racing around the world.

But there must have been many hundreds of explosions of this order along the northwestern edges of the American continent, for the lavas that gushed up in their wake accumulated into the core of a mountain range more than six hundred and fifty miles long.

The exploded rocks of the Cascades had little of the uniformity of the basalts of the coast, Waters noted. Twisting in and out between the andesites were hardened flows of mud and thick beds of volcanic ash. The andesite also was full of big chunks of other kinds of rocks which had been blasted from the walls of craters. Sometimes the inclusions had been coarsely recrystallized and complexly modified by the hot andesite that had surrounded them.

The explosions, and the jarring they had produced, had opened innumerable cracks and fissures in the cones that had been built up and in the land around. Through them more lavas forced their way to the surface. The ultimate solidification of the lavas in these openings left a permanent map of the roadways used by the rising melt.

At last, however, the great explosions ceased. The mountains they had brought into being began to yield, as all mountains must, to the irresistible wearing of erosion. Ash and the weathered debris of the raw volcanic slopes were washed down into the sea on the west, and upon other basalts that were being laid down to the east.

But the belt of violence was not yet ready to subside into quiescence. Millions of years later the Cascades began to stir again. There were new earthquake shocks, and new volcanoes opened. Many of the eruptions this time were smaller and less violent. After piling up enough ashes and lava to form cones fifty to five hundred feet high, most of the volcanoes died into inaction. Only a few grew into the broad, almost flat-topped domes that geologists name "shield volcanoes." Their fluid lavas are spread out horizontally instead of heaping up into a sharp cone.

This episode was a prelude. A little later the Cascades again broke into violence of the first order. Along their crest ran shock after shock; the fracturing produced by these furious earthquakes can easily be seen. Great clouds of ash and volcanic bombs shot from new openings. Falling in thick showers around the volcanoes' throats, they soon piled up high cones. And then torrents of lava came pouring from the craters and from other openings on the flanks. New explosions added new layers of ash and cinders, and additional lava flows overlaid them, until finally huge steep-sided cones made up alternately of the volcano's fine ejecta and of lava were built. Geologists have called them stratovolcanoes; the world today knows them as Mount Rainier, Mount Hood, Mount Baker, Mount Shasta, and the other majestic peaks that crown the Cascades.

Somewhat before the first series of explosions began amassing the core of the Cascade range, fantastic quantities of basalt had started to gush from the earth on the plains to the east. The lava spilled all over the country between the Cascades and the Rocky Mountains of Idaho to form the great lava plateau drained by the Columbia and Snake rivers. Flow upon flow and layer upon layer, it stacked up through millions of years.

The whole overwhelming record is exposed in the walls of the Columbia and Snake river gorges. As Waters mapped and

measured the flows in this show window, he found that many
of them averaged about one hundred feet in thickness, or about
the height of a ten-story building.

Waters decided to trace one of the flows, a large one, varying from 360 to 480 feet in thickness. It had covered the country like a sea for more than 120 miles from north to south and
for more than 50 miles from east to west. On all sides it then
disappeared under younger lava flows. How much farther this
wave of lava may have spread no one could see.

As the molten tide of rock spread against the mountains that
bordered the lava basin on either side, it dammed the rivers
flowing from their slopes and filled the many lakes that clustered
along the margins of the volcanic plain. "The rivers often were
completely displaced by the lava," said Waters, "and we can see
how they made their way back, perhaps only to be displaced
again by a later flow of lava."

All of this was the work of millions of years. As the lava froze
into rock and then slowly crumbled into a rich soil, extensive
forests grew up on the onetime fiery flows. But the black-
crusted burning streams of molten stone pushed forward another time, setting the forests ablaze and burying their remains
under thick beds of volcanic clinkers. The story, repeated many
times over, was clearly depicted in the walls of the canyon.
Waters collected many specimens of the charred, lava-covered
wood.

The Baltimore geologist estimated that about thirty-five
thousand cubic miles of lava were extruded on the Columbia
plateau. More than a hundred thousand square miles were covered with layer after layer of the once-molten rock; a country
had been engulfed.

The lava of the Columbia plateau, like that of the Coast
Range, was remarkably uniform in composition. It seemed to
have come from one brew, a point of significance that Waters
noted down for reference when he should consider the origin of
these rocks.

Waters was constantly on the outlook for the fissures from which the Columbia plateau lavas had come. Oddly enough, over much of the plateau he could find few of the openings. But in northeastern Oregon he came upon a whole "swarm" of dikes. Some of them were ten to fifty feet wide and cracked through the earth for more than five miles. In their day they had been tremendous rents in the earth. And there was strong evidence that these fissures had been used time and again.

The size of the former openings in the earth seemed to match the magnitude of the outflows. "This suggests," said Waters, "that a large part of the Columbia plateau basalt was erupted from the northeast Oregon dike swarm, and that many flows spread more than one hundred miles."

It was thus a varied and tempestuous record that was revealed in this northwestern section of the United States. Along the two sides of the area, basaltic lavas had flooded forth from deep fissures; in between, a different kind of lava had erupted and exploded from volcanoes large and small.

Why was there this difference? What had produced the basalt of the coast and the andesite of the Cascade Mountains? What forces could have caused the mighty explosions?

Under the present coast and under the Columbia plateau, Waters was convinced, there must have been a melting of a deep "uniform earth layer." For the basalts to be so uniform implied that they had come from one kind of material and had made their way to the sea bottom or the land surface with relatively little alteration. But this was not the case with the andesites that had erupted in the area between. They gave every sign of having had a different source or birth. And what it was could fairly well be seen.

The Cascade Mountain region, all the evidence indicated, had once been an ancient shore. Here the sands and muds of the land had piled up year after year and age after age. As the sediments accumulated, the offshore shelf where the pile was deepest slowly sank—it was the classic pattern of a laden subsiding shelf which Hall had pointed up many years before.

But here lavas intruded. Their heat, plus the heat generated in the sinking, metamorphosing pile, may have brought about some melting of the compacting debris of the land. Water and other fluids slowly stewed out. It is a matter of laboratory demonstration that when such rocks are heated, gases, water, and other fluids are the first substances given off.

The fluids then mixed with the molten magmas—molten rock underground is called magma—which were forcing their way upward, and with this dilution their rise was speeded. The mass was becoming a yeasty sort of mixture—a volatile-rich magma. As it approached nearer to the surface and the weight above it decreased slightly, it may have become more fluid. More melting of the sediments may have followed and more steamy fluids may have been added until at last a "steam-rich, highly explosive andesite magma" was formed. The steam and gases perhaps were only a small part of the mass, but that was enough. The potential was great. Very near the surface, when the last earth pressures were nearly gone, it was like removing the top from a pressure boiler. The world has had many demonstrations of the tumultuous explosions that followed.

In Martinique in April 1902 the people of this West Indian island noticed idly that Mount Pelée had begun to smoke again. Picnic parties climbing up the crater to see what was happening reported that rumblings could be heard. Then more ash began to come from the cone and the rumblings sounded in the town of St. Pierre, which lay along the curving bay at the foot of the volcano. There was uneasy talk about the time Mount Pelée had erupted in 1851.

A few talked of leaving, but an election was pending, and officials urged the populace to remain calm. Few departed, though animals began leaving the mountain slopes and the ash clouds increased until everything on the island was white with the dust.

On May 5 a torrent of boiling mud came hurtling down the

mountainside, and the increasingly black cloud hovering over the cone was shot through with flashes of lightning. By May 7 the ash so filled the air that the town was veiled in what seemed like a perpetual twilight. Shock after shock was running through the earth and the sulfur fumes had grown so strong that people and animals were collapsing in the streets. Adding to the horror was the noise—the roar of the volcano, the crash of thunder, the rush of swollen streams, the crunching of the earth. At daybreak after a night of terror many rushed through the murk to the piers, hoping to escape in some of the boats lying in the harbor.

And then a little before eight o'clock on May 8, on the morning that was still night, a final intolerable roar came from the volcano. The mountain seemed to burst. A billowing, swirling cloud of fiery lava particles mounted high into the air before it rolled down the mountainside.

In three seconds it reached the town. In another instant St. Pierre was no more. Its people perished where they stood or lay. Those waiting on the piers were swept into the sea by the hurricane force of the wind that drove before the cloud, and in another second the sea was turned into a boiling caldron. Ships in the way of the cloud burst into flames and capsized.

Nothing was left of the town but the hulks of its once white and tiled-roofed buildings. Searching-parties from a ship that had escaped found only three human beings alive where forty thousand had lived the day before. Two of the three pulled from the wreckage died soon afterward. Only one man, who had been imprisoned in the jail's deep dungeon, survived the explosion and the cloud of fire. Such explosions have since been known as Peléean.

It was with violence of this order that the steam-enriched magmas of the Pacific northwest exploded along the narrow stretch of former shoreline. The torrents of lava that followed the explosions piled up the core of the Cascade Mountains. And it was another cycle of such outbursts that added the cones—

Rainier, Shasta, Hood, and dozens of lesser ones—that are now the glory of that range.

Not all the mixtures of magmas and fluids stewed from sedimentary piles are so explosive. Much depends, Waters points out, on the amount of water and hence of steam. If just enough is added to make the magma fluid, it may erupt or overflow without explosiveness. The Hawaiian volcanic lavas are of this type, though the ominous appearance of a flow, gold and red and white with heat and destroying all before it, seems to belie the use of the word quiet. When Kilauea exploded, as it did in 1924, it was not an andesite mixture that caused the violence, though the explosion resembled one. For some unknown reason the basalt lava that generally boils in the throat of the volcano had suddenly retreated. Ground water running in had taken its place. Then the lava returned, encountering and mixing with the water, and an explosion followed which shook the island.

Nevertheless, the stewing out of the watery fluids scarcely affects the bulk of the sedimentary pile. Only a small part of its mass is thus lost, Waters points out. If the remaining sediments are further heated, they may next become a little slushy. Under such conditions, Waters argues, the silicate part of the mixture begins a slow push upward. If such silicates succeed in reaching the surface, they often form the stone called rhyolite, a rock widely seen in the southern Rocky Mountains.

But there also is a very good chance that the soft, rising silicates may never make their way into the open air. As most of their water has previously been lost, they are apt to be thick and slow-moving. As they push upward they may melt and displace and assimilate the rocks they meet. In this way the hot mixture may remake the part of the crust through which it passes; here is a conquest by absorption. The geologists call such masses batholiths. If they crystallize before reaching the surface, they form granite or one of the wide range of granite-like rocks. Such processes, Waters believes, have produced many of the granites of the Rockies, and they may have created similar

masses under the Cascades. Some granites that are only now being revealed in the deep river gorges along the crest of the Cascades hint that granite in volume may lie below.

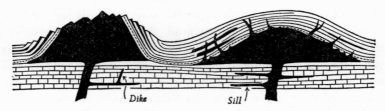

MOLTEN ROCK PUSHES SURFACEWARD. (RIGHT) IT PRODUCES A BULGE
IN THE EARTH, BUT DOES NOT BREAK THROUGH. (LEFT) EROSION
ULTIMATELY BARES THE INTRUSION.

Thus, the kind of rock the silicates form on their upward
journey depends, in Waters's opinion, on the rocks they encounter, the temperatures, pressures, remixing, and a nearly incom-
prehensible complex of conditions. A vast variety of rock might
be produced, and so it is. Complexity below results in the complexity and variety of rock that men know at the surface.

But after the fluids are gone from the onetime sedimentary
pile and after the silicates have separated, a final refractory part
of the rock remains. This dry, thick residue, this sludge, may
under heat and pressure be slowly erupted to form the strange,
banded lavas that harden into the rocks of the continental shields,
the nuclei of the continents.

The whole grand process of the breaking down of the sediments leads, Waters suggests, to a "sort of crude stratification,"
with the granitic rocks above and the more refractory ones below. And thus the sand, the gravel, and the dust washed down
from the mountains and the plains are turned once more, with
aid from volcanic forces and materials, into the igneous stone of
new mountain ranges. One phase of the eternal cycle is ended.
But hundreds of millions of years may have gone into its illimitable transformations.

In a Johns Hopkins geological laboratory sits what newspaper feature writers like to call a "scientific mud pie." It is in fact a clay model that represents a section of the earth's crust.

To study how the earth fractures and what types of movement might produce that fracturing, Dr. Ernst Cloos, chairman of the department of geology at Johns Hopkins, spreads a slab of soft clay two inches thick on a piece of wire screen. The front edge of the wire is bolted to the table, and the back edge is pulled away from the table. Tension fractures open at an angle of about ninety degrees, and sheer at about forty-five degrees to the pull. "This kind of fracturing is common in all zones of movement and is well known," Cloos points out.

Looking down on the model as a passenger in a high-flying plane might look down on the earth, it resembles an actual stretch of the earth. In some of the Cloos models are fractures closely similar to those that opened in the northeast part of Oregon and through which the lavas poured. What is more, each time the same pulls are applied to the underlying wire, the same pattern of cracks appears. The earth's fracturing, the model suggests, is just as certain a function of the forces operating in the earth.

The earth itself has a hard, crystalline crust, made up in large part of the silicates which, Waters pointed out, tend to rise, and of aluminum. For this reason it is sometimes referred to as "sial" —SIlica plus ALuminum. The mantle, on the other hand, is composed largely of silicates and magnesium, "sima"—or SIlica plus MAgnesium—and it is vitreous. Although sima is many times more rigid than steel at atmospheric pressures, under heavy pressure it can flow almost like the clay of Cloos's models.

If there are currents in the mantle, as many scientists now believe, they must set up tremendous tensions by movement under the relatively unyielding crust. Like any rigid thing strained beyond its power to give, the earth's crust might be expected to crack under such strains, as it seemingly does.

Cloos draws no comparison, but it is the movement of the

screen underlying his "crust" which results in the fractures that so closely match those in the crust of the earth. Cloos applies no pressures to the sides or end of his models. It is the underlying movement that does it.

In matters as vastly complex and ultimately untestable as these, no hard and fast conclusions are possible. But the Cloos models add one more clue, a clue that points in the same direction as many others now developing in other branches of the earth sciences.

Significantly, many of the new explanations of the earth's interior and surface fit closely together, whether they come from seismology, from the geophysical study of the grand patterns of development, from an examination of the rocks, or from a scientific mud pie on a laboratory table.

GOLDSCHMIDT AND MASON
ASSORTMENT OF RICHES

THE NOTED NORWEGIAN CHEMIST ground up some rock and melted it in a crucible with alkali. His immediate aim was simply to analyze this sample, to determine what it was made of; but in this and hundreds of similar experiments he would go far toward showing what the earth is made of, and why its rocks and substances are, inevitably perhaps, what they are.

When the melt had cooled, the chemist, V. M. Goldschmidt, added some acid to begin the breaking down of the rock into its components. The man in the laboratory cannot wait a million years, or whatever the time might be, for the decomposition to happen naturally. As the acid went to its immediate work, silica, which makes up most of the world's sands, settled to the bottom of the tube. Then Goldschmidt oxidized the remaining solution and added some ammonia. At this, iron and aluminum were precipitated as a reddish powder, very like some of the iron-bearing clays of the earth.

Again Goldschmidt could not wait for the calcium that was still in the solution to separate, nor, in an experiment, could he have living organisms build it into their shells and bones. He added a different reagent, and the white grains of a calcium compound settled out. It was a calcium similar to that which in the seas and other waters drifts down to the bottom, ultimately to form limestone.

Only one small part of the original rock remained in the solution: the sodium and potassium salts. At this point the chemist broke off his test, for he did not need to go further. He left the salts in solution, just as the salts that are the last fragments of the earth's rock often remain endlessly in that final solution of nature's, the oceans.

As Goldschmidt watched the same materials come from the rocks again and again, he had one of those flashes of insight which sometimes come to men of genius. The separation occurring in the test tube, he saw, was a miniature representation of what was happening in the earth. The groups of materials yielded by the laboratory analysis were similar to those which would have been produced by the natural breaking down of the rocks of the present earth, but, more than this, they were the substances that would have come from the eons-long breaking down of the materials with which the earth began.

Many others had made similar experiments without grasping the analogy. But Goldschmidt was a man of original mind. Born in Switzerland, he had gone to Norway at the age of thirteen. He was such a remarkable student at the University of Oslo that he received his Ph.D. degree at the age of twenty-three, and at the age of twenty-six was made a full professor. He soon became known throughout the world as one of the pioneers of geochemistry, the chemistry of the earth.

In comparing the laboratory analysis to the process of change in the earth, Goldschmidt was not implying that the breaking down of the earth's original rocks was a simple matter. The changes and transformations through which the earth's first materials had passed were so complex as to be perhaps beyond the full accounting of man.

Nevertheless, Goldschmidt understood that the rocks and other substances of this present earth are the end products of that process. The crust of the earth on which we live is the result, he pointed out, of the chemical differentiation of the planet that consolidated out of the matter of the universe.

In a very real sense, therefore, the sand that we idly sift through our fingers at the beach is material that was present when the earth began. It then, of course, had some other form, as did the soil of our gardens and fields, the rocks of the continents, and the ores, the petroleums, and coals of the subsurface. But the elements of which they were made were there at the start.

Goldschmidt could confidently reach this daring and startling conclusion because he knew that in the several billion years since the earth consolidated, very little else had been added, and very little had been lost. The earth is what the geochemist calls a "closed system." It still has only the materials with which it began, vastly altered though they are.

It is true that meteors have fallen on the earth and that there is a constant rain of meteoritic dust from outer space. It is also a fact that some hydrogen and helium are always being lost by escape from the upper atmosphere. But both of these gains and losses are insignificant in comparison to the earth as a whole, and, with these minor exceptions, the earth is no more and no less than it was at the outset.

In searching for the derivation of the materials of the earth, Goldschmidt was pioneering. Geology had gone far in the description of the earth and its processes, but the basic causes that had governed the making of the rocks, and hence of the earth, had not been discovered. The big questions of how and why had scarcely been touched; they lay ahead. Goldschmidt liked to say that what was needed was a tallying of "the account books of the universe." As such a challenging and fruitful prospect always does, this new hope of increasing the understanding of nature drew students to Goldschmidt from all over the world.

One who came from the opposite end of the earth was Brian Mason. Mason was born in New Zealand in 1917, in a region likely to nourish any interest a boy might have in the earth. All around were high mountains, volcanoes, and hot springs, and on this restless margin of the Pacific earthquakes often shook the countryside. After graduating from the University of New Zealand, where he had studied both chemistry and geology, Mason went to Norway in 1939 to study with Goldschmidt.

Before he could take his degree, the Nazi invasion came. Goldschmidt, who had had an earlier, disastrous experience with the Nazis—he was serving as a professor at Göttingen, Germany, when Hitler came to power, and had to abandon the irreplaceable laboratory he had equipped there—went into hiding. He was later captured. Just before he was to be sent to a concentration camp in Poland, he made his escape and ultimately succeeded in reaching England. He returned to Norway at the end of the war, but his health had been broken. He died, honored by the chemists and geologists of the world, in March 1947.

Mason was more fortunate. He had broken a leg in a skiing accident just before the invasion, but a friend picked him up in a car and they made their way to the Swedish border. The young New Zealander was officially interned for the duration of the war, though the Swedish government permitted him to enroll at the University of Stockholm and complete his work for the Ph.D. degree.

At the close of the war Mason returned to New Zealand to teach at the university. In 1947, when a position was offered at the University of Indiana, he accepted, feeling that a geochemist should see as much of the world as possible. He remained in the midwest until 1953, when he was appointed curator of physical geology and mineralogy at the American Museum of Natural History in New York.

Mason carried on the study of the earth along the lines opened by Goldschmidt. In addition he brought together in his book *Principles of Geochemistry,* and in a chapter that he contributed to *The Earth as a Planet,* the remarkable story of the earth which is being revealed by this work.[1]

If the earth as we know it is the end product of the materials present at its beginning, an understanding of the present chemical composition of the earth becomes essential.

[1] Brian Mason: *Principles of Geochemistry.* New York: John Wiley & Sons; 1952.

The geophysicists had established that the earth was made up of a "thin heterogeneous crust," a "fairly homogeneous mantle," and a core of iron. The thickness of each layer also was known with considerable precision, as was the earth's volume. It was therefore possible to compute the earth's bulk chemical composition. Making such a computation, the geochemists found that 90 per cent of the globe as a whole was made up of four elements: iron, which accounted for 35 per cent by weight; oxygen, 28 per cent; magnesium, 17 per cent; and silicon, 13 per cent.

Probably only four other elements—nickel, calcium, aluminum, and sulfur—are present in amounts greater than 1 per cent. Seven other chemical elements may occur in amounts ranging from 0.1 per cent to 1 per cent. Thus, Mason pointed out in his book, the earth is made up almost entirely of fifteen elements. The others, though they may be important to man, occur only in very small amounts. It was clear that the earth as a whole had been put together with a relatively few big blocks of chemical elements.

The crust's assortment of elements differed from that of the whole earth's. The crust's rocky shell was made up almost entirely—99 per cent—of eight elements, and among them oxygen was absolutely predominant. Oxygen (47 per cent) is a major part of practically all the materials of the surface. It has even been suggested, in recognition of oxygen's leading role, that the crust might well be called the oxysphere.

And the crust differed revealingly from the mantle, the core, and the cosmos as a whole. Where the outer layer of the earth was long on oxygen, the mantle was long on iron and magnesium, the core on iron, and the cosmos on hydrogen and helium. The geochemists wanted to know why.

As the earth was assembled in one way or another out of cosmic materials and therefore would almost certainly have had a large amount of hydrogen and helium, the obvious conclusion was that the earth had lost its share of these volatile gases. If the earth was initially a blazing gaseous mass, as some maintained, the volatiles would certainly have escaped. So too, Urey had emphasized, would they have been lost if the earth had been formed by the accretion of solid particles at low or moderate temperatures. Either way, they would have soared up and away, just as inevitably as the helium balloons that we like to set free on festive occasions.

But how did the crust and mantle get their respective chemical make-ups? Suppose, Mason suggested in discussing the problem, that the globe at one time was largely a mass of molten silicates. Suppose it then began to cool. As the temperature dropped, the iron and magnesium compounds in the melt would be the first to crystallize—numerous laboratory tests have shown that this would be the case. Their crystals would sink to the bottom of the liquid mass. The lighter materials left would solidify at the top, probably into granite or a granite-type rock.

Thus, the cooling of such a melt would concentrate the iron and magnesium compounds at the bottom and the granitic ones above, exactly as we find them. As Mason puts it, "the fractional crystallization of an originally homogeneous silicate melt would bring about the differentiation of the mantle and crust."

Superficially this conclusion would seem to favor the theory that the earth was originally molten. But Mason in his book cites the evidence that melting could have resulted later if the earth was formed by the accretion of solid bodies. Compression and radioactivity could have supplied the heat. Thus, on either assumption—of a molten or of a solid beginning—the geochemist's analysis indicated that the earth would have separated into the kind of crust, mantle, and core which the seismographs show does exist. Any way you looked at it, the evidence fitted together.

It is with what happened afterward to the mantle and crust that man is perhaps most concerned. After the earth had sorted itself out in a very early period, how were the materials of the mantle and crust turned into the vast variety of rocks and substances which man knows and depends on today?

"Whatever the nature of the initial crust," said Mason, "it has been subjected to a variety of processes through geological time and has undergone great changes. Vast amounts of magma [molten rock] have poured out on the surface through volcanic vents or have crystallized within the crust.

"The earth's surface has been subjected to weathering and erosion, with the chemical and mechanical breakdown of pre-existing rocks and the transportation of the debris in suspension or solution. Most of this material has eventually come to rest in the sea and some has ultimately returned to the land areas in the form of sedimentary rocks. Then again, both sedimentary and igneous rocks may be transferred through geological processes to the lower parts of the crust, where, by the action of fluids, they have been transformed into metamorphic rocks or perhaps they have been partially or wholly remelted."

The earth's history, as it had been brilliantly worked out by the geologists over the last two hundred years, could not have been more succinctly or clearly summarized. To the geochemists it was another starting-point. The problem to them was what principles had guided or determined this evolution of the earth.

The chemists had early developed what they called the "phase rule." This was the principle that a cooling magma does not all crystallize at once, but that at certain temperatures certain "phases" crystallize and at lower temperatures still others. Sir James Hall had caught a glimpse of the idea one hundred and fifty years before when the Leith glassworks accidentally let a mass of green glass cool slowly and it turned into a white crystalline rock. When Hall re-melted it and quickly cooled it, it went back into non-crystalline glass.[2]

Studying the problem intensively and over a period of years, the Geophysical Laboratory of the Carnegie Institution of Washington, and particularly Dr. Norman L. Bowen, found that one magma, as temperatures and conditions varied, might yield one type of rock or a whole succession of rocks ranging from dunites

[2] See Chapter VIII.

rich in magnesium and iron to lighter granites rich in alkalis and aluminum. Thus, if a magma cooled slowly underground, one kind of rock might be formed; but if the cooling were slow and then rapid, a wholly different range of rocks might be produced. Some of the vast variety in the earth's igneous rocks was becoming understandable.

But the geochemists still needed to know why certain elements always occurred in particular minerals. The search for an answer drove them back to the basic structure of matter.

It was then that Goldschmidt demonstrated that the whole "concourse of matter" depended upon the atom, and upon the arrangement that the atoms of a particular material take on at certain temperatures. As a mineral in a rock crystallizes, its atoms arrange themselves in a pattern that the geochemist calls a lattice, though it is a three-dimensional structure more nearly resembling a playground's jungle gym than what we generally consider a lattice. Any atoms of the right size and shape to fit themselves into the lattice go into the mineral that is forming.

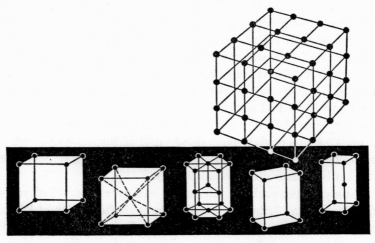

LATTICES. SOME OF THE SIMPLEST OF THE THREE-DIMENSIONAL ARRAYS OF ATOMS WHICH CONSTITUTE ALL SOLIDS. EACH SOLID HAS ITS OWN DISTINCTIVE ARRANGEMENT OF ATOMS.

If, for example, the typical lattice of a ferromagnesian mineral was forming, the small magnesium atoms could edge their way in most easily. A magnesium-rich mineral would be formed first, as it always is in this group.

The crystal lattices act as a sorting mechanism. The process might be compared in one sense to a series of siftings. If a sieve with a special kind of screen were employed, only materials of the right size and shape to get through its mesh would be removed from a mixture. If then another screen with mesh of a different size were introduced, another part of the mixture would be sifted out.

By working out the size and action pattern of each mineral, Goldschmidt was able to predict the order in which both major and minor elements would be removed from a melt. Science, as a result, is well on the way toward understanding why certain groups of rocks are formed in a certain order when molten rock cools. The order of the outcome is as sure as the shape and electrical charge of the atoms; there is nothing hit-or-miss about it.

Magmas, however, also contain water and other volatile material, or at least most scientists now concede that they do. The point was long debated, for it was a critical one. If water were present, it undoubtedly would play a major part in altering the rocks below the surface. But even more, it might be a major source of the earth's surface waters; perhaps it was the water from the depths of the earth that had filled the oceans, and ultimately watered the lands. Certainly no water is received from outer space. The rains, of course, are simply water picked up from the earth and re-showered upon it.

The issue could not be directly settled, for no one has yet devised any way to get red-hot magmas out of the earth for testing. It is dangerous enough to approach them when they are erupting. But there was much indirect proof.

Those who watched the explosion of Vesuvius in 1906 told of the enormous cloud that rose above the volcano. From these accounts some volcanologists estimated that the amount of steam and gas ejected outweighed the solid material. But other scientists studying other volcanoes came to the conclusion that the erupting magmas were very "dry." They could point to the towering spire of lava that pushed up from the throat of Mount Pelée following the disastrous explosion. The thick column rose to tremendous heights, though always with some crumbling away at the top. At its peak, the lava tower was perhaps a third higher than the Washington Monument. That lava must have been very stiff and dry.

Studies of freshly erupted lavas and gases showed a varying content of water. At Kilauea in Hawaii water was the dominant material in volcanic vapors, though they also contained carbon dioxide, hydrogen sulfide, hydrochloric acid, and other humanly unpleasant ingredients. In evaluating the newest findings and discussing the general question of water from volcanoes, Mason did not hesitate to say: "It is evident that igneous activity during geological time has brought vast amounts of water and other volatile matter to the earth's surface."

Thus, from geochemistry and new geological studies came additional evidence that much of the earth's water had come from the hot, hidden depths of the earth. It is beginning to appear, though in a sense wholly unsuspected by the ancients, that the depths were in truth the "'fountains of the deep."

From the earth's earliest beginnings, the molten rock that came from the interior began to wear away as soon as it reached the erosive surface. In time the sands and muds that were ground and dissolved from the hardened lavas collected in the seas and other waters. There they were compacted into the sedimentary rocks that seem to bulk so large in our world and yet are in actuality a thin veneer upon it.

At first it seemed to those studying the earth that the sedimentary rocks should display an average mixture of the chemical materials present in their parent igneous rocks. This proved not to be the case. It was then that the geochemists recognized that weathering, erosion, and sedimentation lead to another separation of the elements, and that out of this second breakdown in the rocks come nearly all of the materials that supply man with food, clothing, shelter, and power. Here are produced the soils, the building materials, the iron, salts, coal, and oil that are the bases of man's world.

And geochemistry suggests that this *must* be the outcome. With the given separation processes—weathering, erosion, and sedimentation—acting upon the materials of the igneous rocks, the materials of the crust are unfailingly produced. As Goldschmidt demonstrated in the experiment described in the opening of this chapter, if rocks are broken down in the test tube the same groups of derivative compounds are produced as in the gigantic laboratory of nature.

Although the rules governing this breakdown of the igneous rocks have not been worked out with the precision of those governing the separation of a cooling magma, the geochemists can now say that six groups of materials are produced:

1. the resistates, or materials that are especially resistant to chemical and mechanical breakdown and thus collect as granular material. The best example is sand, in which the quartz of the rocks concentrates.

2. the hydrolyzates, or the products of the chemical breakdown of the "aluminosilicates." They produce the clays and form the resting-point of the aluminum in the rocks.

3. the oxidates. Their formation precipitates the iron and manganese that existed in the parent rocks.

4. the carbonates, which either through inorganic processes or through the action of living organisms produce the limestones. They come from calcium in the original rocks.

5. the evaporates. They come from the rock salts that collect in the oceans and remain there unless some of the waters are cut off and evaporate.

6. the reduzates. They comprise the coals and oils and other products that take on their form directly or indirectly through organic processes.

This, then, is the fate of more than ninety-nine per cent of the materials locked up in the world's volcanic rocks. What happens to the few traces of minor elements during sedimentation has not yet been investigated thoroughly.

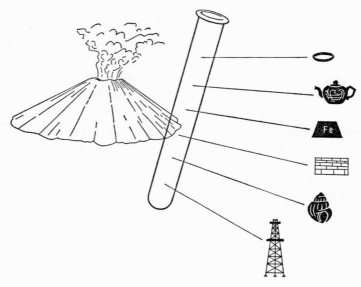

THE VOLCANO, SOURCE OF THE EARTH'S RICHES. FROM THE AGE-LONG BREAKDOWN OF ONCE MOLTEN ROCK COME THE EARTH'S SANDS, INCLUDING THE GOLD SANDS, THE CLAYS, IRON, LIMESTONES, THE SALTS, MOST OF WHICH COLLECT IN THE SEA, AND INDIRECTLY OIL AND COAL.

The process yields great riches to man. The hard, resistant little particles that defy breakdown produce not only the sands, but all the sandstones. From the silica sands we make glass and innumerable other industrial products. But a number of other minerals also collect as sands. One of them is zircon. Occasionally sands are rich enough in it to make possible a profitable separation. Other resistant minerals that accumulate in the sands include magnetite, ilmenite, rutile, monazite, cassiterite, and two metals that have profoundly influenced the course of human history—gold and platinum.

In the very early stages when the earth had consolidated and its materials were separating into crust, mantle, and core, what happened to any particular element depended upon the configuration of its atoms. Uranium and thorium, which fitted into the lattices of the crustal minerals—it might be said that they had an affinity for these materials—were therefore concentrated in the crust. It is here that man has lately been discovering them. But gold and platinum went with iron; they were tied to it.

"Most of the world's gold and platinum metals," said Mason, "are presumably concentrated in the iron core."

Thus there is the possibility that if man should ever bore through to the liquid center of the earth, he might come upon a gold hoard that would exceed even the most fevered dreams of the explorers of the past.

The crustal gold that man has pursued with so much ardor and bloodshed is gold that was linked originally with some of the iron that remained in the mantle and crust. Only occasionally, however, did igneous and sedimentary separation processes bring enough of it together to set off a human gold rush. Gold lodes are considered unusually rich if they carry as much as half an ounce of gold to a ton of rock. More than half the gold obtained in the United States and in all the other countries of the world, with the exception of Canada and South Africa, is gold that is extracted from the sands. Because it resisted the chemical breaking down of nature, it washed out of the rocks and into the sands with the other resistates.

And so is science ending the long and romantic saga of gold's origins—ending it with some curious throwbacks to the beliefs of the ancients.

The alchemist Aurelio Augurelli, in the poem he wrote in 1518, *The Golden Fleece and the Art of Making Gold,* held: "The place where metals take their origin is the inmost and unmoved center of the earth which in shape is like a marble goblet hollowed out of the deep-lying rocks, a vaulted chamber into which the rays of the sun penetrate and the heavenly lights shoot into it innumerable rays which ripen and mature the collected vapours which from thence pass out and tend to fill up all the spaces in the rocks and all crevices traversing them."

Peter Martyr, a councillor to the Emperor Charles V, also insisted, like most others of his day, that gold "grew" within the earth. "The vayne of gold," he wrote, "is a lyving tree." Its roots, declared Peter, "extendeth to the centre of the earth and there taketh nourishment of increase."

And so the old and new have oddly met, for very different reasons, in placing gold at the center of the earth. Man has garnered only the bits.

The aluminum compounds—the hydrolyzates—that weather from the igneous rocks break down in the tropics into aluminum clays and into the bauxites from which industry manufactures aluminum. In other areas, where there is less heat and moisture, the aluminum in the rocks forms ordinary clays. "In either case," Mason said, "the end product represents a concentration of aluminum over the average amount in the earth's crust."

It is only when nature concentrates a scattered material that man can afford to mine it. Although all the rocks and clays of America and Europe contain aluminum compounds, much of the aluminum the world uses comes from the richer bauxites in British Guiana, Malaya, and other areas where a tropical or monsoon climate takes a hand in bringing it together.

Under another very special set of circumstances, the clays from the rocks form black bituminous shales. This usually comes about when the clays collect very slowly in lakes or other waters rich in organic material. The passage of time turns the enriched mud into the rock known as shale. In Colorado and other parts of the west there are whole mountains of it. The beds on the Green River alone are twenty-six hundred feet thick. If the oil were extracted from this shale, it could supply the requirements of the United States for hundreds of years. A government experimental plant once succeeded in extracting the oil at prices approaching those of well-produced oil. At that stage, however, the experiment was halted.

The shales also are fairly rich in uranium. As their carbon content increases, so does the uranium, a fact that does not necessarily imply that the uranium came from the organic material. It may have been present in the clay. "The evidence indicates that the concentration of uranium is not the result of biological activity, but of later chemical processes, probably related, in part at least, to the presence of organic matter in the sediments," Mason explains.

The oxidates, the next major group to form from the crumbling of earlier rocks, include the iron and manganese that are the underpinning of modern industrial development. Although much of the earth's original iron has settled to the core, or perhaps is still settling toward the center, iron remains the fourth most abundant element in the crust. It accounts for a little more than five per cent of the crustal rocks.

But the iron of the crust, like gold and aluminum, is so finely divided and so chemically bound up in the rocks that unless weathering and sedimentation concentrated it, its recovery would be too costly for man. In all probability the rocks in the Lake Superior region and in Labrador did not originally contain much more iron than any others. They must have been about average. At one time in the past, however, waters draining from the Canadian shield ran across shoals and sandbanks that occupied the present site of the Mesabi and Labrador iron deposits. Conditions were right for separating out the iron carried by the waters, and it was deposited in thick beds in the shallows. Enough iron settled down to produce ores with a twenty-five- to sixty-per-cent content of iron. Later it became easy to strip away the shallow beds of gravel and soil which covered the iron ores and scoop them out by steam shovel.

In other places, the iron in the waters came to a halt around shell fragments and sand grains, and formed nodules around

them. In still other places, iron was precipitated in big, vegeta-
tion-filled bogs. The black sludge from the rotting plants piled
up on top of it, and eventually beds of coal were laid down atop
the iron deposits.

The oxidized iron that weathered out of the rocks had a
high absorptive power, and often picked up many minor elements. Vanadium, phosphorus, arsenic, antimony, selenium have
been found in iron ores in amounts larger than their average
abundance in the crust.

Very soon after the rains began streaming across the young
rocks of the earth's surface, they must have carried away large
amounts of the easily dissolved calcium. The carbonates, another
great group derived from the igneous rocks, were washed out in
enormous quantities. Even today in certain places, such as around
the Bahamas, the sea is cloudy with their white powder. If there
is a sudden drop of temperature, precipitation immediately begins. Limestones formed from such deposition often are as much
as ninety-five-per-cent pure calcium carbonate. They are a white,
dense, smooth stone.

But this is an exceptional type of limestone. The calcium
washed down to the seas more often is absorbed by the billions
upon billions of sea creatures and built into their bones, their
shells, and their reefs. The discarded shells and bones slowly accumulate into great beds of limy sediments and ultimately into
limestone. All the while, the coral polyps use the calcium they
take from the sea to keep building up their reefs to the waves that
are their life. Over millions of years they produce undersea mountains of limestone, some of which in their turn become dry-land
mountains. It is through the organism of life that much of the
world's limestone has been formed.

In quantity, the evaporates do not bulk large among the
groups of elements worn from the igneous rocks of the world.
Most of the salts leached out of the rocks and carried down to
the seas remain awash in their waters for time without end.
Only occasionally is an arm of the sea blocked off from the

tides, and only then, after most of the water has been dried away by the sun and wind, are the salts crusted white on the newly formed land. Such deposits are very few in the total of all the rocks, but their importance in the deciphering of the geological history of the earth is in inverse proportion.

Very early in history, men saw that this was one deposit whose formation they could study. They could not easily watch the laying down of iron ores or limestone, but they could watch and themselves initiate the formation of salt deposits. Aristotle was one of the Greeks who undertook this experiment. To test his belief that fresh water was drawn up into the atmosphere and that the salt was left behind, he evaporated some sea water, and satisfied himself that his theory was correct. The experiment enabled him to explain why the sea was salty.

Modern scientists studying the earth also early began to work with salt. They learned that when sea water evaporates under natural conditions, calcium carbonate is the first solid to separate. As evaporation goes on, gypsum and common salt settle out. Only when the solution is down to 1.54 per cent of its original volume do the potassium and magnesium salts crystallize. There are such deposits in Germany, Texas, New Mexico, and in Perm, in the U.S.S.R. In the United States these salts and the common sodium chloride, or table salt, often are "mined" by pumping water down into the beds and taking the salts out in solution.

One final group of products comes, with some indirection, from the breaking down of the igneous rocks. Most important among them are the coals and oils, which are classified as the reduzates. They come from a reduction process in which living things participate.

Sir William Logan proved well over a hundred years ago that coal forms from the decay of dense vegetation that has grown in swamps on the site of the coal seams. Often as much as fifteen feet of rotten trunks and decayed leaves and branches must accumulate to produce one foot of coal. The muck must then be covered with layers of sand, gravel, or mud to create the necessary pressures and other conditions under which the carbon from the plant tissues is concentrated into a solid black coal. The woods and other materials that go into the making of coal have a carbon content of about fifty per cent. In the coal process the carbon becomes so compacted that bituminous coals have a carbon content of about eighty-six per cent, and anthracites of about ninety-four per cent.

Only under such special conditions did the transformation of vegetation into coal take place. And yet the United States has 250,000 square miles underlaid with coal. Although billions of tons have been mined, even more billions of tons remain waiting in the earth.

Coal very frequently betrays its origins. Whole tree trunks often are found embedded in coal seams, and many a lump bears the impress of leaves or bark. But oil, that other reduzate of prime significance to an industrial economy, shows no vestige of its beginnings or of its point of origin. Its background is effectively concealed.

Through most of the last century chemists argued that oil was produced when steamy hot water reacted with carbides of iron and other metals. With its paraffin base, oil seemed to them to be an inorganic compound. Certainly there were no signs that living organisms had anything to do with its formation.

More exact studies shattered this illusion. They indicated that oil was an accumulation of minute droplets that had been formed originally in the bodies of tiny plants and animals. If this were true, it implied an accumulation that taxed even the most willing imagination. For most of the plants and animals from which the oil had to come were microscopic algæ and diatoms and diminutive one-celled foraminifera. Their bodies could have contained only the veriest trace of oil. It seemed impossible that these microscopic bits could have collected into pools totaling millions of gallons.

Only the enormous prolificness of nature over hundreds of millions of years could have achieved such a collection. Slowly the story began to emerge. As the bodies of these uncountable millions of living things had slowly decayed on shallow and often stagnant sea bottoms, the particles of oil in their bodies had been squeezed out. In all probability bacterial action played a part in this extraction. But once the droplet was in a free state it began a migration.

Lighter than fresh water and much lighter than salt water, it worked its way through cracks in the rocks, carried along as a film on the water. Sometimes it came to a place where it was halted. Perhaps there were rocks above through which it could not seep, and perhaps there were sands in which it could accumulate, or a dome-like structure in which it could find space.

There it remained, buried and unknown until men discovered its presence just about a hundred years ago. It was in 1859 that "Colonel" Drake of Pennsylvania drilled a seventy-foot well and found to his amazement that it yielded twenty barrels of oil a day. He sold it as a medicine guaranteed to cure all ailments.

Since that day billions of barrels have been drawn from the earth in Pennsylvania, Texas, California, and many other parts of the United States as well as from huge fields in the Middle East and elsewhere in the world. The oil that began as microscopic droplets in the tiny bodies of sea fauna and became a cure-all medicine has since powered two wars and an increasing amount of the world's industrial development. The reduzates count heavily in man's scheme of things.

The unceasing process of sedimentation which began when the first rains washed across the young rocks of the crust has concentrated the minerals of the earth in quantities that man finds useful and essential. Nature thus has served as a vast factory changing undifferentiated, scattered raw materials into semi-finished stores of materials which we call ores, seams, pools, banks. And we draw upon these supplies with a recklessness that might seem to imply that they are an accumulation of a few years rather than of hundreds of millions.

The geochemists have tried repeatedly to estimate just how

much sedimentation has occurred. It is a calculation beset by many difficulties and uncertainties. Goldschmidt once calculated, however, that enough sediments had been deposited in the world's waters to form a shell about two thousand feet thick enveloping the entire earth.

But P. H. Kuenen maintains that these figures are too low. Studies by Wilson at Toronto point in the same direction. Insufficient account was taken earlier, these scientists believe, of the red clays, the fine "rock flour" that eventually reaches the depths of the ocean and endlessly settles there. Recent electronic soundings of the red clays indicate that they have attained great thickness. Kuenen estimates, therefore, that the sediments deposited in all time may reach a thickness of about 1.8 miles or three kilometers. This accords very well with the measurements being made by the oceanographers.

But this is not the end of the story. It is, in fact, only the beginning of a new cycle. No sooner is a weight of sediments deposited in the waters than this finely divided substance of the land begins to pack into solid rock and to undergo change. The geologist calls this process metamorphism. It is induced in the once fluffy and grainy sediments by the great changes of temperature, pressure, and chemical environment which they encounter as they subside deeper and deeper into the earth.

"In this way the constituents of a rock are changed to minerals which are more stable under the new conditions, and these minerals may arrange themselves with the production of structures which are likewise more suited to the new environment," explains Mason.

The heat that acts upon the subsiding sediments may come from the general increase of temperature with depth, or from adjacent areas of molten rocks, or magmas. The pressure also is of two kinds: a uniform pressure that packs the sediments into a smaller volume, and a directed pressure or stress that produces banded or parallel structures. The banded gneisses of the Canadian shield are an excellent example of the latter.

Most of the chemical alteration is produced, Mason thinks, by chemically active fluids. Others argue that the migration of atoms in and through the solid rock is a more important factor in metamorphism. Mason points out, in support of the position that he and A. C. Waters take in this controversy, that water and other volatile substances are present, at least in small amounts, in all rocks, and that large amounts of water are set free in the earth by igneous activity.

Such waters would provide a universal and effective medium for the transportation of underground materials. Both field observations and laboratory tests indicate that most chemical alteration of the rocks results from the circulation of such waters.

Of course, if the temperatures rise high enough, the rocks melt, just as certainly as a lump of butter over a flame. And then the age-old process has begun all over again. Once again there are magmas ready to move toward the surface. In fact, this has been the history of the earth since its beginning.

Up to the point where the rocks begin to alter under metamorphism, and to re-melt, everything that happened went toward breaking them down, toward separating the elements of which they are made. At first, as the young earth came together, there was a separation of elements according to weight. The heavy parts of the material that had been gathered from the dust of space were concentrated by the force of gravity toward the center of the sphere, and the lighter parts toward the surface.

Next the materials of the earth separated a little further into shells or layers of different density. At this point, Goldschmidt saw, the elements that oxidized more readily than iron went into the mantle and crust, and the less readily oxidized materials concentrated in the core. This "primary geochemical differentiation" depended upon the number and arrangement of the electrons in the atoms involved. Through this separation, the outer part of the earth, the mantle and crust, became what the geochemist calls a "distinct physio-chemical system."

Then the elements concentrated in the crust were further

separated by the processes of magma formation and sedimentation. In the end, when the breaking down, the dividing, and the
separating had progressed far, the building-stone, the metals,
the chemical raw materials, and the salts so necessary to man
were produced.

Only at this point was the inexorable process reversed. As the
deeply buried sediments began to undergo transformation and to
melt, the whole direction of change was altered. After the long
breaking down, the earth began to put Humpty Dumpty together
again.

"In general," explains Mason, "metamorphism tends toward
uniformity of distribution of the elements. One can visualize unlimited metamorphism as resulting in an ideal condition in which
the whole lithosphere [the rocky shell of the earth] reaches a
uniform composition. This may seem an exaggerated view, but
that such a tendency exists is evidenced by the comparatively
monotonous chemical and mineralogical composition of ancient
geological formations as compared to the chemically diverse
rock types of younger ages."

Mason picks up a sheet of paper and draws a large circle
on it. At the center bottom is magma. Continuing around the
circle counter-clockwise, he points out, there come the crystallization of the igneous rocks, their weathering into the sediments,
their settling down into the sedimentary rocks, their alteration
into metamorphic rocks, and their re-melting into magma. The
cycle has gone full turn.

"Like any ideal cycle," warns Mason, "this geochemical cycle
may not be realized in practice; it may be indefinitely halted
at some stage, short circuited, or its direction reversed."

But it is a cycle of breakdown and regeneration. Out of the
separation of the materials with which the earth began comes
a new beginning of the majestic processes that have fashioned
and sculptured the crust we live on.

XVIII

KULP

THE AGE OF THE EARTH

LORD RUTHERFORD—then Ernest Rutherford—was strolling across the campus of McGill University in Montreal, where he had been serving for several years as professor of physics. In his hand he tossed a small piece of pitchblende, the natural ore of uranium. When he met one of his faculty colleagues, a professor of geology, he stopped him and asked: "How old is the earth supposed to be?" The geologist told him that the weight of opinion favored an age of about a hundred million years.

"I *know*," said Rutherford quietly but with full effect, "that this piece of pitchblende is seven hundred million years old."

Here perhaps was the first collision—for the year was 1904 —between the old estimates of the age of the earth and the vastly larger figures that would grow out of a wholly new kind of dating. Rutherford was just beginning to apply the recent discovery of radioactivity to the determination of the age of uranium ore, and hence—in part, at least—to the determination of the age of the earth.

The announcement soon afterward of his findings went a long way toward upsetting all that the Western world then believed about the age of the earth. The brilliant New Zealand-born physicist administered a severe shock to geological thought.

And yet this increase in the estimate of the age of the earth was only the first in a long series of upward revisions. Within the next fifty years scientists working with radioactivity would not only begin the dating of the major events of the earth's past; they would bring about a startling change in our very concept of time.

Some of the most dramatic of these discoveries, making it possible to pinpoint happenings a billion years and more in the past, have come in the decade following the close of World War II. Science now has learned to read the past with uranium and thorium, and with the radioactive isotopes of rubidium, potassium, carbon, oxygen, and other similar materials whose very existence was unsuspected not long before.

Whole laboratories, like the geochemistry laboratory of Columbia University's Lamont Geological Observatory, have been organized to work with the new methods of dating and to focus them on the primary problems of the earth. And young men like Lamont's J. Laurence Kulp have brought the new atomic physics and chemistry to bear in these studies of the earth. But their striking findings, revealing many a long-hidden secret of the earth, are an outgrowth of much that went before.

Man long has wanted to know how old the earth is. The sages of Greece probably were not the first to try to devise a chronology. Their unknown predecessors may have worked at the same baffling problem. But of all the ancient prophecies which have come down to us, that of the Hindus was, as Arthur Holmes points out in his *Age of the Earth,* the most remarkable. The Manusmitri, the Hindu sacred book, fixed the whole existence of the earth, past and future, at 4.32 billion years or one "day" in the life of Brahma. Beyond, it was believed, would come the night of Brahma where the finite would merge into the infinite. Brahma's "day" was divided into fourteen great cycles, the seventh of which, it is said, has now been reached. According to this reckoning, the earth is now slightly less than 2 billion years old.

The Western world had no similar concept of time. When Archbishop Ussher, early in the seventeenth century, worked out the age of the earth from his interpretation of the ages recorded in the narratives of the Old Testament, he fixed the date of the earth's creation at 4004 B.C. It was printed in the

In flow after flow molten rock poured from the earth in the Pacific Northwest. Here at Battleship Rock in Dry Falls State Park in Washington the flows stand forth in clear outline.

The deep somber canyon of the Snake River. Here between eastern Oregon and western Idaho the gorge is 6,478 feet or nearly a mile and a quarter deep. Only the upper part of the canyon is lava. Below lies older metamorphic rock.

PLATE XVII

Volcanic ash, not the soft fall of snow, covers land
and trees in this valley near Michoacan, Mexico

PLATE XVIII

Along the crest of the Cascade Mountains. Above their jagged tops rises the snow-covered peak of Mount Rainier, the great extinct volcano that crowns this range.

The sky is reflected in the perfect mirror of Devil's Hole Lake in Siskiyou National Forest. This is the placid end of a crater that once exploded with fire.

PLATE XIX

Scar of an earthquake. Seen from a plane this crack in the California earth becomes a sharply defined, seemingly endless rift.

Record of an earthquake. The arrival of P (pressure) waves set off by a sharp cracking of the rocks of the earth produced the first large ups and downs in this seismograph record. As the S (shake) waves came in a few seconds later the motion was more violent.

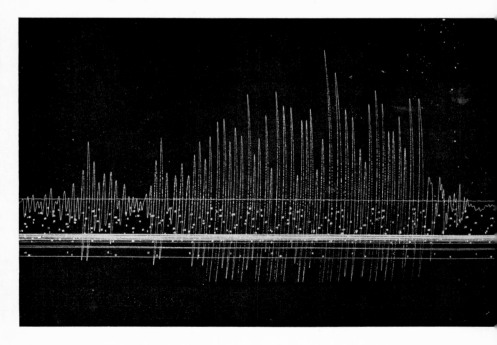

PLATE XX

A miniature, model volcano erupts. As in nature, a cone forms and "lava" flows down into "the valley." Professor Ernst Cloos of Johns Hopkins University produces the eruption with mud, dry ice, and a caulking gun.

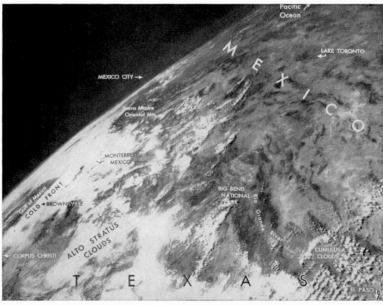

The twentieth century's additional proof that the world is round. As the camera in a Viking rocket photographed the earth from one hundred and fifty-eight miles out in space the earth's roundness was dramatically evident. Approximately 600,000 square miles of surface are shown in this remarkable photograph.

PLATE XXI

J. Tuzo Wilson. He has accumulated new evidence showing that the continents have grown and are growing.

Sir Harold Jeffreys. His work has helped to outline the long unknown and mysterious interior of the earth.

Stanley Keith Runcorn. "Fossil magnets" that he has discovered in many parts of the world indicate that the earth may once have "rolled about."

Sir Edward Bullard. His studies of the heat of the earth have contributed to the increasing knowledge of the earth's interior.

PLATE XXII

J. Laurence Kulp. His laboratory is one of those now dating the past.

Brian Mason. The story of the earth's chemical development and assortment is told in his books. Here he tests a uranium specimen.

Harold Clayton Urey. An earth that originated cool and has since been warming up is pictured by this winner of the Nobel Prize.

PLATE XXIII

Uranium mine. The Happy Jack on the Colorado River near Hite, Utah. An old river-bed formation deep in this once abandoned copper mine was found to be rich in uranium.

PLATE XXIV

margins of many Bibles, and was largely accepted by Christian peoples as the authoritative and incontrovertible date of the earth's beginning. The West was certain that the earth was thus only a few thousand years old.

Geologists of the late nineteenth century were not deterred. They could not accept this constrictive limitation when they saw the changes the earth had undergone, for such changes could not have come about in a few thousand years. Joly, who in 1899 attempted to measure the age of the earth by computing the amount of salt washed into the seas, arrived at a figure of 80 million to 90 million years. Another scientist set an age of 57 million years, based on the separation of the earth from the moon; and others, studying the thickness of the sediments, estimated it at about 100 million years.

It was at about this time, in 1897, that the scientific attempts to establish an age for the earth received the famed setback from Lord Kelvin. Kelvin's estimate that the earth could not be less than 20 million years old or more than 40 million was carefully calculated. It could be held invalid, he accurately declared, "only if sources of heat now unknown to us are prepared in the great storehouse of creation."

Almost at the moment that Kelvin was speaking, exactly such new sources of heat were being discovered. Professor Henri Becquerel of France had followed with great interest Röntgen's discovery of X rays in 1895. Was it possible, Becquerel wondered, that the phosphorescence that he was studying might also be produced by invisible rays? Perhaps certain substances absorbed light from the sun and later reflected it. Becquerel exposed a large number of substances to the sun and then laid them on photographic paper to see if they would fog it as X rays did.

None of them produced the slightest effect until one day he tried a salt of the rare metal uranium, the heaviest of all the elements.

Then he found that the uranium salts blurred the paper in the same way whether or not they were previously placed in the sun. Some form of radiation was being given off by the uranium, Becquerel saw, and it was being given off continuously and spontaneously. Here was a new form of radiation. He announced his discovery in 1896.

Marie and Pierre Curie, who were interested in the same general problems, at once began to work on the mystifying radiation. By the laborious process of testing all the elements, they learned that thorium also gave off the strange radiation. But even more puzzling was the behavior of a piece of the natural uranium ore called pitchblende which came from a mine at Joachimsthal in Bohemia.

The intensity of the radiation it emitted far surpassed the combined amount that should have come from both the uranium and the thorium it contained. Only one conclusion was possible: some unknown material in the ore also was radioactive (the term Marie Curie had coined for the phenomenon). For four years the Curies labored in their drafty, shed-like laboratory, trying to isolate the elusive material. In the end, as all the world knows, they found radium—only a tenth of a gram of it, but a substance a million times more radioactive than uranium. It was one of the classic achievements of science, and for it the Curies and Becquerel shared a Nobel Prize.

Such discoveries have their own radiance. Ernest Rutherford, then a young science student at the Cavendish Laboratory at Cambridge, was inspired by the reports coming from France, and in his turn went to work with the new phenomenon.

Before the year 1902 had ended, Rutherford was ready to announce that radioactivity was nothing less than the spontaneous disintegration of radioactive atoms and their conversion into wholly different atoms. The atom, up to that time, had been considered the eternal and unchangeable base of all matter. But here was a transmutation of matter, almost as fabulous as the transmutations the alchemists had dreamed of. A new era in science was suddenly opened.

Rutherford, in the meanwhile, had gone to Canada, to Mc-

Gill University. He had realized almost at once that if the particles were given off at a fixed rate (and every sign indicated that they were), the loss in radioactivity would afford a new kind of measurement of the age of minerals and of the earth of which they were a part.

Later it was to be learned that this disintegration of radioactive substances is one of the steadiest, most undeviating things in existence; the particles are thrown off at the same rate regardless of changes in temperature, time, or condition. Research revealed, however, that each radioactive material disintegrates at its own distinctive rate, and that the decay of uranium is almost inconceivably slow. At the end of 4.5 billion years only half of its radioactivity is gone; only half of it has changed into another substance. At the end of a second 4.5 billion years another half would be altered, and so it continues in ever diminishing halves. Rutherford understood enough of this "half-life" system of measurement to estimate that the uranium he was studying was at least 700 million years old, and that the earth also had to be that old.

In 1904 Rutherford was invited to discuss the whole exciting question of radioactivity and its indications about the age of the earth at a London meeting. He tells of what happened in his own ebullient way:

"I came into the room which was half dark, and presently spotted Lord Kelvin in the audience and realized that I was in for trouble at the last part of my speech dealing with the age of the Earth where my views conflicted with his. To my relief Kelvin fell fast asleep, but as I came to the important point, I saw the old boy sit up, open an eye and cock a baleful glance at me! Then a sudden inspiration came and I said that Lord Kelvin had limited the age of the Earth *provided no new source* (of heat) *was discovered.* 'That prophetic utterance refers to what we are considering tonight, radium!' Behold! the old boy beamed upon me!" [1]

[1] A. S. Eve: *Rutherford.* New York: MacMillan and Co.; 1939.

Discoveries continued to come in a great surge, for scientists everywhere were working intensively at the new findings. In 1906, B. B. Boltwood, professor of chemistry at Yale University, noted that lead was nearly always present in uranium-bearing rocks. Could lead, he asked, be the final disintegration product of the radioactive uranium?

To test the point, Boltwood collected ore samples from all parts of the world and measured their lead and uranium contents. Both varied widely. That suggested another idea; he would line them up according to their lead-uranium ratios.

When he did so, the results were highly enlightening. The greater the amount of lead, the older was the geological formation from which the mineral had come. His hunch that there was a relationship between lead and age was thus supported by the geological evidence. With this encouragement Boltwood calculated the time that would have been required for the uranium to deteriorate into the lead in each sample. For one specimen he obtained the startling figure of 2.2 billion years. The earth certainly was as old as its oldest rocks, but the suggestion that the earth could have had a life of more than 2 billion years seemed fantastic.

The time had come to test and consolidate the new discoveries. As this was done, it became apparent that many serious errors could creep into the computation of ages by a simple lead-uranium ratio. A better method was needed, and it was found. Science learned that uranium is in fact a mixture of two isotopes, and that each of them decays into a different kind of radiogenic or radioaction-derived lead. For uranium and thorium the atomic transformation may be set out in this way:

URANIUM 238 *decays to* LEAD 206
URANIUM 235 *decays to* LEAD 207
THORIUM 232 *decays to* LEAD 208

As soon as the complex nature of uranium was recognized, scientists saw that three age-determinations might be made from one specimen. In a specimen containing uranium alone the decay of uranium 238 to lead 206 would provide one measurement, and the disintegration of uranium 235 to lead 207 a second. The ratio of lead 206 to lead 207 provided a third, for the amount of lead 207 increases proportionately with time—uranium 235 decaying more rapidly than uranium 238. In effect, therefore, each piece of uranium ore had three clocks built within it, or at least two clocks and a continuous record of their performance. Age could be read by each of the three and the answers compared. Still, many problems of technique remained to be solved.

When Alfred O. Nier, then of Harvard University, published the first isotopic dates in 1939, it was certain that a new phase in dating was beginning. The war, however, intervened and many of the physicists who had been working with these problems joined the Manhattan Project.

One of the young scientists who gained experience in radioactive work during the war was J. Laurence Kulp. The director of geochemistry at the Lamont Observatory was born at Trenton, New Jersey, on February 11, 1921. He went to the midwest to college, graduating from Wheaton, near Chicago, in 1942. After taking a master's degree in science at Ohio State University he returned east, to Princeton, for his Ph.D. He received the latter degree in 1945. Work with the Manhattan Project had fitted in, and at the close of the war Kulp joined the faculty of Columbia University.

Kulp had been trained as a physical chemist, but after four years in the laboratory he thought longingly of work that would get a man out of doors at least once in a while. More than this, the possibilities of applying the new physics and chemistry to the study of the earth and its large unsolved problems offered an auspicious and exciting prospect. Geochemistry, which obviously was on the threshold of a rapid development, offered exactly the combination that Kulp wanted.

Columbia University at the time was expanding its work in this and related fields. Mrs. Thomas W. Lamont had presented the university with a beautiful estate on the west bank of the Hudson about thirteen miles above the city, for a geological observatory. Under the direction of Dr. W. Maurice Ewing it was dedicated to the application of the methods of physics, chemistry, mathematics, and engineering to the study of the earth. In 1955 a special building, clean-lined, modern in design, and fitting well into the wooded Palisades, was completed for the geochemistry laboratory. The latter is in fact something quite new in the world: a center for radioactive dating, for studying the chronology of the earth.

Potentially any long-lived radioactive isotope may be used for what might be called a time clock, if that term may be recovered from industry. The three isotopes of uranium were only the first to be employed. Indeed, the scientists of the world are in something of a race to identify and develop others.

Immediately after the war Dr. Willard F. Libby, of the University of Chicago and later a member of the Atomic Energy Commission, demonstrated that radioactive carbon, Carbon-14, may be used to determine the age of recent organic remains, like charcoal from a fire of prehistoric man. "Recent" at first meant up to twenty-five thousand years. It was then extended to fifty thousand.

Kulp set up extensive programs at Lamont both to carry on lead and Carbon-14 dating and to improve these techniques. The laboratory also went to work on the promising new rubidium and potassium dating and on other possible dating materials.

In all of these studies, extremely small amounts of the radioactive materials and of their end products must be extracted from the raw ores. Analyses must be made, and radioactivity measured in supersensitive Geiger counters. Elaborate computations also are necessary.

To cope with this intricate chemistry, Lamont has a vacuum fusion laboratory, an emission spectograph and X-ray diffraction laboratory, a natural radioacarbon laboratory, and laboratories of general geochemistry, electrochemistry, analytical chemistry, mass spectrometry, and low-level counting.

In these rooms is a forest of equipment. Miles of glass tubing, it seems, turn and twist, enter flasks of all sizes and shapes, and emerge from them only to intertangle with pumps and other equipment confounding and awesome to the non-scientist. In other rooms are batteries of computing machines, their dial-studded faces alight with the flickering of red and green bulbs. And there are recording instruments whose pens trace back and forth across fine-lined graph paper. Here is all the panoply of science at its most imposing.

To these laboratories come specimens from all parts of the world. At this point, though, the formal terminology of science is thoroughly snubbed. Many of the specimens that are fed into the spectrometers, the diffraction apparatus, and all the rest of it, originate in such non-scientifically named mines as the Hoot Owl, Brown Derby, Deep Creek, and Happy Jack's. So are they known as they go through the laboratory, and so are they reported in the journals of science.

Lamont has one other unique measuring implement. It is a handsome brass balance that stands on Kulp's desk. One of its shining pans holds a perfect white crystal, sharp-planed, symmetrical, and clear. The other bears a chunk of grayish black, slag-like rock, pitted, rough, and contorted. This burned, fused piece with its small twisted inclusions came from zero point at Hiroshima.

As this laboratory and others ran uranium specimens through their apparatus, they sometimes found that all three clocks showed remarkable agreement. Nier dated one sample of pitchblende from Joachimsthal—the same pitchblende that Mme Curie had used—which revealed an age of 244 million years on the lead-206-uranium-238 test, an age of 249 million years on the 207/235 test, and one of 242 million years on the 207/ 206 ratio.

Another ore from Connecticut showed, respectively, ages of 250 million years, 266 million, and 280 million.[2]

Such an agreement is remarkable. What makes it one of the astonishing facts of science is that both uranium and thorium decay at different rates. They also have different chemical characteristics, and occur in different concentrations. It is as if three entirely different clocks, each of which had been running for hundreds of millions of years, pointed in the present to the same hour and minute. Even though the ages recorded by these natural clocks go back several billion years there is virtually no doubt, when all three agree, that the ages are correct.

"Agreement between them is strong evidence of the reliability of the calculated age," said Kulp. Adolph Knopf, former chairman of the Committee on the Age of the Earth, has made the same point: "If all three determinations agree, assurance is rendered trebly sure."

But occasionally there is a wide discrepancy in some of the dates. A pitchblende from northern Canada had an age of 337 million years on the 206/238 ratio and one of 389 million years on the 207/235 determination, but jumped to an unacceptable 705 million years on the third. More disturbing was the discrepancy in a radioactive mineral from Sweden known as kolm. It is the one known radioactive material that contains fossils. Nearly all other uranium ores occur in masses that have intruded into unstratified rocks, and afford no evidence of where they stand in the geological sequence. But the fossils embedded in the kolm are trilobites and other forms that trace back to the early stages of life on this earth, or at least to its first appearance in the rocks. That definitely helps to place the kolm among the oldest of the fossil-bearing rocks. On the 206/238 test the kolm gave an age of 380 million years, on 207/235 an age of

---

[2] All dates are presented with the scientist's familiar ± although it is omitted here. If a date is given as, say, 2,400 ± 200 years, it means that from the evidence of the measurement alone, the chance is 68 per cent that the true value is between 2,200 and 2,600 years.

440 million years, and on the 207/206 determination one of 800 million years. Something unquestionably had gone wrong.

For a while the investigators were baffled. As the work went on, however, and more was learned about the complex way in which uranium decays, the source of the trouble was spotted. Uranium does not disintegrate directly into lead. According to the latest tables, uranium 238 goes through fifteen transformations before it emerges as the plain grub lead.

At one of the stages on its diminishing course the uranium 238 transmutes very briefly into an inert gas, called radon. At this stage it is fairly easy for some of the gas to leak away. If this occurs, the uranium-238 stock is reduced, and ultimately less lead 206 is formed. Both the 206/238 and the 207/206 ratios would be thrown into error.

But all is not lost, as far as dating goes. In the first place, any radon lost in the uranium-238 chain does not affect thorium decomposition. And even the value of 238 time is not destroyed by what might figuratively be called the loss of a fraction of a second. The loss can be taken into account, and allowance made for it.

Kulp began to study radon leakage in the laboratory. At room temperatures, he found, uranianites and pitchblendes lose from 0.1 to 10 per cent of their radon. At higher temperatures the leakage may be larger. But if a loss of about this amount is allowed for at the sixteen-hundred-year-long radon stage, the U-238 dates of very young minerals often are brought closely into line. It is like knowing that the clock is a minute slow and allowing for it. In that way, the discrepancy is overcome.

Other alterations that affect the radioactive clocks are being studied in much the same way. Lead, for example, is commonly lost if the mineral in which it is contained has been reheated since it was first formed.

As the trouble spots were singled out and dealt with, improvements also were made in the apparatus that does the measuring. A mass spectrometer has been developed that on one runthrough of a single sample supplies the data on all three types of radiogenic lead. The amounts of each present in the sample are registered by a pen that makes red zigzags on green graph paper. Kulp also has worked out charts that make it possible to obtain the age directly from the figures shown on the graphs. A sample can now be prepared for testing in about a week, and after half a day in the spectrometer its age may be read. Formerly, weeks of work were involved in making one determination.

With the greater number of tests the improved techniques have made possible, and with the solution of some of the major problems of making measurements, Kulp and his associates have reported that there are at least eight localities in the world where the age of the rocks can now be established to within five per cent of the true and absolute figure. The geochemists thus are saying that science at last can accurately time the last several billion years. It is a striking achievement—to reach back through time and fix the birthday of a rock in an unknown and almost unimaginable era.

The following ages—which science now regards as "nearly sure"—have been set for areas in two continents:

Southeast Manitoba, Canada	2,650 MILLION YEARS
Southern Rhodesia, Africa	2,650 MILLION YEARS
Great Bear Lake, Canada	1,400 MILLION YEARS
Parry Sound, Ontario, Canada	1,040 MILLION YEARS
Wilberforce, Ontario, Canada	1,030 MILLION YEARS
Katanga, Belgian Congo, Africa	610 MILLION YEARS
Bedford, New York	350 MILLION YEARS
Middletown, Connecticut	260 MILLION YEARS
Gilpin County, Colorado	60 MILLION YEARS

In addition, there is a long list of dates that the scientists are willing to say are correct to within twenty per cent.

But the uranium-lead methods made possible the dating of

only a scanty part of the rocks of the earth. In many parts of the world there are no uranium ores suitable for dating. Technical difficulties also block the dating of uranium-derived lead that is less than a million years of age.

Carbon-14 dating also is limited. Even with the latest improvements in method, it can reach back into the past no further than fifty thousand years.

Thus, there was no quantitative way of dating rocks too old for the Carbon-14 method and too young for the uranium-lead system, and an undatable gap was left between fifty thousand years and a million. It was a crucial gap, for therein lies the larger part of human history.

Additional methods of dating that could reach more rocks and more eras were badly needed. Scientists concentrated on the problem, and research already is well advanced on two additional new dating methods that hold great promise.

One of the two methods is based on rubidium, a soft, silvery metal that explodes if it comes in contact with water. This metal consists of two isotopes: radioactive rubidium 87 and rubidium 85. Over a period of billions of years the former decays to strontium 87—about seven per cent of ordinary strontium is made up of this end-product strontium. It follows that any mineral relatively rich in rubidium and low in ordinary strontium can be dated.

Goldschmidt was the first to see the possibilities of the rubidium-strontium decay chain. That was in 1937. Ten years later, scientists had sufficiently developed the new method to date a number of rubidium specimens from areas where lead-uranium dates had already been obtained. That provided a nice check on the uncertain new method, and at first both sets of dates seemed to agree closely. It looked as though an accurate new dating tool was at hand.

Later, however, as new mass spectrometers were used for additional rubidium studies, it was discovered that the rubidium dates ran regularly fifteen- to twenty-per-cent higher than the

best uranium dates. Again something was wrong. Apparently
defective analyses had produced the early agreement. The disagreement therefore had to be explained.

Scientists at Lamont and other laboratories dug into the problem. They found that the trouble probably lay in the lack of
an exact "half-life" for rubidium. It was assumed in the tests
that half of any rubidium 87 present would decay to the next
product in the chain in 6.3 billion years. But this had not been
positively determined, and Kulp pointed out that if a possible
twenty-five-per-cent error had been made, the half-life would
become 4.9 billion years. If the latter figure turns out to be the
right one, it would bring the uranium-lead and the rubidium-
strontium ages into agreement.

As Kulp notes, the decay of radioactive rubidium is immensely slow, even slower than the protracted decay of uranium, and when the technical difficulties are solved, it will be
an extremely valuable new clock for dating the most ancient
of rocks.

The other new dating tool on which research is far along
also holds great promise. When the work with radioactivity was
in its early stages in 1907, scientists saw that a rare form of
potassium is radioactive. Not until 1943, however, was it possible
to track down its end product. Von Weizsächer had earlier predicted that potassium 40 might decay under some circumstances
to calcium 40 and under others to the colorless, odorless gas
argon 40; this proved to be the case.

Excitement ran high in scientific circles, for potassium is one
of the most common elements in the rocks. If it could be used
for dating, vast areas would be opened to research. Uranium,
thorium, and rubidium all are relatively rare, but there are
rich concentrations of potassium in the basalts that underlie a
large part of the oceanic areas of the globe. Their study might
reveal much about the age of the oceans and about some of
the deep movements of the crust of the earth. And besides,
there is potassium aplenty in such hard ancient rocks as the

schist and gneiss that often form part of the continent's "basement complex" and crop up in the shields.

Extremely difficult technical problems at first blocked the use of the new potassium clue. The exact steps in the decay chain that converts the radioactive potassium to argon had to be worked out. It also seemed quite likely that some of the end-product argon might leak from the rocks, and that would further complicate the measurements.

Kulp and the Lamont staff were among many who labored steadily at this problem. Step by step, using radioactive tracer materials from the piles of the Atomic Energy Commission, they were able to demonstrate that argon in the rocks may be released and measured to an accuracy of within three per cent.

Some samples of rock from the highly metamorphosed southern Appalachians were among the first measured. The argon/potassium clock showed that the rocks had undergone two periods of metamorphism, the first about 600 to 700 million years ago and the second about 350 million years ago. The argon gas imprisoned in the rocks also revealed that the "Storm King" granite at Bear Mountain, in New York, had pushed its way up through the older rocks of the area about 700 to 800 million years ago. The "Canada Hill" granite gneiss of the same area showed an age of about 1,200 to 1,400 million years.

Although much more research must be done before the argon-potassium clock is perfected, Kulp predicts its ultimate success. "If the branching ratio and retentivity can be established with high precision," he said, "this method may become the most useful of all isotopic chronometers."

As precise ages were established for a significant number of rock areas of the earth, science gave its renewed attention to that venerable question: how old is the earth itself?

Prior to 1946, estimates, as the radioactivity scientists politely say, were not based on "quantitative reasoning." They were rather informed guesses. Such guesses had then placed the age of the oldest rocks at about 2 billion years, which meant that the earth was somewhat older.

But the new isotopic data on the age of the rocks provided a basis for some exact computations. Arthur Holmes assumed that when the earth began it contained no lead 207, and that all the lead 207 present in the modern crust had therefore been generated from uranium 235. Calculating the time it would have taken the lead to form, he arrived at an age of 3.3 billion years for the earth. A number of other scientists working with the same data also found that the earth was from 3 to 3.5 billion years old. The figures showed notable agreement.

"But," Kulp warns, "the ages obtained should probably be considered a minimum, particularly if the continental areas are becoming increasingly granitic as well as expanding." Wilson has made the point that they are.

The first isotopic calculations of the age of the earth were thus made uncertain by doubts as to the accuracy of the figures on the amount of lead 207 in the crust today. Lead, it is known, is not concentrated heavily in the outer part of the crust, as is uranium. The age-old remaking of the crust, with the upward movement of the granites and the growth of the nucleus areas, may have affected the distribution of lead in the samples on which the figures were based. If some lead was being overlooked, the figures on the age of the earth would be low.

The search went on for a more exact way to determine the age of the earth. The scientists saw that if they could obtain the isotopic *composition* of the lead that was present when the earth was formed, and compare it with the isotopic *composition* of the lead in the crust today, simple subtraction would supply a measure of what lead had been added by the decomposition of uranium. This might perhaps be compared to saying that if we started with two lead coins and ended with three, it would be easy to tell what had been added during the life of the earth. And if the added coin could have been produced only by the decay of uranium and if the rate of that decay was known, the exact time that it had taken to produce the extra coin could be calculated. The age of the earth could be fixed absolutely.

But how was the composition of primeval lead, of the earth's starting quota, to be found? One possibility suggested itself to C. C. Patterson of the California Institute of Technology: the answer, he suspected, might lie in meteorites. There was a strong likelihood that the chunks of stone and metal which occasionally rain down on the earth from outer space have the same composition as the original earth. Many scientists believe that they are the debris of a shattered planet that came into existence at the same time as the earth and the other planets. Patterson and his associates obtained samples from metal meteorites that had fallen in Iowa, Mexico, Kansas, and, later, in Australia.[3]

The metal meteorites contained virtually no uranium or thorium, but they were rich in lead. Because such quantities of lead could not have been produced by uranium decay after the consolidation of the meteorites, Patterson concluded that the lead was present in the materials from which the meteorites were formed. It was, then, primeval lead.

Another problem had to be solved simultaneously. Patterson and his associates needed to know the average isotopic composition of the earth's lead today, and they had to be certain it was the average composition of the lead in the crust as a whole, and not of that in some particular locality. The scientists found what they were seeking in the fine red clay that accumulates endlessly in the great depths of the Pacific Ocean. By the time this extremely fine "rock flour" reaches the bottom of the ocean, so much mixing has occurred that it represents an average of the rocks of all the continents. As an additional check in determining the composition of the earth's lead, the Patterson group wanted data on the lead in the lower parts of the earth's crust. They obtained samples of such rock and lead

[3] Meteorites are the solid bodies that fall to earth. Meteors or shooting stars burn themselves out as they flash across the heavens.

from the basalts in some of the deeper, undisturbed lava flows in the Snake River area.

When analyses were made of the isotopic composition of the lead in the red clay, in the basalt, and in the meteorites, dramatic results appeared:

Lead	206	207	206/207 age
Oceanic	18.93	15.73	
Meteoritic	9.41	10.27	
Radiogenic	9.52	5.46	4.5 billion years
Basaltic	18.12	15.45	
Meteoritic	9.41	10.27	
Radiogenic	8.71	5.18	4.6 billion years

In the meteorites, in which almost no lead could have been formed by radioactive decay, there was strikingly less lead than in the clay and the basalt, where lead had been added by the breakdown of uranium. In fact, the figures vividly showed that the earth today contains almost twice as much lead 206 as the meteorites, and about a third more lead 207. And this was true whether the earth's lead came from the bottom of the ocean or from the lower part of the crust. The effect of the decay of uranium was definitively established: radioactive decay was adding large amounts of lead to the earth.

Knowing how much radiogenic lead the earth had gained and knowing the rate of uranium decay, Patterson could calculate the time that had gone into its formation. It had taken 4.5 billion years to accumulate the earth's uranium-derived lead; some 4.5 billion years had passed since the earth had consolidated out of the dusts of space. This, then, was the age of the earth: 4.5 billion years!

Remarkable additional proof that this vast age is in truth the correct age of the earth or very close to it was soon to come.

If meteorites were formed at the same time as the earth, and if their age could be measured, the scientists working in this field quickly saw that they would have an accurate check on the age revealed by the isotopic comparison. By 1956 several groups had succeeded in making three distinct measurements of the age of meteorites.

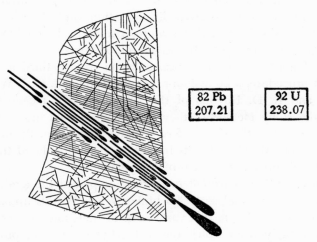

82 Pb
207.21

92 U
238.07

METEORS AND METEORITE (A METEOR COME TO EARTH). A CROSS-SECTION DISPLAYS THE CHARACTERISTIC MARKINGS OF A METEORITE, (TO THE RIGHT) THE ATOMIC WEIGHTS OF LEAD AND URANIUM, BOTH USED IN DETERMINATIONS WHICH SHOW THAT THE METEORITES ARE ABOUT 4.5 BILLION YEARS OLD.

Studying certain stony types of meteorites which contained uranium that had partially decayed into lead 206 and 207, Patterson, Harrison Brown, and Mark Inghram, all three then at the University of Chicago, and George Tilton, of the Carnegie Institution, separated enough lead to obtain a 206/207 ratio. It showed that the meteorites they tested were 4.5 billion years old!

One of the newest methods of dating, rubidium-strontium, was used for another determination. Ernst Schumacher found that the metal meteorites held no rubidium, and that their strontium therefore had to be primeval strontium, present when the black

386Into Invisible Forces

piece of metal was formed. On the other hand, the stony meteorites, which crash into the earth more frequently than their metal counterparts, contained rubidium, and its decay had produced measurable amounts of radiogenic strontium. By simple subtraction Schumacher could tell how much strontium had been created by radioactive disintegration, and by calculating how long it had taken that strontium to form, he could obtain the age of the meteorite. It was 4.5 billion years!

Still more confirmation was to come from a third and different procedure, a potassium-argon measurement. G. J. Wasserburg and R. D. Hayden of the University of Chicago found that the stony meteorites they studied contained argon which had come from the decay of radioactive potassium. By measuring the time required for its formation, they calculated the age of the meteorites. It was 4.6 billion years!

Three entirely different methods thus placed the age of the meteorites at very close to 4.5 billion years. Worlds apparently were in the making in that vast recess of time, and among them was the body from which the meteorites came, and probably the earth as well. For the evidence of that most certain of all clocks, radioactivity, said that the earth, too, had come into existence at that time, 4.5 billion years ago. The agreement was overwhelming.

So strong and convincing was this converging of proofs that most scientists in the field concluded that the age of the earth had at last "been reasonably well defined." After the fluctuation of centuries, after the earth's age had been variously estimated at less than 6,000 years, at 100 million, at 2 billion, at 3.5 billion, it is now expected that the true and absolute age will be found to be very close to the 4.5 billion years recorded in the laboratories in 1955 and 1956. Man at last, it seems, has reached back to the very beginnings of this earth; we know at the middle of the twentieth century approximately where our earth stands in the endless panorama of time.

Only one major doubt remains. There is, as Patterson has

reminded the scientific world, no absolute proof that the newly born earth had the same composition as the meteorites. That still is an assumption, though it is one that most scientists make and it is supported by powerful evidence.[4] But it is a doubt that is not likely to be completely resolved until we learn finally and fully the still-veiled story of the origin of the solar system.

An age of 4.5 billion years at once created havoc in the traditional geologic time scale, the scale developed to indicate the time and order of the formation of the rocks and of the life of the earth.

In nearly all of the scales, the time from the present back to the first appearance of the fossils in the rocks is generally set at 500 million years. The new dating does not change this span allotted to fossil life; it confirms it. The time set for the three divisions in this great period, the Paleozoic, the Mesozoic, and the Cenozoic, is thus unchanged.

Before life came upon the scene, however, or before the tiny creatures swarming in the early seas developed shells or bony structures that could survive as fossils, the time scales assumed two great, vague preceding periods totaling about 1.5 billion years. These periods—pre-Cambrian periods—were called the Proterozoic and the Archeozoic. A few recently corrected scales even set this opening age of the earth at 2.5 billion years.

It is here that a great change must now be made. With the revision of the earth's time and perhaps with its definition, this period—which man has traditionally regarded as prelude—has been extended to 4 billion years. No longer prelude but the major portion of the earth's time, it has become a span eight times longer than that of fossil life upon the earth. The age of recorded life has now diminished to a relatively brief one, the occupancy of humans to a mere minute, and the tenancy of homo

---

[4] The meteorites also contain diamonds. The pressures necessary for their formation could only have been secured in a "large object." Calculations indicate that this parent body from which the meteorites came must have been about the size of the moon.

sapiens, or men like ourselves, to a fleeting moment in the long history of the earth.[5]

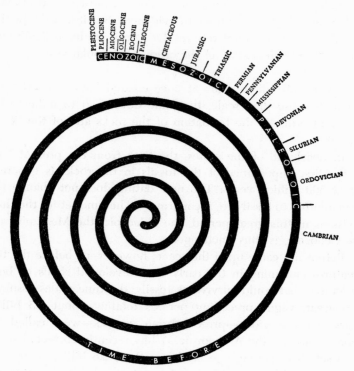

THE 4.5 BILLION YEARS OF THE EARTH. THE 500 MILLION YEARS THAT HAVE PASSED SINCE THE FIRST FOSSILS APPEARED IN THE ROCKS ARE NOW ONLY A TAIL ON THIS COIL THAT REPRESENTS THE TIME OF THE EARTH. STRUCTURED ANIMALS, INCLUDING MAN, ARE VERY LATE COMERS.

Even the scientist who ordinarily speaks only in restrictive terms cannot restrain his wonder when he regards this lengthen-

[5] If the 4.5-billion-year age of the earth is thought of as one year, the 500 million years of the fossil record is equivalent to about forty days. The time of humans, assuming that it is about 1 million years, would amount to less than two hours, and that of modern man, giving him 50,000 years, to a little more than five minutes.

ing of the earth's time. "It is somewhat shocking," said Kulp, to find such an enormous age going before.

A re-study of the oldest rocks has underwritten the new time scale growing out of the comparison of meteoritic and earthly lead. The oldest rocks measured so far, the 2,650-million-year-old uranium ores of Canada and Africa, occur in what are called pegmatites. They are minerals that intruded into an older complex of greatly altered sedimentary and volcanic rocks. Thus, they pushed their way in among rocks that had already been on the earth long enough to have crumbled into sand and dust, to have been washed down into primordial waters, and to have re-formed and undergone great change.

"There was a great deal of earth history before the regional metamorphism which culminated in the southern Manitoba pegmatites," Kulp points out. The Columbia University geochemist expects that new refinements in lead-uranium dating, particularly with zircons, will make it possible to date some of the ancestral rocks, the rocks whose detritus made the rocks the pegmatites invaded. The identification and dating of still older rocks seems certain to come, and the expansion of this very early period in the earth's history promises to fit well into a total 4.5-billion-year time for the earth.

And the new dating is fixing the time and order of earth-shaping events that followed. In North America, Kulp points out, a series of events now appears well defined. Around the 2,650-million-year-old rocks that formed part of the nucleus of the continent—the inner Canadian shield—rose younger rocks. Work at Lamont has already timed the Lake Athabasca mineralization in north central Canada at about 2 billion years, the metamorphism in the Black Hills at 1.5 billion years, and the Great Bear Lake mineralization—in the Canadian northwestern territories —at 1.4 billion years.

If the Swedish kolm—the earliest fossil-bearing rock that can be dated by radioactive techniques—is finally timed at about 440 million years, as the Lamont studies have shown it may well be, another highly significant point in the earth's history will have been confirmed. When the simple, minute animals entombed in the kolm swarmed in the early seas, life had already taken a long step forward. The 500-million-year date long set for the beginning of such life would appear correct.

And further along in the earth's development, radioactive dating has shown the formation of the southern Appalachians at about 340 million years ago, and the buckling up of the Rocky Mountains about 60 million years ago. Events whose beginning man could only imagine are being dated with as much precision as modern historians might bring to setting the birth date of some early king or dynasty. And the pattern is consistent, consistent with itself and with all that the layering of the earth and the order of the fossils reveals about the earth.

But the dates so far recorded are only the opening figures. They are only a foretaste of the filling in of the record which is certain to come. "Geochronometry should produce many details of geologic history in the next decade," says Kulp.

Even now, however, man knows more about his earth than the most sanguine might have expected just a few decades ago. We know, as none of our human predecessors could have known with any assurance, that this is a tremendously old earth that we live on, a 4.5-billion-year-old earth. We know that it probably came together out of the dusts of space and that it has sorted itself into a crust, a mantle, and a core. We know that continents grew from island-like nuclei and are still growing. We know that this is an earth whose orderly, inevitable breakdown is matched only by its endless regeneration. Many utterly unsuspected answers have been supplied to the questions that Hesiod began to ask and that man has asked through his brief centuries.

It is an amazing, an ever changing, a never wholly revealing earth we live on.

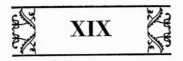

WEGENER

THE GREATEST ENIGMA IS SOLVED

IT WAS GEOPOETRY.

Alfred Wegener was proposing a scientific theory of the earth. In 1915 many of the answers were still missing, but the German scientist built up a theory of the earth so sweeping and so supremely inclusive in its explanation of the earth, its continents, its mountains, its volcanoes, and its earthquakes that it could well have been called geopoetry. It had the quality of poetry, and as a matter of fact the term was later to be used.

Since the seventeenth century and early eighteenth, not many had dared to think that there might be essentially a single explanation of what Burnet had called the "ruine" of the earth— its rugged unaccountable topography and its often destructive upheavals. The nineteenth- and twentieth-century scientists had concentrated generally on one phase or another, for the grand scheme had seemed beyond the reach of science in their time.

Unlike the philosophers and poets who had dealt with the "originale" of the earth to justify myth or religion, Wegener began with an insight and then brought all of modern science to bear upon it.

One day in 1910, when Wegener was a lecturer in astronomy and meteorology at the University of Marburg, Germany, he happened to be poring over a map of the world. He looked at Brazil and the large rectangular bulge in its coastline. He then looked at Africa, at the huge indentation along the Cameroon Coast. If the two continents had been shoved together, the Brazilian bulge and the African indentation would have fitted together almost as though they had once been one.

Wegener pulled out a globe and a pair of compasses. Spreading out the compass points, he made a few measurements. In size the Brazilian bulge and the African concavity were "precisely commensurate." Was it possible that the two could once have been joined? Like innumerable others who had noted the same congruence, Wegener dismissed the idea as improbable, if not impossible.

Some months later, quite by accident, he came upon a report summarizing paleontological evidence for an ancient land bridge between Africa and Brazil. Wegener had not realized before how remarkably similar the ancient animals and plants of the two areas had been. He immediately recalled his earlier thought about the conformity of the two continents, and he was so interested that he undertook a "cursory" examination of the geological as well as the paleontological research that had been done.

"A conviction of the fundamental soundness of the idea took root in my mind," he said.

Wegener went to work on the basic hypothesis that the two continents might in fact have been one. He was equipped for a study that would have to draw upon a number of fields in addition to geology, being a well-rounded and thoroughly trained scientist.

Wegener had been born on November 1, 1880, in Berlin, the youngest child of Dr. Richard Wegener, an evangelical preacher. After studying at the universities of Heidelberg, Innsbruck, and Berlin, he entered the "Urania" of Berlin as an astronomer. Soon afterward he was appointed an assistant to his brother at the Prussian Aeronautical Observatory at Tegel. The two brothers soon set a record with a balloon flight over Germany that lasted fifty-two and a half hours. They were testing a spirit-level clinometer as an instrument for flight navigation, and just by chance created a sports record.

In 1906 Wegener was invited to go as a meteorologist with a Danish expedition to the northeast coast of Greenland. In two years there he not only learned Arctic work, but also formed a clear idea of the effect of ice on the geology of the earth.

Upon his return he went to Marburg. His lectures on the thermodynamics of the atmosphere later were incorporated in a book on the same subject. But his interest in the relationship of continents was beginning to crowd out meteorology.

On January 6, 1912, Wegener was ready to lay his theory before his fellow scientists. He gave an address before the Geological Association on "The Geophysical Basis of the Evolution of the Large Scale Features of Earth's Crust (Continents and Oceans)."

Instead of being permanent, fixed parts of this predominantly watery globe, Wegener argued, the continents had shifted their positions. He traced the possible odyssey.

At one time the entire land mass of the world had formed one vast continent. South America had lain beside Africa as part of the big block. Then a split had developed. The two began to pull apart, and the rift widened until South America reached its present position, some 3,700 miles distant. The Atlantic Ocean filled the basin between them.

Also, originally North America had abutted Europe and formed a coherent block with it. Antarctica, Australia, and India also lay alongside South Africa and thus formed another part of the huge original land mass.

As the two Americas drifted westward, something like great ice floes in a frozen but moving sea, their leading edges were compressed and folded by the resistance of the Pacific Ocean floor. The westward-moving continent overrode the eastward-moving Pacific floor and in the collision the huge mountain ranges extending from Alaska on the north to Antarctica on the south were upthrust and folded.

After Australia broke away from India, India moved closer to Asia. As the subcontinent jammed against the continent, the largest folded mountains on earth, the Himalayas, were shoved up.

Wegener was not only reorganizing the earth and shifting continents, he was also proposing a different explanation of how the mountains, "the wild ruines" of the seventeenth century and a conundrum of all time, came to be.

ONE WORLD SURROUNDED BY ONE OCEAN. SOME 200,000,000 YEARS AGO ALL THE CONTINENTS FORMED ONE LAND MASS. IT HAS BEEN CALLED GONDWANALAND BY SOME AND PANGAEA BY OTHERS.

His hypothesis was a plausible one, but it certainly needed proof and support if it was to have any more effect than similar ideas advanced in the past. Sir Francis Bacon had considered the possibility of continental drift, and in the middle of the nineteenth century there was lively discussion on the subject. In 1857 W. L. Green wrote of "segments of the earth's crust which float on the liquid core," and Darwin, who had to establish connections between land masses if the spread of life around the earth was to be explained, still complained to a friend that some naturalists were making continents "the way a cook makes pancakes." Darwin feared that the continent movers were simply taking too easy a way out of the problem of connections. Others argued that the oceans covered sunken continents.

Only a few years before, in 1909 and 1910, R. Manto-
vani and F. B. Taylor had published suggestions that the continents might have broken away from an earlier single land
mass.

The majority insisted, however, that the continents and
oceans were features of great antiquity. They were believed to

THE PRESENT WORLD WITH ITS SEPARATE CONTINENTS. NORTH AND
SOUTH AMERICA HAVE DRIFTED WEST TO THEIR PRESENT POSITIONS
AND THE ATLANTIC OCEAN HAS FILLED IN THE RIFT CREATED BY THE
MOVEMENT. INDIA AND ARABIA HAVE COMPLETED A LONG ODYSSEY
TO THE NORTH. AUSTRALIA HAS ALSO MADE A LONG JOURNEY AWAY
FROM ITS FORMER BASE, AND ANTARCTICA HAS SEPARATED FROM THE
AFRICAN LAND MASS.

have held unchanged positions almost from the beginning of the
earth's formation, though, it was conceded, repeated changes in
sea level had covered and uncovered shallow land lying between
them and large parts of the continents themselves.

"Other authors," said Darwin, "have hypothetically bridged
over every ocean and united almost every island with some mainland."

In his turn Wegener added: "It is a strange fact and characteristic of the incomplete state of our present knowledge, that

totally opposing conclusions are drawn about prehistoric conditions on our planet."

Before Wegener could further explore the question that was
increasingly preoccupying him, he joined a second two-year expedition to Greenland. The goal was to spend a winter on the
eastern edge of the ice and then to make a crossing of the island's
widest part. The expedition was nearly lost during an ascent of
the inland glacier and barely succeeded in reaching the west
coast.

When Wegener returned to Germany, World War I was
breaking out, and as a reserve lieutenant, he was quickly drafted
and assigned to a field regiment. During the advance into Bel-
gium he was shot in the arm. He made a rapid recovery, but
two weeks after his return to duty he was wounded again, this
time by a bullet in the neck. He was unable to return to the
service a second time and was assigned to a field meteorological unit.

He was finally free to work on the compelling idea that had
come to him as he casually studied the map of the south Atlantic,
and for the next fourteen years he devoted himself to this task.
He brought together for the first time all the information geology, geography, geophysics, and paleontology could offer. Previously scientists had used only the evidence of their own fields
to advance hypotheses about the earth.

Wegener first had to confront the concept of land bridges
and the accompanying theory that "the great ocean basins constitute permanent features of the earth's surface and have with
little change in shape occupied the same positions as now since
the ocean waters were first gathered." Both theories obviated the
idea of continental drift.

The assumption of bridges and sunken, long-lost continents
that had become part of the sea floor was based on the idea of a
cooling, shrinking globe. Just as a drying apple wrinkles, so the
slow shriveling of the earth was believed to have compressed the
surface into mountains and sea basins.

Wegener pointed out that there were many objections to the "shrinking" hypothesis. The earth had not wrinkled uniformly, as such a contracting body should. Its mountains—wrinkles—were instead concentrated in specific belts. The basic idea of contraction also had virtually been negated by the discovery of radioactivity. Instead of continuously cooling, the earth was continuously being warmed by heat from radioactive substances in the crust and mantle.

Wegener also cited Dutton's isostasy [1] or the theory of the balance between the heights and depths of the crust.

"It seems impossible," he said, "that a continental block the size of a land bridge of the required size could sink to the ocean bottom without a load or that the reverse should happen. Isostasy is a contradiction not only to contraction theory but also to the theory of sunken land bridges."

The old theory could effectively be demolished, but this in itself did not establish the fact that the continents had once formed a single land mass and had drifted apart. Wegener began to pile up his evidence.

He began with the startling acknowledgment that if the continents had drifted apart in the past, they would still have to be moving in the present. Such a claim would have to be provable. According to Wegener's estimates, active movement could be expected between Greenland and Europe. Here he knew that a test might possibly be made, comparing old longitudinal measurements with newer ones. The difficulty lay in using the old— they had been made with different methods and from a different point. In 1922, however, a Danish survey, using radiotelegraphy time transmission, made new measurements and some comparisons became possible.

Wegener concluded from these comparisons that Greenland had drifted west between 1873 (when the earlier longitudinal measurements had been taken) and 1922. He estimated that Greenland was still moving away from Europe at a steady rate.

[1] See Chapter XII.

Wegener presented other data showing that North America was moving and that Madagascar too was drifting. This was about all the physical evidence available to him, but it was persuasive and valid as far as it went.

Wegener then proceeded with the geophysical, geological, paleontological, and paleoclimatic arguments for continental drift. He particularly gave weight to the geophysical data.

The ocean floors were composed of heavier materials; the continents of lighter. He emphasized again that the buoying up of the thicker, lighter continents and their elevation above the waters was wholly in accord with isostasy.

"To put it in picturesque terms," he said, "the two layers (floor and continents) behave like open water and large ice floes.

"The whole isostasy theory depends upon the idea that the crustal layer has a certain degree of fluidity. But if this is so and the continental blocks do float on a fluid, even though a very viscous one, there is clearly no reason why their movement should only occur vertically, and not also horizontally, provided only there are forces in existence which tend to displace continents, and that these forces last for geological epochs."

Certainly there had been a vertical rise in the land when former ice sheets melted. Lyell had seen it earlier in Scandinavia, and had made his own markers to record the rise for the future. More modern measurement had established that both Scandinavia and Canada had been rising at the rate of about one centimeter a year since the ice cap had drawn back about eleven thousand years ago. As Wegener observed, there was little dispute about up and down movements.

But could Wegener's proviso be satisfied? Could he demonstrate the existence of a force capable of moving the continents horizontally? Wegener knew that he would have to face the question and he tried. First, however, he presented the other arguments for drift.

Wegener could cite the seismic and geomagnetic evidence showing the variations in the earth layers. Earthquake waves, as Jeffreys and others had demonstrated, change their speed when they pass under the continents and under the oceans. The varied speeds bore out Wegener's contention that the sea floors consisted of a very dense rock. To substantiate his point, he suggested that the ideal would be to procure test samples of deep layer rock from the ocean floors themselves.

"However," he added, "it will be impossible for a long time yet to bring up samples of rock outcrops from the depths by dragnet or by other means."

The few loose samples brought to the surface by dredging were volcanic and heavy. They were basalt, a rock that fulfilled the requirements Wegener was specifying for the sea floor. Basalt also lay below the lighter granite that formed much of the continents.

To the laymen, the earth and particularly the continents seemed as solid as steel and the embodiment of immovability. In actual comparison, the granite did prove nearly as stiff as steel. Wegener argued, however, that it was not plasticity (stiffness) that mattered but viscosity (internal friction).

All attempts to determine the actual viscosity of the various layers of the earth had proved indecisive, and Wegener, who always eschewed the dogmatic, cautioned, "All that can be said with certainty is that the earth behaves as a solid elastic body when acted upon by short term forces, such as seismic waves, and there is no question of plastic flow here. However, under forces applied over geological time, the earth must behave as a fluid; for example, this is shown by the fact that its oblateness corresponds exactly to its period of rotation."

All that geophysics could then say about the earth seemed to support the drift theory.

Another test could be made, in geology. If the American continents were once a part of the African land mass and if the two

continents had pulled apart, the geologic formations and folds
that existed before the split should conform on both sides. This
was the same argument Desmerest had used in the eighteenth
century about France and the British Isles. When he found more
or less identical chalk cliffs on both sides of the English channel
he had no difficulty in concluding that the two had once been
part of a continuous formation.

In South Africa there was an ancient folded mountain range,
the Swartberg. It had an east-west strike, or direction. Just south
of Buenos Aires was an extension of the same range. In structure
the two were identical. The same fossils were found in the same
beds. The rock series were the same—sandstone, fossil-bearing
shists, glacial conglomerate, and sedimentary rocks.

"We have here an elongated ancient fold that traverses the
southern tip of Africa, then is continued across South America
south of Buenos Aires and finally turns north to join the Andes,"
said Wegener. "Today the fragments of this fold are separated
from each other by an ocean of more than 6,000 kilometers
[3,726 miles] . . ."

In a model Wegener shoved the pieces together. The continuity of the mountains was certainly visible. Even the great
gneiss plateau of Africa showed a striking similarity to the main
plateau in Brazil. The igneous roots conformed, as did the
original direction of the folding. Altogether five parallels were
pointed out in the rock formations of Africa and Brazil, including the diamond fields in both. White diamonds came from the
same peculiar "pipes" in the same kimberlite rock on both sides
of the Atlantic.

Many who examined the two continents were struck by these
and many other similarities. R. Maach wrote: "Anyone who
knows something of Africa will find the geology of this [the
Brazilian] landscape startling. At every step I am reminded of
the formations of Namaland and the Transvaal. The Brazilian
strata correspond perfectly in every detail to the southern African shield."

The South African geologist A. L. DuToit, who was later to advance the theory of continental drift, said in his book comparing South Africa and Brazil that he had great difficulty in realizing that he was on another continent than his own.

"Conformities between the two sides of the ocean are now known in such numbers," he said, "that it is no longer possible to imagine them accidentally co-existing, particularly since they cover vast stretches of land and the time span from the pre-Devonian to the Tertiary."

The similarities piled up in great detail. Farther north the American coal fields seemed to be a direct continuation of the European ones. The Caledonian range in Norway and northern Britain matched the Canadian Caledonians or Appalachians. Still farther north the gneiss mountain ranges of the Hebrides and northern Scotland continued on into the gneiss mountains of Labrador. Even the terminal remains of the ice sheets in Europe and North America could have joined without a gap or break. Such conformity would have been "highly improbable" if the moraines had been formed when the two continents were separated by some twelve hundred miles as they are today.

When Wegener looked at the "totality" of the geological similarities he concluded that they offered "almost incontrovertible proof" that the Atlantic was an "expanded rift."

"It is just as if we were to refit the torn pieces of a newspaper and then check whether the lines of print run smoothly across," Wegener wrote. "If they do there is nothing left but to conclude that the pieces were in fact joined."

If even just one line of print had continued across, Wegener remarked, that would indicate a high probability of fit. With a fit in more than six geological areas, he argued, "we can bet a million to one on the theory being right."

Wegener extended his geological proof throughout the world. The correspondence in geological structure held between Greenland and North America, between Madagascar and Africa, be-

tween India, Madagascar, and Africa. Furthermore, he demonstrated, the Himalayas displayed it again.

According to Wegener's theory Australia once had been
joined to India. If the gneiss folds of Australia were laid next to
those of India their strike also conformed. Wegener even undertook an examination of the South Pacific archipelago, where
drift, according to his theory, had been complicated. He found
similarities that accounted as little else could for that complex
part of the world.

Many objections were made to his jigsaw-puzzle figuring of
the world and to the one-time unified land mass to which it
pointed. One critic claimed that with the proper imagination
North America would have fitted as well as South America to
the African coast. Others insisted that continental drift was not
necessary to explain geological coincidence. The Wegenerian
case, admittedly, was not perfect, but it was difficult to refute.
E. Argnand, an unbiased observer, said flatly "it . . . has not
been refuted."

Since Darwin's time students of ancient and modern animals
and plants had particularly required land connections to account for their distribution through most of the world. Only if
there had been some connections between the continents could
life have spread around the earth as it had. Wegener complained
with some bitterness that most of the biologists did not care
whether the connections were made with sunken continental
bridges or by the drift of continents.

"A perfectly preposterous attitude," he exclaimed with exas-
peration.

In the middle of the last century Alfred Russel Wallace had
shown that the most ancient animals of Australia bore some resemblance to those of India, Madagascar, and South Africa.

Wegener answered this observation by asserting, "Of course.
Australia once was joined to India."

Australia's second faunal group, the marsupials and mono-
tremes, bore points of relationship with the South American

fauna. Even the parasites of the Australian and South American marsupials were the same—a very telling point, as Darwin had observed many years before.

Wegener again in effect said, "Of course. The second faunal group dated back to the time when Australia still was joined to South America via Antarctica."

The third and most recent Australian "faunal element," the dingo (wild dog), rodents, bats, and other mammals, had emigrated from New Guinea and the Sunda Islands.

A third "Of course" followed. The two had been connected.

"This threefold division of the Australian fauna agrees most elegantly with drift theory," said Wegener, ". . . these very circumstances show in the clearest possible way the great superiority of the drift theory over that of sunken bridges. The distance between points in South America and Australia . . . today amounts to 80 degrees, making a great circle as large as that between Germany and Japan. . . . Can one really be expected to believe that a mere land bridge is enough in this case to ensure the interchange of biological forms?"

Wegener arrayed extensive evidence of the distribution of plants and earthworms to further support his argument. The Australian flora presented the same three-way pattern as the animal kingdom.

Botanists long had been puzzled by the distribution of some of the conifers. Why did closely related species occur in Australia, New Zealand, and Tasmania, and also in South Africa, southern Brazil, and Chile, areas widely separated by ocean? If these land masses formerly all had been one, the problem was solved. Some of the outstanding botanists accepted Wegener's way out. They really had no other.

Earthworms made an equally convincing case. They could not endure salt water or frozen ground and could only be transported with difficulty, except by man. And yet eight forms were the same on both sides of the Atlantic. All eight were ancient ones. That was further substantiation for drift theory, which held that the Atlantic had opened first at the south and that this was the oldest part of the rift.

Certainly since Chamberlain's day it had been granted that sections of the earth had undergone great climatic fluctuations. The coal and the magnolia fossils at the far north and the marks of glaciers in the steaming Amazon valley left no doubts, however incredible both seemed. The reversal of the poles and the earth's "rolling around" in its course through space offered an explanation.[2] The explanation, though, brought new difficulties.

One problem was the location of the huge coal beds of North America, Europe, Asia Minor, and China. All four areas, at the time of the coal deposition, must have lain in a continuous equatorial rain belt, similar to the rain belt that circles the globe today.

"It is clear," said Wegener, "that not only the Permo-Carboniferous traces of glaciation, but the total climatic evidence of that period falls into place with the application of drift theory and forms a climatic system which corresponds completely to that of today, provided the South Pole is displaced to southern Africa. With the present day position of the continent, however, it is altogether impossible to combine the data with an intelligible system of climates.

"Polar wandering and continental drift here form in mutual supplementation, the cardinal principle; by its use the previous confusion of disordered, apparently self-contradictory facts link up to form a pattern of simplicity . . . in complete analogy with the present climatic system (great climatic belts circling the earth.)"

The geodetic, geophysical, geological, biological, and climatic data that Wegener arrayed in support of his theory were impressive and nearly compelling. Much of the data was not to be denied. But it was all premised on the breaking up of the original land mass and the drifting away of the continents. How

[2] See Chapter XIII.

could continents, those enormous masses of land, have gone sailing around, almost like ships at sea, or at least like ice floes drifting through the oceans?

Wegener answered that the fact could be established without explaining it. There was ample precedent for this position. Newton did not derive the laws of falling bodies and planetary orbits until long after both had been determined indirectly by observation.

"The Newton of the drift theory has not yet appeared," said Wegener, with his characteristic refusal to go further than necessary.

There were, however, a number of possibilities for explanation. Among them was a "flight from the poles." Possibly an internal axial shift might have initiated it and set the continents moving. Such a flight, Wegener noted, might have moved the continental blocks through the crust. He was doubtful, however, that it would have been enough to produce the great folded mountains, the Andes and the Himalayas.

Some scientists had speculated that the friction of tidal waves could have been the driving force in producing a rotation of the crust over the core. Others proposed that deviations in the earth's shape could have given rise to a flow in the mantle and therewith the drift of the continents. Still others argued for convection currents in the mantle. Wegener felt that the last proposal held promise and could account not only for the break-up of a single land mass, but also for the opening up of the Atlantic Ocean.

"The investigation is still in its infancy," he conceded and warned: "We may, however, assume one thing as certain. The forces which displace continents are the same as those which produce great-fold mountain ranges. Continental drift, faults, compressions, earthquakes, volcanicity, transgression cycles, and polar wanderings are undoubtedly connected on a grand scale . . . However, what is cause and what is effect, only the future will unveil."

From 1915, when he published his book *Die Entstehung der Kontinente und Ozeane* (*The Origin of Continents and Oceans*), until 1928 Wegener brought out three other editions. In each he continued to pile up the evidence bearing on his far-reaching theory. In 1924 Wegener had become professor of meteorology and geophysics at Graz University in Austria. He interrupted both his teaching and his work on the theory to join another expedition to Greenland. The expedition established that the inland ice was more than eighteen hundred meters thick; then, in an accident on the inland ice cap, in November 1930, Wegener met his death.

Many scientists, particularly those in related fields where otherwise insoluble problems were solved by the drift theory, enthusiastically accepted the hypothesis. The main body of science held back. The theory was studied and given a respectful hearing. At the same time it was firmly rejected, particularly in the United States. Unless and until forces capable of moving bodies of land as immense as the continents could be demonstrated, all the evidence for drift was held in abeyance. If drift could not occur, observations indicating it were questionable and perhaps stretched far beyond their reality. *The Origin of Continents and Mountains* was not forgotten. It was, somewhat regretfully, relegated to the shelf.

It refused, however, to stay there very long. In 1937 the mechanisms for moving continents were still missing, but other objections to the theory looked increasingly niggling. The strengths of drift theory were becoming more substantial. By the thirties the earth looked less fixed and rigid to the scientists than it had in the past. Research was more and more pointing to a "pulsating, restless" body and if this were the case, movements of the continents became more plausible.

DuToit, in a book called *Our Wandering Continents,* called attention again to the "wonderfully similar histories—stratographic, tectonic, climatic, biological and eruptive—of such pairs of land masses as South Africa and South America, East Africa and India, and South Africa and Australia.

"That they should have reacted so similarly while at so great a distance from one another is improbable, accepting orthodox views, whereas under the Displacement Hypothesis, such is not only reasonable, but inevitable," he wrote.

The majority still was not convinced. One critic charged that the congruities were largely built out of the imagination, much as dragon's heads are seen in the stalactites in every other cave.

New findings, however, kept forcing the renewed consideration of the drift theory. In the thirties Vening Meinesz, the Dutch geophysicist, carried a gravimeter aboard a submarine, and proved that a sub was a sufficiently stable platform for measuring the gravity of the ocean floors. Over the abyssal trenches in the sea floor in the western Pacific he found some of the largest deficiencies in gravity ever recorded. Some force stronger than gravity was pulling the sea floor into the depths, it seemed.

If this were true, and the measurements were repeatedly confirmed, perhaps the interior of the earth was different than had been postulated. Perhaps it was more plastic and viscous. Harold Urey had suggested that the heat created by radioactivity might have softened the rocks of the mantle enough for them to move in response to pressure, somewhat in the way that soft clay does. Arthur Holmes of the University of Edinburgh and D. T. Griggs of the University of California, Los Angeles, then put into modern geophysical terms the earlier idea that extremely slow convection currents might be pushing the plastic material up through the crust, and dragging it down again at the ocean trenches. There was perhaps a continuous pushing up and down, an overturn in the earth's crust. The convection currents that Wegener had favored as a prime mechanism for drift were taking on a high degree of probability. They probably moved in the layer just below the brittle crust. It was named the asthenosphere.

During the fifties and in the sixties the sea floor was explored
as never before. Three ships, the *Vema* and the *Robert D. Conrad*
of Columbia University's Lamont Geological Observatory and
the National Science Foundation's USNS *Eltanin* explored about a
hundred thousand miles of ocean each year.

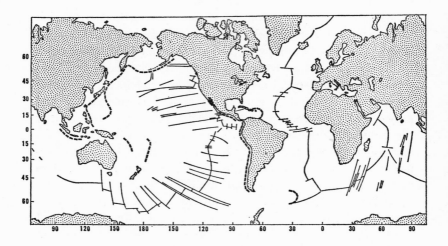

THE MID-OCEAN RIDGES WHERE NEW CRUSTAL MATERIAL PUSHES
UP FROM BELOW. THE 47,000 MILES OF OFFSET RIDGES ARE SHOWN
BY THE SOLID LINE.

THE DOTTED LINES SHOW THE TRENCHES. HERE ALONG THE EDGES
OF THE PLATES, THE SEA FLOORS THAT HAVE SPREAD OUT FROM THE
RIDGES TURN DOWN AND BEGIN THEIR RETURN TO THE ASTHENO-
SPHERE BELOW.

Their echo sounders and other instruments began to define
the true dimensions of the areas of up-flow, the ridges that ran
down the middle of the Atlantic and twisted through the other
oceans for a total distance of about forty-seven thousand miles.
And then it was discovered that these formerly almost unknown
underwater ridges actually were the earth's largest topographic
features. Some of their peaks reared higher than Everest.

Data also was coming in on the abyssal depths of the trenches in both the Atlantic and Pacific. They were being accurately plumbed and identified as the possible points of downturn, where the crust returned to the lower depths. Far from being the smooth billiard table that had been envisioned in earlier days, the sea floors as a whole were found to be as jagged, rugged, and broken as the land.

The theory of continental drift steadily looked better. Perhaps a mechanism with the infinite power to move sea floors and continents was coming into sight. Harry Hammond Hess of Princeton University proposed such a mechanism in 1962. Nevertheless, in a paper which he contributed to the Buddington Memorial Volume published by the Geological Sociey of America, Hess called the revised theory of the earth and of drift, a grand scheme of nearly overwhelming power and scope, "an essay in geopoetry." He also guarded against charges of over-reaching by describing his proposal as a "useful framework for testing."

In this modest guise, Hess laid out his geofacts with clarity and conciseness:

1. The mantle of the earth is convecting—moving—even today at an average rate of one centimeter a year.
2. The convection currents have rising limbs under the mid-ocean ridges.
3. This accounts for the rise of the ridges and for the observed high heat flow in the ridge areas.
4. The mantle material comes to the surface on the crest of these ridges.
5. The ocean crust is hydrated mantle material.

In the massing of his argument, Hess also suggested that the ridges are "ephemeral features," with a probable life of only 200,000,000 to 300,000,000 years. As long as molten or plastic material continued to come up from the mantle below, the earlier ridge rock would be shoved outward by the newer, just as a finger thrust up between two stiffly held figures shoves them aside. The outward movement from the flanks of the ridges would in time reach the continents and shove them in turn.

"The continents are carried passively on the mantle," said Hess. "They do not plow through the ocean crust."

Hess pointed out that the leading edge of a moving continent might be strongly deformed if it impinged on a "downward moving limb of the convecting mantle." At an abyss or trench, the advancing continent or sea floor would not plunge over like water going over Niagara. There would be an infinitely slow buckling that would carry the surface down into the mantle. The exchange begun at the rising mounts of the ridges would be complete.

"The ocean basins are impermanent features and the continents are permanent, though they may be torn apart or welded together and their margins deformed [cast up into folded mountains]," said Hess. "The earth is a dynamic body with its surface constantly changing. The spherical harmonics of its topography show unexpected regularities, a reflection of the regularities of its mantle convecting systems and their secondary effects."

This was both geopoetry and geofact, a theory to stir the imagination and one to move scientists into further explorations of its challenges. Here also was a scientifically more sophisticated presentation, one well in harmony with geophysical and geological observations and very possibly a force sufficient to move ocean floors and even continents, to make and unmake the earth's crust.

Like Wegener, Hess urged that the theory be put to the test. How some of the major premises could be tested he still was unable to say. That again had to await the future and further scientific advances.

At Toronto, J. Tuzo Wilson, professor of geophysics and Arctic explorer, had long been studying the great system of oceanic ridges and trenches. One system circled the globe in generally a north-to-south direction and the other ran east to west. At their point of crossing a huge T seemed to be formed.

Wilson had been associated with the aerial survey of Canada. In the photographs of the land a number of faults appeared— enormous gashes in the earth. Wilson found that the Canadian faults connected with another long fault—the Cabot—extending from Boston to northern Newfoundland. If Europe and North America had once adjoined, the American faults also would have connected with a deep and ancient fault that bisects Scotland along the Great Glen in the Caledonian Mountains. It was as though Wegener's line of print had matched.

The finding sent Wilson back to Wegener. The German scientist had predicted exactly such a system of faults. It was along this line, he had said, that Ellesmere Island had been pulled apart from Greenland.

Wilson undertook a review of Wegener and the drift theory in the light of the latest knowledge. It was published in *Scientific American* in April 1963. Wilson argued that Wegener's case had been greatly strengthened and that it had newly been opened to examination. Wilson proposed one specific test.

The oceanographers had been reporting that the Atlantic ridge was not in fact an unbroken range. Sections of it were offset, stepped in effect.

If the ridge had been all one, like an uncut loaf of French bread, and if the upthrust of lava had not only cracked it apart at the crest but had also caused it to break into chunks as a loaf of bread might be broken, earthquakes should have occurred all along these horizontal lines of breakage. But, said Wilson, this did not appear to be the case.

If, however, sections of the ridge were offset, Wilson suggested, there would be a very different pattern of earthquakes. He hypothesized that only a part of the fracture zone between the two chunks would be subjected to the opposite movements away from the flank. The fault between them would be a transform one, rather than a transcurrent one. Wilson proposed that a study of earthquake patterns along the ridges would determine if this was the case.

Not long afterward Lynn R. Sykes and other seismologists at the Lamont Observatory determined on a worldwide basis that the earthquakes associated with ocean fracture zones occur in

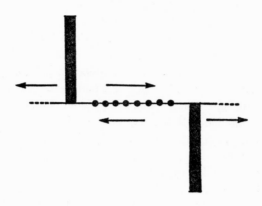

EARTHQUAKE AREA IN THE MID-OCEAN RIDGES. SHALLOW EARTHQUAKES OCCUR BETWEEN TWO OFFSET SECTIONS OF THE RIDGE. HERE OPPOSING MOTIONS COME INTO CONFLICT. AS NEW SEA FLOOR ALONG THE UPPER RIDGE (UPPER LINE IN DIAGRAM) PUSHES TO THE RIGHT, IT CONFLICTS WITH SEA FLOOR SPREADING TO THE LEFT FROM THE LOWER OFFSET PART OF THE RIDGE. THE RESULT: COUNTER-PULLS AND EARTHQUAKES.

the limited opposite-pull zone between the ridge axes. It was a dramatic confirmation of Wilson's hypothesis. The test had been made and it upheld the prediction. The discovery of the earthquake directions along the ridges at the same time offered substantiating and striking evidence that the sea floors were spreading out from the constantly growing mid-ocean ridges. And since the earthquakes were happening in the present, their shocks and directions said emphatically that spreading was going on today.

Frederick J. Vine and D. H. Matthews at Cambridge University also read the Hess geopoetry and were stirred by it. Could it be proved? Vine, a twenty-four-year-old graduate student, had an idea that might open the way for at least one test. It was in fact a corollary hypothesis, built upon the amazing magnetic "pointers" fixed forever, or for extremely long periods, in the earth's rock. Runcorn had shown that grains of iron in lavas pouring out to the surface of the earth and in sediments forming into rock are weakly magnetized by the earth's magnetic field.[3] The uncountable billions of metallic grains align themselves to point to the nearest magnetic pole. They are an abiding record of where the magnetic poles stood at the time of the rock's formation.

It had also been established that the magnetic poles frequently—in geologic terms—reverse themselves. Continuing research had revealed that the magnetic field had reversed itself about 171 times in the last 76,000,000 years. The north magnetic pole had become south, and the south, north, although the directions were not absolute.

Vine and Matthews pointed out that the reversing polarity might leave a readable record in the rock of the ocean floors. Lavas consolidating at the ridge crests of today would point to the magnetic poles of today. The magnetized grains in the rocks being pushed outward along the ridge flanks should in turn point to the poles of their day. Thus on both sides of the ridge there should be bands of "up"-pointing grains and bands of "down"-pointing grains, something like the up-and-down strips of lighted arrows installed in some of the most elaborate new elevators.

And so it would continue in all of the rocks pushed still further away from the ridge, figuratively speaking, up and down, up and down. The bands of pointing grains, if the theory was correct, should run parallel to the ridge.

Each band might vary in width, for the periods of positive and reverse magnetization had varied. Some periods had lasted for as little as 33,000 years, and some for more than 70,000. A few had continued for several million years. If a "normal" period had been a long one the band of pointers would be a wide one; if a short one, it would be narrower, much as the varied bands in

[3] See Chapter XV.

striped ribbon or a soldier's campaign ribbons. Would such a pattern be found in the sea floors? Were they magnetically zebra-striped?

Many were dubious. But this again was a thesis that could be tested. Oceanographic vessels and planes routinely drag a magnetometer after them—the instrument must be towed to avoid the magnetic field of the ship. The magnetometers record the magnetization of the ocean floor below, or of what is called the anomalous field, the magnetization field produced by sources within the crust, as distinct from the fields originating in the earth's core. If such a magnetometer were towed over an ocean floor consisting of alternate strips of normal and reversely magnetized grains it should record the bands as clearly as so many lines drawn on a piece of paper.

In 1963 the United States Naval Oceonographic Office did what had not been done before. Its planes, dragging their magnetometers behind them, flew fifty-eight traverses over the Reykjanes Ridge, a little southwest of Iceland. It was a northern part of the main Atlantic ridge. On both sides of the ridge, the instruments recorded linear stripes of normal and reversed magnetization in a veritable zebra-stripe pattern.

Another profile was taken at 51 degrees south in the Pacific Ocean. Here was another banded pattern. The stripes appeared with remarkable symmetry on both sides of the Pacific Ridge.

By this time other scientists, using paleomagnetic and radiogenic measurements on lavas in many parts of the world, had worked out the time scale for every magnetic reversal in the last 3,500,000 years. The once-disputed reversals were accurately timed and profiled in line drawings. The scientists could show, for example, that Band A with normal magnetization and all of its pointers turned in one direction had lasted for 700,000 years, that Band B next to it had continued for only 33,000 years, and that the next period of changed magnetization had continued for 300,000 years. The width of the stripes varied with the time their period of magnetization had prevailed.

Using this data Columbia scientists made models—profiles—of what the magnetic pattern should be in the Atlantic and in the south Pacific. Their computed lines rose in peaks of various heights and widths for each normal period and plunged in similarly varied dips for each reverse period. Their next step was to profile similarly the actual measurements made by the magnetometers of the ships and planes.

"Considering the utter simplicity of the model," said W. C. Pitman, a Lamont participant in the study, "the correlation between the profile computed from the model and the measured profile is quite good." This was careful scientific understatement. Peak nearly matched peak in model and actuality. The widths and the dips came at virtually the same points. Prediction and actuality once again were extremely close.

With the dates for each period and a record of how long it had lasted, the scientists at once had a history of what had occurred in the ocean areas. At the ridges, the record showed that the rocks were new. On both sides the history was traced for the full 3,500,000 years that had been timed. However, the rate of spreading could easily be calculated from the data at hand. In the South Pacific the older formations were being pushed away from the ridge at the rate of 4.5 centimeters, or about one and three-fourths inches, a year on either side of the mountainous ridge. And knowing the rate of spreading, the scientists could time the bands farther out. They could extend their profiles far beyond 3,500,000 years.

It was the same in the north Atlantic. Pitman and J. R. Heirtzler of Lamont computed a model profile of the Reykjanes Ridge. Then actual measurements were made by Navy planes.

"The correlation between the measured and computed profiles seems quite remarkable," said Pitman.

Over millions of years the sea floor had been pushing out from the ridge at the rate of one centimeter a year on either side. Some of the rocks in the northwest of Scotland had been dated by potassium-argon at 60,000,000 years. This meant that it had taken them 60,000,000 years to move from the mid-ocean ridge to Scotland. At the one-centimeter rate of spread that was exactly how far they should have gone. The answer checked.

Vine and Matthews then applied the method to new data on the Carlsberg Ridge in the Indian Ocean, to the Juan de Fuca Ridge in the northeast Pacific, and to the Red Sea Rift, which many considered an embryonic ridge. Again prediction tallied with the actual findings.

In all parts of the world, the Pacific, the Atlantic, and the Indian Oceans, the magnetization investigations showed that new sea floor was being created at the ridges, and that as the new lavas pushed up from below, the older ridges were shoved farther and farther away from their point of origin. Over millions of years they had gone far from their place of birth.

Wegener had thought, a little despairingly perhaps, that it would be a "long time" before scientists could investigate the sea floor itself. But only thirty years later Lamont, under the direction of Maurice Ewing, sent out research ships to cut cores from the sediments spread on the ocean floors, sediments that undisturbed had accumulated over millions of years. The piston corer used for these investigations could not, however, push into the underlying rocks or some of the deepest sediments.

The attempts to drill a hole all the way through the crust of the earth, in the Mohole Project, had not succeeded. Nevertheless, the techniques developed made it possible to drill into the hard ocean floor. Dating techniques enabled the scientists to fix the time of the deposit of the materials brought up in the cores. It was at last possible to make a thorough scientific study of the ocean floors.

The National Science Foundation in 1966 made a $12,600,000 grant for an eighteen-month "Deep Sea Drilling Project" and later extended it for another three years. Five institutions joined the project—the Scripps Institution for Oceanography, Columbia's Lamont-Doherty Observatory,[4] the University of Miami's

[4] Formerly Lamont Observatory.

Institute of Marine Sciences, the Woods Hole Oceanographic Institution, and the University of Washington.

A research vessel was built to special design and named the *Glomar Challenger, Glomar* for the builder, Global Marine Inc., and *Challenger* for a proud predecessor, the H.M.S. *Challenger,* which from 1872 to 1876 had sailed the seas, sampling, sounding, and studying all the oceans. Her work established the broad contours of the ocean basins and laid the foundation for the science of oceanography.

Special "thrusters" would hold the *Glomar Challenger* steady while she dropped from one to four miles of line through the ocean's waters and drilled through as much as a half mile of sediments and rock that lay below.

Satellites orbiting above would give her almost hourly corrections of her position and enable her to locate a tiny hole in the midst of the ocean's trackless expanse. On August 11, 1968, the *Glomar Challenger* sailed on the first of the two-month "legs" that would carry her back and forth across the oceans and chart a still largely unexplored world far below.

On Leg 3, from Dakar to Rio de Janeiro, the *Glomar Challenger* drilled her way across the Atlantic Ridge, dropping her line through nearly three miles of water, and recovered cores of the floor rock. It was the first time such a feat had been accomplished.

At the ridge the rock was virtually new—on the geologic time scale it stood at zero. About 100 nautical miles out from the ridge the cores were about 11,000,000 years old. At about 205 miles, the age of the rock came to 24,000,000 years, and at 872 miles, the age was close to 76,000,000 years. It was the same on the other side of the ridge; the age of the rocks advanced from zero to 70,000,000 as the distance from the ridge increased. On this leg eight sites were drilled. On later voyages the same increase in age, as the core drilling moved away from the ridges, was found in the Pacific Ocean.

Wegener could not have dreamed of a more striking confirmation. Once again scientists had predicted, and had been proved to be right. The magnetic measurements guided by the tiny magnetic "pointers" in the rocks had shown a progression from young to old in the magnetization of the rocks paralleling the long stretches of the 47,000 miles of underseas ridges. Studies of the earthquakes along the ridges had shown once again that the ridges were spreading and how they were doing it.

Then this totally different kind of test, penetrating the floor of the ocean itself, had revealed the same consistent pattern. Few could any longer doubt the theory. The sea floors were spreading out, pushing out, moving continually away from the ridge crests where molten or soft materials had welled up from the still unknown sub-crustal depths. The crust's birthplace during most of geologic time had been found.

"This suggests continuous spreading during the Cenozoic [the last 65,000,000 or 70,000,000 years] at an essentially constant rate," said Vine. The rate varied from about one centimeter per ridge flank in the North and South Atlantic to six centimeters in the equatorial Pacific. Some of the floors had moved as much as 1,000 miles in the last 100,000,000 years and several thousand in the last 200,000,000. It was calculated that some of the sea floors might easily move the length of a man's body during his lifetime.

Without titantic upheaval, but slowly and inexorably, the moving sea floor pushed up against the nearest continental land masses and rafted or shoved them along. The Atlantic sea floor west of the middle ocean ridge came so firmly against the North American continent that the two parts, sea and land, formed one vast crustal plate. It was almost as though they were welded together. The plate pushed on westward.

But along the Pacific coast this westward-inching plate collided with the edge of the Pacific plate pushing eastward from the mid-Pacific ridge. Land going in one direction met sea floor moving in the opposite. On the geological scale it was a colossal head-on clash. The lighter land mass—with its lighter rocks—ran up and over the heavier Pacific sea floor and turned it down into the depths.

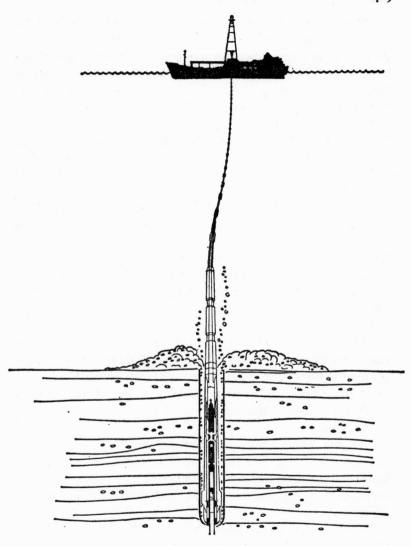

EXPLORING THE OCEAN FLOOR. THE "GLOMAR-CHALLENGER" DROPS
HER LINE AND CORER-DRILL THROUGH SOME FOUR MILES OF WATER
AND CUTS OUT UNDISTURBED CORES OF THE ACCUMULATED SEDIMENTS
AND THE FLOOR BELOW. THE CORES GIVE A CLEAR RECORD OF MIL-
LIONS OF YEARS OF OCEAN HISTORY AND MAKE IT POSSIBLE TO DETER-
MINE THE TIME OF DEPOSIT OF EACH OF THE LAYERS.

The results of this encounter were registered in some of the mightiest phenomena the earth has known. The land was up-thrust into the vast, towering mountains that run from Alaska south along the entire coast, and the sea floor was downthrust into some of the deep Pacific trenches that lie just offshore. As the downgoing sea floor was crunched back into the mantle and rock forced into rock under the unrelenting pressures and weight, there was fracturing and distortion. The stupendous forces generated repeatedly shook the coast with devastating earthquakes and erupted into volcanic outbursts violent enough to create mountain ranges as vast as the Cascades.

In one sense this collision of land and sea floor was an ending. Masses of material pushed up from the mantle millions of years before were returning to their beginnings. Some maintained that it was a regeneration. The sea floor going back to the astheno-sphere or under-crustal world might in the illimitable lengths of time and further subterranean movements once again upwell in some other part of the globe to create new sea floor and start the re-making of the crust all over again.

Scientists began to see that on a globe—a sphere—where new extrusions split sea floor ridges and pushed their flanks outward in opposite directions, the meeting and clash of the blocks was inevitable. Oppositely moving blocks were bound to collide as they pushed around this nearly round globe; irresistible forces had to meet.

In South America the same westward-moving American plate encountered part of the eastward-moving Pacific plate. Here the Andes and the deep trenches off Chile and Peru were created by the conflict. And again there were prodigious earthquakes and volcanoes.

In other parts of the world, sea floors have met sea floors, with one or the other being turned downward at the profoundly deep trenches. And continent has crashed into continent, with the uplifting of mountains as lofty and mighty as the Himalayas.

The trenches, those gashes in the earth, were mapped and measured. Cores were taken from them and scientists descended to their generally smooth though narrow floors by bathysphere. In addition, studies of the earthquakes originating along their downslopes defined them in the deep areas where no man can penetrate.

James D. Hays, of Lamont, was the chief scientist aboard Leg 9 of the Deep Sea Drilling Project. His scientific team sent their drill down under two and a half miles of water west of the East Pacific Ridge. From 35,000,000 years ago to 10,000,000, Hays found that the speed of the moving floor increased from three inches a year to five and a half, and then abruptly slowed to about two and one half inches a year.

"This observed acceleration," Hays said, "suggests the possibility that the principal Pacific Ocean plate was drawn laterally westward by the force of gravity pulling the edge of the plate down into the earth at the deep-sea trenches near the Asian continent."

To explain, Hays used an analogy: "It's like laying a terry-cloth towel on water. It sinks first at the edge and the more towel that goes under water, the faster it sinks and the faster the part of the surface is pulled along."

Hays estimated that the plate turning down at an angle at the big trench systems was about sixty miles thick. He questioned that convection currents alone, as had previously been assumed, would be sufficient to draw the plate back down into the depths. He questioned too whether the push initiated by the steady upwelling of rock along the distant ridges could alone explain the downturn. The pushout from the ridges and through the plates would be constant. But the evidence from Leg 9 showed that the Pacific movement down into the trenches was not constant.

"This one [Pacific] Ocean floor plate at least may have been pulled rather than pushed," said Hays. "However, future research may show all three mechanisms at work, the pushing of upwelling rock, the carrying of convection currents and the pulling of gravity, at various times and in varying combinations through geological time."

Vine had estimated that about half of the present sea floor was created during the last 65,000,000 years. A concomitant estimate became possible and inescapable. Half of the earth's crust must have been destroyed in the same geologically modern period of 65,000,000 years in those great crunching trench systems, and particularly in the deep trenches of the north and south Pacific. The ocean floors then had been made and unmade in prodigious quantities in what is only a brief time in the earth's total life of 4.5 billion years. And the ocean floors were young, almost juvenile in comparison to the continents, for rocks taken from the continents have been dated at 3.5 billion years. The oldest sea floor rocks dated so far have an age of only about 150,000,000 years. The continents may prove to be ten to twenty times older than the frequently remade sea floors.

As the huge sixty-mile-thick slabs of sea floor moved down into the maw of the trenches, they were relatively cold. The asthenosphere to which they were returning was much hotter, possibly 800 to 1,000 degrees.

"At the rates of underthrusting being considered," said Sykes, "the downgoing slab of lithosphere would remain quite cold relative to its surroundings. . . . The injection of cold exotic materials into the asthenosphere opens a number of new possibilities for explaining the mechanisms of volcanoes and of deep earthquakes."

Sykes calculated that the down-turning crust might remain cold and brittle enough to be subject to fracture for as much as 437 miles into the earth. The shocks generated might shake the surface in major earthquakes.

Sykes, Jack Oliver, and Bryan Isacks, all seismologists, undertook a worldwide survey of earthquakes in the light of the new global tectonics, as the entire majestic process was called. On maps of the earth they dotted in the locations of the deepest shocks. The dots formed a broad band defining the downgoing edge of the crustal plates.

On another map they marked the shallow shocks. These zones came at the edges of the plates, but also at the ridges.

On a third map the location of all of the world's active volcanoes was noted. They all lay along the edges where one plate was underthrusting another.

The seismologists then drew in the locations of the earthquakes that had produced large *tsunamis* or the tidal waves that sweep, destructively for man, across the oceans. They also lay along the edges of the trenches.

Even the direction of the sub-surface flow at the trenches was shown by the earthquakes. The shocks seemed to follow the direction of the downward movement, eastward and downward under the Pacific coast of South America and westward and downward under the island arcs on the opposite side of the Pacific.

"Perhaps the strongest and most convincing evidence supporting the new global tectonics comes from the information about worldwide seismicity," said Sykes. "The concentration of seismic activity in narrow belts that outline large stable blocks is immediately apparent."

Thus earthquakes and volcanoes—fire, shock, and tidal waves—defined the great blocks into which the earth was cracked and their direction of movement. Upheaval outlined the borders.

The belts of fire and shock outlined at least six crustal plates. Xavier LePichon suggested the six as a base for study until further examination of the complex worldwide data might indicate a need for revision.

The six plates that Le Pichon proposed were variously composed and sized:

1. The American—made up of North and South America and the western half of the Atlantic floor

2. The African—the continent of Africa and the eastern half of the Atlantic floor
3. The European-Asian—all of both land masses except India and Arabia and some adjoining sea floors
4. The Indian-Arabic—and adjoining sea floors
5. The Pacific—entirely oceanic
6. The Australian-Antarctic—and adjoining sea floors

All were in movement and probably always had been. Within a few years the actual movements may be measured. After observation stations are established in Hawaii and Japan, instruments placed on the moon are expected to give the longitudes of these stations with such accuracy that the predicted motion— here a movement toward Japan of about four inches a year— should be observable.

It must constantly be remembered that this is a spherical earth. The big plates with their high-riding land masses probably are slowly rotating around poles.

"The motion can be described as the rotation of rigid blocks on the spherical surface of the earth," said J. R. Heirtzler of Lamont. "The only modification of the blocks occurs at the crests of the ridges, along the trenches, and within regions of major compressive folding."

The mechanisms that Wegener could not supply had been defined to the satisfaction of most, though not all, of the scientific world. Wegener's other evidence, the jigsaw fit of the continents and the continuity of rock formations, species, and paleoclimates became largely incontrovertible—as Wegener had considered it many years before.

How the earth's sixty-mile thick and relatively brittle crust was formed was another problem, but the new research strongly suggested that by some 250,000,000 years ago all of the crust was assembled in one big land mass. Around it rolled a single ocean, which then as well as now covered about three fourths of the globe. Eduard Suess, the Austrian geologist, named this proposed early world Gondwanaland land, for a geologically ancient province in India. Wegener generally called it Pangaea. (Neither should be confused with the mythical sunken continent of Atlantis.)

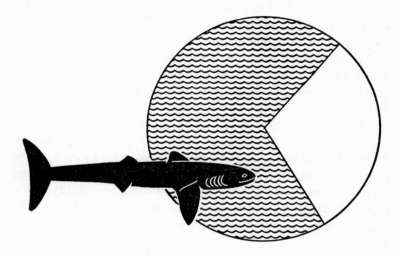

THIS IS A WATER WORLD. A LITTLE MORE THAN SEVENTY PER CENT OF THE EARTH'S SURFACE IS COVERED BY WATER.

F. B. Taylor suggested, however, that there had been two land masses at this early period, Gondwana and a northern mass that he called Laurasia. Wegener and others studying drift at about the same time had put their super-continent together by in effect shoving the present continents back together. The fit of some of the pieces was loose, though perhaps no looser than might have been expected after some 120,000,000 or more years of erosion of the continental shorelines. In general the pieces went together convincingly well.

The data on the seas developed during the 1950's and 1960's afforded additional clues for the reconstitution of the early super-continent. Wilson pointed out that if two of today's continents had once been adjacent, a median ridge should now lie between them—the outpouring of lavas along the ridge would have separated them. Under certain circumstances lateral ridges also should presently lie between the one-time continental mates. By mapping the ridges, Wilson said, geologists should have a unique method of reassembling continents that had drifted apart.

Wilson put his proposal to the most severe of tests—in the Indian Ocean. The geological and paleomagnetic evidence indicated that here four continents, Africa, India, Australia, and Antarctica, had drifted apart. If this was the case, the four should be separated by four mid-ocean ridges.

Wilson traced out three of them. There were signs of the fourth. All had been located by oceanic surveys. In each of the quadrants marked off by the ridges there was also a lateral ridge. "What is remarkable is not that there is some irregularity in the present configuration of these ridges, but that the floor of the Indian Ocean should show such a symmetrical pattern," said Wilson.

The predicted pattern held in the Pacific. The mid-ocean ridge separating Australia from Antarctica continued north through the Pacific and into the Caribbean to form the rift that divided North and South America. Another branch of the Pacific ridge separated South America from Antarctica. The oceanic islands extending at right angles along the east Pacific rise—the Tubai, Society, Tuamotu, and Marquesas Islands—were older the farther they lay from the rise. The east Pacific rise had rifted the Pacific, the greatest of the oceans.

Wilson in turn drew the continents together along the lines represented by the ridges. On paper and in model they fit together in one super-continent. The single land mass was not exactly the Pangaea of Wegener and DuToit, but the two were highly similar.

Wilson warned that the Gondwanaland he was assembling was not primeval. He suggested that it had been brought together from two still older fragments. Before that and far back in the dim early history of the earth there might have been many times of assembly, fracturing, and disjunction. The land and the seas had probably always been rotating around the earth in their stately and changing dance.

The Canadian geophysicist also set out to track the splitting up that had broken Gondwanaland into the continents of the present. About 120,000,000 years ago, he suggested, a ridge rift developed that pushed Africa and South America apart. The waters of the earlier ocean poured into the basin to form the Atlantic. In the south the rift and the ocean were quite wide.

A continuation of the split separated Antarctica from Africa, and spreading diagonally across the Indian Ocean, moved Africa farther north. The big continent was further separated from the Antarctic and Australian land masses.

By 60,000,000 years ago, as Wilson reconstructs events, the ridge and rift had become somewhat less active. But a new rift opened. India was separated from Africa, and Australia from Antarctica.

India continued to drift north until it collided colossally with Asia, and the Himalayas were upthrust at the line of impact. Wilson attributed the lengthy northward migration of the Indian subcontinent to the successive activity of the two main ridges in the Indian Ocean. This, he argued, could explain why India moved twice as far north in relation to Antarctica as did Africa and Australia. As proof of the double shoving there was the now somewhat indistinct older northeast ridge on the floor of the Indian Ocean.

The young Indian Ocean rift may then have extended along the east Pacific rise to the Cocos Ridge and may even have gone farther to cross the Caribbean. A branch also passed south of South America. This was virtually global fracturing and ridge creation.

"As these median ridges have continued to widen they have been forced by this growth to migrate northward, forming great shears or faults off the coast of Chile and through California [the San Andreas fault]. Indeed a case can be made for the idea that every mid-ocean ridge normally ends at a great fault or at a pivot point," said Wilson.

A few million years ago activity along part of the 47,000-mile-long meandering ridge may have decreased. This would have allowed the north and south American continents to be joined by the Isthmus of Panama.

But the signs indicated that the north Atlantic ridge once more became active. The new activity produced renewed uplift in the Verkloyansk Mountains of Siberia and in five still-active volcanoes in the Atlantic.

"And thence," added Wilson, "by two arms along the rift valleys of the Jordan River and through the African rift valleys where the breakup of a continent apparently has begun."

Another division of Africa might have already started, and in the very valleys and gorges where the cracking open of the earth has revealed the nearly unbroken fossil record of man from his earliest apeman beginnings to today.

The continuing upflow from the mantle, from the depths, had initiated movements that largely created the earth known to its human inhabitants of today. The familiar continents separated by the wide familiar oceans proved to be a phase, a passing, shifting phase in the history of the planet. They had changed and would change in the future almost like the drifting clouds above.

Once again, it had been learned, movements undiscernible to the human eyes or senses were shaping the earth—the mountains that had always awed men, and the earthquakes, volcanoes, and tidal waves they had always feared, were all the workings of these slow, slow movements. And, as Hutton had observed many years earlier, there was no sign of either a beginning or an end.

Even a decade earlier there had been little expectation that the enigma of the earth would be largely solved in any near time. The immensity of the problem seemed to place it beyond even the reach of modern science. Many of the answers, though, came in a rush. The exploration of the sea floors, the reading of the minute magnetized grains pointing to the poles of their time, the pinpointing of the origins and movements of earthquakes, and the wide-scale sampling of rocks lying below miles of water and of deep beds of sediments suddenly and collectively supplied understanding of the format of the earth, its mountains, its oceans, and its upheavals. The clues in themselves sometimes were tiny. Their implications were huge.

"It is a revolution," said Julian R. Goldsmith, geophysicist of the University of Chicago. Others repeatedly used the same word to describe the radical change in the understanding of the earth. Wilson compared the new findings to the classic atomic breakthrough in physics. Pitman warned that the textbooks will have to be rewritten.

Not all the mysteries of the earth were solved. The details of how the crustal movements shaped the earth still had to be worked out in years of patient research. Corrections and refinements would have to be made. But at long last the basic understandings had been gained. We can now understand as none of our predecessors "the outward forms and inner workings of Nature."

[430]

NOTE ON BOOKS AND MATERIALS

THERE ARE great libraries devoted wholly to books about the earth. In this note I shall attempt only to indicate the principal books with which I worked, a few others that I think might be particularly useful or interesting, and some of the bibliographies where full references may be found.

A few books range across certain large sections of this almost limitless subject. At the head of those dealing with the history of geology should be placed Sir Archibald Geikie's beautifully written and clear-sighted *The Founders of Geology* (London: MacMillan and Co.; 1897). It is the story both of the development of geological ideas and of the men who gave them form. Frank Dawson Adams took an entirely different approach. Over many years this noted Canadian geologist tracked down the early writing and thought about the earth, and his book *The Birth and Development of the Geological Sciences* (New York: Dover Publications; 1954) is a fascinating study, particularly of the Middle Ages. George Perkins Merrill's *The First Hundred Years of American Geology* (New Haven: Yale University Press; 1924) is a scholarly review of the work of American geologists.

In their very readable *Giants of Geology* (Garden City: Doubleday & Co.; 1952) Carroll Lane Fenton and M. A. Fenton emphasize the lives of leading geologists. Also useful are *A Source Book in Geology*, by K. F. Mather and S. L. Mason (New York: McGraw-Hill Book Co.; 1939), and *Geology, 1888–1938*, a 1941 publication of the Geological Society of America (New York).

The principles of geology and the processes that have shaped the earth are set forth in a number of distinguished textbooks. Among the newer or those that have appeared in recent editions are: *Down to Earth*, in which Carey Croneis and William C. Krumbein take an unsolemn but authoritative look at geology (Chicago: University of Chicago Press; 1955); *Geology, Principles and Processes*, by William H. Emmons and others (New York: McGraw-Hill Book Co.; 1955); *Principles of Physical Geology*, by Arthur Holmes (New York: The Ronald Press Company; 1945); *A Textbook of Geology*, by R. M. Garrels (New York: Harper & Bros.; 1951); *Principles of Geology*, by James Gilluly (San Francisco: W. H. Freeman & Co.; 1951); *Physical Geology*, by Chester R. Longwell, Adolph Knopf, and Richard F. Flint (Third edition. New York: John Wiley & Sons; 1948); *Geology: An Introduction to Earth History*, by Herbert H. Read (London: Oxford University Press; 1949); and *The Earth's Crust*, by Laurence Dudley Stamp, which shows many of the earth's most important structures in colored models that often are more vivid than many words (New York: Crown Publishers; 1951).

Authoritative scientific reports on much of the new work in geology, geophysics, and geochemistry which is so dramatically changing older theories of the earth may be found in three books, all symposia: *The Earth as a Planet*, edited by Gerard P. Kuiper (Chicago: University of Chicago Press: 1954); *Crust of the Earth: A Symposium*, Arie Poldervaart, editor (New York: The Geological Society of America, Special Paper 62; 1955); and *Internal Constitution of the Earth*, edited by Beno Gutenberg (Second edition. New York: Dover Publications; 1951). The world's most noted scientists have contributed chapters on their own specialties. Although all three books are technical and designed for the use of scientists, they may be read with pleasure and profit by a layman well grounded in the physical sciences. Each of the chapters is followed by an extensive bibliography. Here may be found nearly all of the papers and books that have contributed to the new findings.

Two well-classified bibliographies will be of the greatest assistance to anyone looking for additional general materials. They are: *The Literature of Geology*, compiled by Brian Mason of the American Museum of Natural History, Central Park West at 79th Street, New York ($2); and *The Earth for the Layman*, which lists books and pamphlets for children and adults, and is a publication of the American Geological Institute of the National Research Council, 2101 Constitution Avenue, Washington, D. C. ($1). The present report was issued in 1950, but a later and fuller edition is planned.

Chapter by chapter, the materials also are voluminous. Only a few can be listed.

I

HESIOD. The excellent prose translation by Hugh G. Evelyn White (Cambridge: Harvard University Press; 1936) was principally used. Edith Hamilton's sensitive and moving *The Greek Way to Western Civilization* (New York: The New American Library; 1948) is essential for background. Miss Hamilton's *Mythology* (New York: The New American Library; 1954) and *The Greek Myths*, by Robert Graves (Baltimore: Penguin Books; 1955), treat the myths in the light of modern anthropological research. C. E. Robinson's *Hellas* (Boston: Beacon Press; 1955) provides an excellent and fascinating short history of Greece. W. K. C. Guthrie's *The Greeks and Their Gods* (Boston: Beacon Press; 1954) and H. D. F. Kitto's *The Greeks* (London: Penguin Books; 1954) should not be overlooked, and many will wish to turn too to Milton's *Paradise Lost* for another treatment of the Hesiod myths.

ARISTOTLE. H. D. P. Lee's translation of Aristotle's *Meteorologica* (Cambridge: Harvard University Press; 1952) was the choice here. Aristotle's other writings on the earth may conveniently be found in *The Basic Works of Aristotle*, by Richard McKeon (New York: Random House; 1941). There is an interesting account of Aristotle's life and work in W. D. Ross's *Aristotle* (London: Methuen & Co.; 1949). This book also provides a classified bibliography. Professor Henry Jackson of Cambridge University in an article in the *Journal of Philology* (Vol. XXXV, 1910) reconstructed Aristotle's classroom from clues given in his work. This technique was borrowed to build the scenes used in this chapter and to determine attitudes.

II

Sir Leonard Woolley tells the story of his discovery of Noah's Flood in his books *Ur of the Chaldees* (London: Penguin Books; 1954) and *Excavations at Ur* (New York: Thomas Y. Crowell Company; 1954). The Gilgamesh Epic and other early accounts of the Flood are brought together with precision and scholarship in *The Gilgamesh Epic and Old Testament Parallels*, by Alexander Heidel (Chicago: University of Chicago Press; 1949). Indispensable to a study of the Flood and the legends it inspired is Don Cameron Allen's *The Legend of Noah* (Urbana: University of Illinois Press; 1949). The seventeenth-century theories of the Flood are best seen in the work of Burnet, Woodward, Ray, and Whiston—the lengthy titles of their works are given in the text.

III

The life and work of Guettard is presented with clarity, understanding, and a rare grace in the *éloge* that the Marquis de Condorcet delivered before the French Academy; it is included in *Œuvres de Condorcet* (Paris: Firmin Dido Frères; 1847). Geikie's fine chapter on Guettard draws most of its biographical material from this source. Guettard's own work is well summarized in the following memoir in the *Histoires de l'Académie Royale des Sciences: "Sur quelques montagnes de France qui ont été volcans"* (1752), and in nine memoirs on related subjects and the Auvergne in the *histoire* of 1768.

IV

Cuvier, when he became perpetual secretary of the Institut des Sciences, made his *éloges* of deceased members scientific summaries of their work. He also always emphasized the man and the circumstances of his life which influenced what he did. The *éloges* are therefore an invaluable source of material. Those of Desmarest and Werner were delivered at the same session of the Institut. Both are reprinted in the *Recueil des éloges historiques lus dans l'Institut Royal de France* (Strasbourg; 1819). Memoirs covering the work of Desmarest are found in the *histoires* of the Institut over a period of years. Geikie has excellent chapters on Desmarest and Werner.

V

Hutton's first publication of his theory appears in the *Transactions of the Royal Society of Edinburgh*, Vol. I (1783–6). A fine account of the life of Dr. Hutton and Playfair's *Illustrations of the Huttonian Theory* are printed in *The Works of John Playfair* (Edinburgh: Archibald Constable & Co.; 1822). A report of Hall's work is in the *Transactions of the Royal Society*, Vol. III (1790).

VI

Three of Cuvier's books encompass most of his work on the earth: *Description géologique des environs de Paris* (Paris: G. Dufour; 1822); *Discours sur les révolutions du globe* (Paris: Firmin Didot Frères; 1850);

and, in English translation by Professor Robert Jameson, *Essay on the Theory of the Earth* (Edinburgh: William Blackwood; 1827). Cuvier's own *éloge*, guided by the notes he left, is included in *Éloges historiques*, by M. Flourens (Paris: Ducrocq; 1860). The one hundredth anniversary of Cuvier's death was observed in 1932 by the publication of the "*Centenaire de G. Cuvier*" in the *Archives du Muséum National d'Histoire Naturelle* (Paris: Masson et Cie.; 1932). It includes essays on Cuvier's life and career, on Cuvier as the founder of paleontology, and a complete and handsomely engraved iconography.

VII

Agassiz's European studies of glaciers are summed up in two books: *Étude sur les glaciers* (Neuchâtel: Jent & Gassmann; 1840), with its accompanying atlas of magnificent drawings (Neuchâtel: H. Nicolet; 1840), and *Système glaciaire* (Paris: V. Masson; 1847). Some of his American work on glaciers is reported in *Geological Sketches* (Boston: James R. Osgood & Co.; 1873). The story of Agassiz's life and of the experiences that helped to produce his scientific findings is vividly told in *Louis Agassiz —His Life and Correspondence*, edited by Elizabeth Cary Agassiz (Two volumes. Boston: Houghton, Mifflin and Company; 1886). Several other biographies of Agassiz have been written, and are of varying quality.

VIII

Lyell's most famous book, *The Principles of Geology* (Two volumes. Twelfth edition. London: John Murray; 1875), continues to be a geological classic and is eminently readable even today. Also useful is his *Elements of Geology* (London: Spottiswoode; 1838). The man behind these monumental works is clearly revealed in *The Life, Letters, and Journals of Sir Charles Lyell, Bart.* (Two volumes. London: John Murray; 1881). G. A. J. Cole wrote a short, excellent life of Lyell for the *Dictionary of National Biography* (London: Smith, Elder & Co.; 1909). The obituary written by Sir Archibald Geikie for *Nature* (August 27, 1875) assesses Lyell's place in his own time.

IX

The results of Logan's work are presented in his highly respected *Geology of Canada* (Montreal: Geological Survey of Canada; 1863). The book is a geological study and entirely impersonal. Two biographies, however, give a picture of the man as well as of his work: *The Life of Sir William Logan*, by Bernard J. Harrington (London: Sampson-Low; 1883), and *Sir William E. Logan and the Geological Survey of Canada*, by Dr. Robert Bell (Ottawa: The Mortimer Co.; 1907). Frank Dawson Adams and many others have made later studies of the Canadian shield.

X

Hall's theory of mountains is set forth most clearly in his presidential address before the American Association for the Advancement of Science in 1856, which was printed in 1859 in Volume III of *Paleontology of New York* (Albany: printed by C. van Benthuysen; 1847–94). Other volumes of *Paleontology* demonstrate Hall's vast work with fossils, as does *Geology of*

New York (Albany: Carroll & Cook; 1842). A full account of Hall's life and work is given in *James Hall of Albany,* by John M. Clarke (Albany; 1923).

XI

Powell's own first-person account of the exploration of the Colorado—*Exploration of the Colorado River of the West and Its Tributaries*—was first printed under the direction of the Smithsonian Institution in 1875. In addition, some of his conclusions and later work were published by the Smithsonian in 1874. A biographical memoir written by W. M. Davis appeared in Volume VIII, National Academy of Sciences, Washington, 1915. Two full and scholarly biographies were published half a century after Powell's death: *Powell of the Colorado,* by William Culp Darrah (Princeton: Princeton University Press; 1951), and *Beyond the Hundredth Meridian—John Wesley Powell and the Second Opening of the West,* by Wallace Stegner (Boston: Houghton Mifflin Company; 1954). Many of the documents relating to the Powell expedition may be found in the *Utah Historical Quarterly,* Vol. XV (1947). These last three items provide many references to other sources.

XII

Dutton's work in the west is reported scientifically and colorfully in his *Tertiary History of the Grand Cañon District* (Washington: U. S. Geological Survey; 1882), in the accompanying atlas of drawings by William Henry Holmes, and in *The Geology of the High Plateaus of Utah* (Washington: U. S. Geological Survey; 1880). Dutton's first proposal of the theory of isostasy is in Volume XI of the *Proceedings of the Philosophical Society of Washington* (1889). A whole literature has since grown up on the subject. Among the outstanding volumes are William Bowie's *Isostasy* (New York: A. P. Dutton & Co.; 1927); Walter H. Bucher's *Deformation of the Earth's Crust* (Princeton: Princeton University Press; 1941); and J. H. F. Umbgrove's *The Pulse of the Earth* (The Hague: M. Nijhoff; 1947). There is biographical material in Stegner's *Beyond the Hundredth Meridian,* and in his *Clarence Edward Dutton: An Appraisal* (Salt Lake City; 1936); in "C. E. Dutton, Explorer, Geologist and Nature Writer," *Scientific Monthly,* Vol. XLV (July 1937); and in *Dictionary of American Biography,* Vol. XIII.

XIII

Chamberlin's theory of the earth is developed principally in the following: *The Origin of the Earth* (Chicago: University of Chicago Press; 1916); *Two Solar Families* (Chicago: University of Chicago Press; 1928); and "On Lord Kelvin's Address on the Age of the Earth as an Abode Fitted for Life," *Science* (Smithsonian Institution), June 30, 1899. Two books report much of his glacial work: *Kettle Moraines of the Great Lakes District of North America* (Paris: T. Symonds; 1878), and *The Classification of American Glacial Deposits* (Chicago: University of Chicago Press; 1895). Two careful memoirs tell of the life and work of Chamberlin: "Chamberlin," by Bailey Willis (Bulletin of the Geological Society of America, Vol. XL, March 1929), and one by his son Rollin T. Chamberlin, published by National Academy of Sciences, 1930.

XIV

Urey makes his most extensive presentation of his theory of the earth in his book *The Planets: Their Origin and Development* (New Haven: Yale University Press; 1952). Most of his work that has so profoundly influenced the study of the earth is reported in papers appearing in scientific journals. Among them are: "The Separation of Isotopes" (The Physical Society, London: Vol. VI, 1940); "Atomic Energy in International Politics" (*Foreign Policy Reports*, Vol. XXII, 1946); "The State of the Primitive Earth" (*The Technion Society Yearbook*, Vol. IX, 1950); "Measurement of Paleotemperatures" (*Bulletin of the Geological Society of America*, Vol. LXII, 1951); "Cosmic Abundances of the Elements, and the Chemical Composition of the Solar System" (*American Scientist*, Vol. XXXIX, 1951); "The Origin and Development of the Earth and Other Terrestrial Planets" (*Geochimica et Cosmochimica*, Acta I, 1951), and "A Correction" in the same journal (Acta II, 1952); "The Origin of the Earth" (*Scientific American*, Vol. CLXXXVII, 1952); "Comments on Planetary Convection as Applied to the Earth" (*Philosophical Magazine*, Vol. XLIV, 1953); "On the Concentration of Certain Elements at the Earth's Surface" (*Proceedings of the Royal Society*, Vol. CCXIX, 1953); "On the Origin of Continents and Mountains" (*Proceedings of the National Academy of Sciences*, Vol. XXXIX, 1953); "Chemical Evidence Regarding the Earth's Origin" (XIIIth International Congress of Pure and Applied Chemistry, Stockholm, 1953); "On the Origin and Age of Meteorites" (*Nature*, Vol. CLXXV, 1955); "Distribution of Elements in the Meteorites and the Earth and the Origin of Heat in the Earth's Core" (*Annales de Géophysique*, Vol. XI, January–March; 1955); and "Chemical Heating for Meteorites" (unpublished, 1956).

XV

Sir Harold Jeffreys brings together his studies of the earth and its interior in *The Earth, Its Origin, History, and Physical Constitution* (Third edition. Cambridge: University Press; 1952), and in *The Future of the Earth* (New York: W. W. Norton & Co.; 1929). Also essential is his popularly written study of the physics of the earth, *Earthquakes and Mountains* (Second edition. London: Methuen & Co.; 1950). Attention also is called to the chapters that Sir Harold contributed to *The Earth as a Planet*, and to *Internal Constitution of the Earth*. His latest scientific papers may be found listed in the two latter books.

Sir Edward Bullard's chapter on "Interior of the Earth" in *The Earth as a Planet* was used as the basis of the section of this book which discusses his work. Other publications of Bullard on the interior of the earth, its heat flow, and magnetism include "Heat Flow through the Floor of the Eastern North Pacific Ocean" (*Nature*, Vol. CLXX, 1952); "A Comparison of Oceans and Continents" (*Proceedings of the Royal Society*, A, Vol. CCXXII, 1954); "The Flow of Heat through the Floor of the Atlantic Ocean" (*Proceedings of the Royal Society*, A, Vol. CCXXII, 1954); and "Homogeneous Dynamos and Terrestrial Magnetism" (*Philosophical Transactions of the Royal Society*, A, Vol. CCXLVII, 1954).

Other books on this subject, all of them technical though important, are K. E. Bullen's *An Introduction to the Theory of Seismology* (Cambridge; University Press; 1947); chapters by Beno Gutenberg in *Internal Constitu-*

tion of the Earth; and R. A. Daly's *Strength and Structure of the Earth* (New York: Prentice-Hall; 1940).

Runcorn's latest findings on the magnetism of the earth are popularly presented in "The Earth's Magnetism" in the September 1955 issue of *Scientific American.* The problem also is discussed in an article on "Rock Magnetism," by G. D. Nicholls, Louis Neel, and Runcorn, in *Advances in Physics,* Vol. XIV (April 1955); by Walter M. Elsasser in "The Earth's Interior and Geomagnetism," in *Review of Modern Physics,* Vol. XXII (January 1950); by Gerard P. Kuiper in an address before the Royal Canadian Institute in November 1955; and by Bullard in his studies of magnetism. See also "The Earth's Core," by Runcorn (*Transactions of the American Geophysical Union,* Vol. XXXVI (1955).

XVI

Waters discusses his work in the Pacific northwest, and the conclusions about igneous action to which it led him, in his chapter "Volcanic Rocks and the Tectonic Cycle in the Crust of the Earth" in *Crust of the Earth,* and in "Geomorphology of South Central Washington, Illustrated by the Yakima East Quadrangle" (*Geological Society of America Bulletin,* Vol. LXVI, 1955).

The work of Cloos on fracture patterns is reported in "Experimental Analysis of Fracture Patterns" (*Geological Society of American Bulletin,* Vol. LXVI, 1955).

XVII

Mason reports the development of geochemistry in his book *Principles of Geochemistry* (New York: John Wiley & Sons; 1952), and in his chapter "The Geochemistry of the Crust" in *The Earth as a Planet.* An address by Norman L. Bowen, reprinted in *Scientific Monthly,* June 1935, is still an excellent explanation for the layman of "Igneous Rocks in the Light of High Temperature Research." "The Chemistry of the Earth's Crust," by Arie Poldervaart, in *Crust of the Earth* is a technical but enlightening round-up. Reference is also made to the previously cited work of Urey. Another important work in the field is *Geochemistry,* by Kalervo Rankama and T. G. Saharna (Chicago: University of Chicago Press; 1950).

XVIII

Kulp sums up much of the work that has been done on the age of the earth in "Isotopic Dating and the Geologic Time Scale," the chapter he contributed to *Crust of the Earth.* He and a group of associates report on "The Present Status of the Lead Method of Age Determination" in the *American Journal of Science,* Vol. CCLII (June 1954). Materials under preparation at the Lamont Geological Observatory present additional data on rubidium and potassium dating.

A popular report on the work of Patterson, Brown, Tilton, and Inghram in fixing the age of the earth at 4.5 billion years appears in *University of Chicago Reports,* January 1954, and a fuller scientific report in *Science,* January 21, 1955. Patterson's work on the dating of meteorites may be found in *Geochimica et Cosmochimica,* Acta 7 (1955).

A full discussion of the new dating may be seen in *Isotope Geology,* by Kalervo Rankama (New York: McGraw-Hill Book Co.; 1954). A somewhat older presentation of the same subject, but also including dating by tree rings, varves, and other methods, is found in Frederick E. Zeuner's *Dating The Past—An Introduction to Geochronology* (Second edition. London: Methuen & Co.; 1950).

XIX
The fourth and revised edition of Wegener's book *The Origin of Continents and Oceans* may be obtained in a translation by John Biram in a paperback issued by Dover Publications, Inc. (New York, 1966). The Hess theory is set forth in the *Buddington Memorial Volume, Geological Society of America* (1962), pages 599–620. DuToit's *Our Wandering Continents* was published by Oliver & Boyd (Edinburgh, 1937). Two excellent reviews bring together significant newer work: "Sea Floor Spreading" by W. C. Pitman in *Science Journal,* Feb. 1969 (published by Iliffe Industrial Publications Ltd, London), and "Sea Floor Spreading—New Evidence" by F. J. Vine in *Journal of Geological Education,* Vol. XVII, No. 1 (Feb. 1969).

These are the principal published materials that have been used in the writing of this book. Unless there was some special reason for doing so, I did not attempt to list other books that were consulted.

In addition to studying published materials, I talked personally to all the living American scientists whose work is reported and visited their laboratories. This offered an invaluable opportunity to ask questions and to obtain additional materials. Sometimes it was possible, too, to talk to their friends and associates. In another part of the book I have expressed my gratitude to the scientists, but here, in speaking of the gathering of materials, I should like to underscore it.

INDEX

RUTH MOORE *is one of the best-known popular-science writers in the country. She was born in St. Louis, Missouri, and received her B.A. and M.A. degrees from Washington University there. She has worked as Washington correspondent for the Chicago Sun, and again in Chicago on the Sun-Times, where science feature stories were one of her specialties. Her deep concern about housing and the many continuing problems relating to urban renewal have made her a specialist in these questions. In May 1960 she received the first individual award given by the American Association of Planning Officials for a series on urban renewal in seven major cities, and in 1970 the "Champion Fighter For a Better Chicago" award of the Metropolitan Housing and Planning Council. She and her husband, Raymond W. Garbe, a noted hospital architect, live in Chicago.*

The Earth We Live On, first published in 1956, has now been issued in nine languages; The Coil of Life (1961) has been published in eight languages so far, and Man, Time, and Fossils (1953) in fourteen languages. She is the author also of Charles Darwin: A Great Life in Brief (1955) *and* Niels Bohr (1966).

A NOTE ON THE TYPE

The text of this book is set in Caledonia, a type face designed by William Addison Dwiggins for the Mergenthaler Linotype Company in 1939. Dwiggins chose to call his new type face Caledonia, the Roman name for Scotland, because it was inspired by the Scotch types cast about 1833 by Alexander Wilson & Son, Glasgow type founders. However, there is a calligraphic quality about Caledonia that is totally lacking in the Wilson types. Dwiggins referred to an even earlier type face for this "liveliness of action"—one cut around 1790 by William Martin for the printer William Bulmer. Caledonia has more weight than the Martin letters, and the bottom finishing strokes (serifs) of the letters are cut straight across, without brackets, to make sharp angles with the upright stems, thus giving a "modern face" appearance.

W. A. Dwiggins (1880–1956) began an association with the Mergenthaler Linotype Company in 1929 and over the next twenty-seven years designed a number of book types, the most interesting of which are the Metro series, Electra, Caledonia, Eldorado, and Falcon.

This book was composed, printed and bound by the Kingsport Press, Inc., Kingsport, Tennessee.